18 17

UNDER THE EDITORSHIP OF GARDNER MURPHY

Inhibition and Choice

A NEUROBEHAVIORAL APPROACH TO PROBLEMS OF PLASTICITY IN BEHAVIOR

Solomon Diamond
Richard S. Balvin
Florence Rand Diamond

HARPER & ROW, PUBLISHERS, *New York and Evanston*

 For information address Harper & Row, Publishers, Incorporated, 49 East 33rd Street, New York 16, N.Y.

M–M

LIBRARY OF CONGRESS CATALOG CARD NUMBER: 63–7102

CONTENTS

PREFACE

That a book should make *inhibition* and *choice,* rather than *response* and *learning,* central to psychology, will startle many readers. The physical sciences provide an analogy which may help to clarify our purpose. Man's scientific efforts were first directed toward understanding the forces that move objects, forces that make for change, and it was a long time before the genius of a Newton recognized that a "balance of forces" is needed to explain the simple rest of a stationary object. Yet modern physics recognizes that the energies which are locked in the nucleus of the atom, which to our ordinary perception seems so inert, are immeasurably greater than those we associate with moving things.

In the biological sciences, too, men wondered first about the vital forces that move muscles and fluids and are responsible for the behaving activity of men and animals, and were slow to appreciate the need for study of inaction. Our habits of scientific thinking escape with difficulty from the patterns set by our naive perception of the world, as an arrangement of intrinsically inert objects which must be pushed into action. However, the inactivity of a living thing is a very remarkable phenomenon. Given an action mechanism, there is nothing remarkable about its activity. We may wonder at the causes that have put it together so that it acts at all, but we cannot wonder that it acts in the way that it does, being constituted as it is. But when we have reached this level of scientific understanding, when we have ceased to regard the activity of living things as miraculous and come to regard it in terms of physical process, we have still to understand what added complexities enable this action mechanism to be restrained from action.

In any complete account of behavior, we must be able to explain the organism's inaction as well as its action. If now it runs, why does it not run at other times? If now it eats, why does it not eat at other times? Failure to recognize this as a part of the problem betrays a latent belief in some qualitative distinction between one state—behaving—and another state—not behaving. The behaving animal is still looked upon as an object of wonder, whereas the nonbehaver is simply an accepted part of the physical world. Actually, a complex organism has many varieties of inaction, including such different states as sleep, repression, catalepsy, and meditative thought. Oddly enough, man in his obstinate perversity has made a mystery of the only form of inaction which is completely comprehensible in everyday terms: death.

It is not surprising that the fuller understanding of this neglected aspect of behavior should lead to a changed view of behavior generally. Out of the study of inaction there arises a picture of the behaving organism as an arrangement of action systems which exert mutually restraining influences, and in which each overt act is a phase of disequilibrium that must be quickly arrested, before it becomes maladaptive. This model of behavior has historical antecedents, and it also receives much substance from modern neurophysiology.

Our references are a formal but necessarily inadequate acknowledgment of our debt to the past and to our contemporaries. Specific thanks are due also to Basic Books, Inc., for permission to reproduce Freud's sketch (on page 169) from their book, *The Origins of Psychoanalysis;* to the Clarendon Press for permission to reproduce (on pages 191 and 195) two tables from Pavlov's *Conditioned Reflexes;* to Pergamon Press, Inc., for permission to reproduce (on page 101) a table from *Inhibition in the Nervous System and Gamma-Aminobutyric Acid,* edited by E. Roberts; and to John Wiley & Sons, Inc., for permission to reproduce (on page 342) a table from *Drugs and Behavior,* edited by L. Uhr and J. G. Miller. Our colleagues, Dr. Ann Richardson and Dr. Herbert Moscowitz, read portions of the manuscript and made helpful suggestions. Appreciation no less warm is due to "Jan, Lois, Lily, Robin, Roy, Tony, and Willy," children whose cases are described in Chapter 14, who have also helped us to understand. We owe most special thanks to Dean Horace W. Magoun, who found time in an overburdened schedule to read the galleys and to make insightful comments from which we have tried to profit. These kind friends have had no responsibility for rooting out all our errors, which must be charged to us alone. To all our readers, we are grateful for the effort they will make to understand; we hope that in time we shall become more deeply indebted to a few, who will contribute to the further clarification of the ideas here presented.

S. D.
R. S. B.
F. R. D.

July, 1962

INHIBITION: A PHYSIOLOGICAL REALITY

I

STATEMENT OF THE PROBLEM 1

The development of psychological theory has always been tied to changing conceptions of the nervous system. This influence has not always been a fortunate one, since physiologists are no more immune to error than other men, and psychologists no less disposed to attempt the scaling of impregnable walls on bean stalks. It is therefore not difficult to understand the point of view of those who decry this form of dependence on foreign manufactures and who urge psychologists to an abstemious reliance on home-grown products exclusively. However sound the arguments for such a program may appear, they are bound to lose much of their appeal whenever, as at the present time, our sister science is able to exhibit a tempting array of startling new discoveries.

During the past decade, progress in neurophysiology has outstripped the most sanguine hopes of the patient men who, a few years earlier, had been doggedly pursuing what seemed at times like a will-o'-the-wisp: the neural pattern of a behavioral event. New discoveries have led to a radically new conception of the role of the nervous system in behavior, and it is inevitable that this should give rise to many new developments in psychological theory. Even if we grant in advance that some of these developments will be in error, can we afford to forego the opportunity offered for new insights?

The situation is not unlike that with respect to the relations between psychological theory and philosophy. It has so often been said that the issue is not whether psychology can get along without philosophy, but whether it can afford to bungle along with the out-of-date philosophy of the man in the street, or whether it must seek the best available model. In this case, the issue is not whether psychology shall be influenced by neurophysiology, but whether it shall make studied use of the best available neurophysiology, or go bungling along with an antiquated form. Hebb (1951) has pointed out that the attempt to exclude neurological thinking from our theory construction only means that, without planning to do so, we work in terms of ideas which, although they are now put forth as "'purely behavioral' conceptions," actually had their origins in late nineteenth-century theories of nervous functioning.

This book does not attempt to consider all of the implications which contemporary neurophysiological findings have for psychological theories. It is concerned only with the concept of neural inhibition—its history, its present status, and its applications to certain specific problems of psychology. Our labors had their starting point in an interest in inhibition as a factor in personality integration, with particular reference to the problem of anxiety (Diamond, 1957, ch. 17); but the pursuit of that problem led inevitably to a study of the relevant physiological research. Although we shall give considerable attention to physiological findings in the very recent period, we will begin with a historical review in order to show, on the one hand, that the need for some kind of neural inhibitory process has been recognized repeatedly by psychologists and, on the other, that the understanding of inhibition has been hindered by certain methodological assumptions which are still all too prevalent. Thus the isolationist will find some material which will tend to support his argument that psychology, left to itself, could have developed the concept of neural inhibition quite successfully, and that its failure to do so may be traced to the malign influence of neurologists who looked with skepticism on the concept. However, it would seem that a sounder reading of history is to the effect that the full potential of the concept of inhibition could not be realized by psychologists until it was given a sound physiological basis.

From this point of view, we stand today at the point which was anticipated by Lloyd Morgan when he wrote the following sentence, seventy years ago: "When physiologists have solved the problem of inhibition, they will be in a position to consider that of volition." This quotation is from *Animal Life and Intelligence,* which appeared in 1891, at the start of a decade when psychologists generally were more intensely interested in the theoretical significance of physiological inhibition than at any time before or since. It was written by the man whose name was to become, in the professional parlance of psychologists, a synonym for scientific rectitude. Three years later, in his *Introduction to Comparative Psychology,* Morgan (1894) was to enunciate his famous canon: "In no case may we interpret an action as the outcome of the exercise of a higher psychical faculty, if it can be interpreted as the outcome of the exercise of one which stands lower in the psychological scale." His speculation that physiological inhibition is the basis for volition (or, as we should say today, for choice behavior) is entirely in the spirit of such parsimonious theorizing, since it sought to explain one of the most complex problems of behavior on the basis of a phenomenon which had been repeatedly demonstrated in the physiological laboratory. Ironically, the commitment of neurologists to parsimonious theorizing was to become a major impediment to wider acceptance of the concept of inhibition among psychologists, as it had already prevented its general acceptance by physiologists.

At the time when Morgan was writing, the interest of psychologists in the subject of neural inhibition was high. Recent events had led William James to declare, in *Principles of Psychology* (1890): "Inhibition is a *vera causa,* of that there can be no doubt." Freud, before writing any of his major psychoanalytic works, would soon be engaged in speculations concerning the relation between neural inhibition and the repressions which took place in neurotic defense. Wundt was to revise his theory of apperception, the very heart of his system, by pointing to inhibition as its physiological substrate. However, this interest was destined to subside soon after the opening of the new century, as psychologists became more and more concerned with "doing" rather than with "thinking."

Sherrington's great work, *The Integrative Action of the Nervous System* (1906), might just as readily have carried the title: The importance of inhibition for nervous integration. But it was not so titled, and physiologists somehow succeeded in recognizing all the facts relating to posture and locomotion without drawing implications for their wider significance. The interest of physiologists in the subject of inhibition was only spasmodic throughout the first half of the twentieth century. There was a continuing accumulation of examples of inhibition exercised by "higher" over "lower" levels of the nervous system, but neither physiologists nor psychologists seemed to regard this as a problem of central importance. Instances of inhibition of sensory afferentation were also known, but they were accorded no systematic importance.

The prominence of inhibition in current neurophysiological research and theory did not come about as the direct result of research dealing with inhibition per se, although progress in that area was stimulated when Renshaw (1941) and Lloyd (1941) demonstrated the existence of inhibitory interneurons in the spine. Paradoxically, the great contemporary flood of research dealing with inhibition, at least in its behavioral aspects, arose out of the interest of neurophysiologists in the phenomenon of cortical "arousal," that is, in what seemed to be a mechanism for generalized excitation of the brain. This discovery was made by Moruzzi and Magoun (1949), who half accidentally observed that stimulation of the brain stem reticular formation produced a change in the general character of cortical activity, as reflected in the electroencephalogram (EEG), of the same kind as that which is evoked by attention-capturing stimulation. Their report proved to be the starting-point for a great surge of neurophysiological research, concerned especially with the functions of the reticular formation, which has highlighted the part played by inhibitory effects in higher nervous activities. Perhaps this crucial discovery would not have been made if it had not been preceded by the earlier finding, by Magoun and Rhines (1946), that stimulation of a certain portion of the brain stem reticular formation caused inhibition of spinal reflexes. In a broad sense, this was little more than confirmation and elaboration of what Sechenov had found more than eighty years earlier, and in itself it would have received no special recognition aside from its significance for the understanding of locomotor reflexes, and particularly the phenomena of spasticity (Magoun & Rhines, 1947). It was the converse phenomenon of arousal—that is, the apparently widespread excitation of cortical areas originating in a subcortical structure and without specific sensory content—which stirred the interest and imagination of neurophysiologists generally, and at once became the focus of a large number of research programs, all initially concerned with the phenomenon of arousal, but all inevitably producing facts about inhibition.

Currently, a great deal of interdisciplinary work by neurophysiologists, pharmacologists, and psychologists is serving to demonstrate correlations between behavioral phenomena and measurable inhibition of neural processes. Furthermore, very recent dramatic advances in biochemistry and microphysiology have made it possible for neurophysiologists to penetrate into the secrets of the synapse, in a manner which seemed only a decade ago to be reserved for the fantasies of science fiction. Today, the problem of inhibition can be considered as solved, to the extent that the physicochemical nature of neural inhibition has been clearly differentiated from neural excitation, and its effects have been detected, not merely as a decrement of overt activity, but in the recorded action of individual neurons. Thus, although Morgan's term *volition* is dated, the problem of *choice* has clearly been placed on the agenda of behavioral scientists.

What is meant by inhibition? In a general sense, it is any act of prevention or hindrance. It is obvious that one bodily act will occasionally hinder or prevent another bodily act, with which it is incompatible. However, we are not concerned with incompatibilities which may be defined in terms of muscles or bone structure, but with the effects of inhibition within the nervous system, that is, with instances in which one neural event prevents or hinders another neural event. In behavioral terms, it should not be assumed that the effects of inhibition are limited to phenomena which are designated by terms like *repression, act-inhibition,* and *response decrement.* These are its most conspicuous, but not necessarily its most important effects. It will be shown later that in all higher organisms tonic inhibitions play an indispensable part in nervous control, and that the momentary (phasic) inhibition of a tonic inhibition is very often the means by which an overt act is precipitated.

The classical definition of physiological inhibition is that which was offered by Brunton (1883): "By inhibition we mean the arrest of the functions of a structure or organ, by the action upon it of another, while its power to execute those functions is still retained, and can be manifested as soon as the restraining power is removed. It is thus distinguished from paralysis, in which the function is abolished, and not merely restrained."

This definition reflects the atmosphere of controversy which prevailed at the time it was written. Careful workers had reported the slowing of the heart by stimulation of the vagus nerve, the slowing of respiration by the upper laryngeal nerve, the interruption of intestinal peristalsis by stimulation of the splanchnic nerve, the suppression of reflex avoidance movements to painful stimulation by coincident stimulation of other channels, etc. But physiologists could not agree on the nature of the process underlying such phenomena. The most eager protagonists of inhibition believed that there were special inhibitory centers, dispatching inhibitory impulses, probably along inhibitory nerves. The most skeptical group contended that these phenomena could all be explained as indirect consequences of fatigue, or anemia, or some other condition which interfered with normal nervous function. Between, there were some who vaguely believed that nervous impulses could somehow "interfere" with one another, like contrary tides, mutually destroying their effectiveness. There were others who thought that inhibition resulted from some sort of antiexcitatory process inside the nerve cell, probably associated with some restorative phase of the cell's activity.

The "arrest" of function in Brunton's definition is to be interpreted as implying prevention of exercise of the *function,* and not merely interference with its effects. Thus, the inhibition of a muscle eliminates the muscular contraction, and does not merely counteract the expected movement. For example, when an angry man raises his clenched fist, but restrains himself from delivering a punch while his arm trembles with all of its muscles tensed, it may be said in a colloquial sense that he "inhibits" himself. Actually, this situation represents a default of inhibition in the technical sense, since effective neural inhibition would eliminate the innervations which are giving rise to excessive muscular contractions, and would enable him to hold his arm up and his fingers closed with only the amount of effort needed to counter the force of gravity, that is, without the simultaneous wasteful contraction of antagonistic muscles. Brunton's definition also excludes the possibility that inhibition is to be explained as an effect of fatigue, which is a kind of temporary paralysis. However, it does not exclude the possibility that inhibition results from interference, somewhere within the nervous system, between two or more sets of excitatory impulses. Indeed, it is just such a theory that Brunton himself advanced, in the article containing the definition which we have quoted. Nor does it necessarily exclude a variety of other possible explanations of inhibitory effects, some of which will be mentioned in due course. In short, this is a broad definition, which is useful for discussion of the many ways in which physiologists and psychologists have used the concept of inhibition.

However, we shall have need also of a "narrow" definition, which corresponds to the concept of inhibition as it is defined by contemporary research. Let us, for this purpose, use the designation *synaptic inhibition,* and define this as an event which begins with the release by an activated neuron of an inhibitory transmitter substance, the effect of which is to prevent, or tend to prevent, the discharge of another neuron (or the contraction of a muscle fiber, or secretion by a gland) under conditions which would otherwise lead to such discharge (or contraction, or secretion). The process of synaptic inhibition will be described in some detail in Chapter 5. However, it is this understanding of the inhibitory process which permits us to state with confidence that the time foreseen by Lloyd Morgan has arrived, and that psychology at last has the tools with which to approach the problems of choice behavior.

Nevertheless, it is not likely that this breakthrough will be successfully exploited by psychologists unless we recognize that the neglect of inhibition, as a phenomenon comparable to excitation and every bit as important to the proper functioning of the nervous system, has been something more than an oversight. The idea of active inhibition has been actively suppressed. Generations of psychologists and physiologists have dismissed it as an illusion, as a merely figurative expression for some other undefined processes, or, after reluctantly acknowledging it as a reality, they have turned away and proceeded to deal with other problems exactly as if the matter of inhibition had never been broached. As already indicated above, there was a period starting about 1890 when many leading psychologists displayed an intense interest in the subject of inhibition. But this interest was short-lived, partly because it could not be sustained in the face of a fairly general skepticism among physiologists, and partly because other developments captured the attention of psychologists. For the past fifty years, the concept of inhibition has not held a place of honor in the mainstream of psychological thought, outside of Russia. Many leading textbooks of general psychology do not mention it at all, even when they take pains to explain the operation of the nervous system as an organ of communication and control. Some have a passing word for retroactive or proactive inhibition, as oddities of the learning process which result from a presumed interference between associative excitations. Discussions of learning theory refer condescendingly to Pavlov's strange notions about an inhibitory process in the cerebral cortex, "induced" by the excitatory process and somehow complementary to it. Advanced texts respectfully state Hull's postulates about reactive and conditioned inhibition, but the reader is usually asked to remember that Hull was never really clear about the extent to which his postulated relationships corresponded to physiological processes. To avoid the neurological taint, many of Hull's followers now speak instead of "response decrement." Textbooks of physiological psychology properly point out that there is in the nervous system a process or function of inhibition as well as one of excitation, but they uniformly fail to convey to the student reader any real comprehension of the importance of inhibition. The technical usage of the term is so rare among psychologists that most of them think of *inhibition* just as laymen do, as a close synonym of *repression* in the Freudian sense. Skinner (1953) employs it to designate a pathological aspect of behavior which is the unfortunate aftermath of excessive punishment. These facts indicate that before we can utilize our new knowledge effectively, we shall have to free ourselves from some long-standing prejudices.

Indeed, it is a simple fact of daily observation that just as some stimuli lead to action, others lead to inaction, but in the absence of a convincing physiological account of how a stimulus can lead to decrement of neural action, these behavioral data have not received adequate interpretation. The historical record shows that there has been more inclination to explain inhibition away than to utilize it as a behavioral fact. Morgan was right: as long as the concept of inhibition remained poorly defined by physiologists, psychologists were unable to make effective use of it in dealing with their problems.

Nevertheless, the early history of psychology provides many instances of interest in behavioral phenomena which apparently require inhibitory processes for their explanation.

Every penetrating observer of behavior has always been aware of the existence of simultaneous and incompatible tendencies in behavior, one of which can come to full expression only by suppressing the other. Thus, in the *Phaedrus,* Plato described the soul as consisting of three parts, which he likened to "a pair of winged horses and a charioteer." One of the horses is a noble animal, who "needs not the touch of the whip, but is guided by word and admonition only." The other is "the mate of insolence and pride, shag-eared, deaf, hardly yielding to blow or spur." To drive these two horses as a team is a difficult task. When the soul is tempted to carnal pleasures, it often happens that the charioteer succeeds in reining "both the steeds on their haunches, the one willing and unresisting, the unruly one very unwilling." However, it may also happen that the unruly horse takes the charioteer off his guard, and brings him, half unwilling, to "accomplish that desire (which has) not the approval of the whole soul."

This poetic description of the struggle between reason and desire may be compared with the account which was given about 2,200 years later by Alexander Bain, in *The Emotions and the Will* (1859). Bain wrote at a time when a good deal had been learned about the gross anatomy of the nervous system and about neuromuscular innervation, and he was disposed to make the most of it. In fact, it is he who set the fashion for succeeding generations of psychologists by devoting a lengthy chapter in the first part of his composite treatise on psychology (*The Senses and the Intellect,* 1855) to a fairly thorough statement of contemporary knowledge about the structure and function of the nervous system. At that time, however, neural inhibition was a secret of nature which had been hinted only darkly to physiologists; and the hints did not pertain to the possible inhibition of voluntary acts. Bain could only guess at the manner in which conflict was represented in and resolved by the brain. He even conjectured that one reason why voluntary control of the emotions is relatively ineffective is because "the check given to the actual movement of a member does not arrest the circulation of nervous influences, on which an emotional state depends." Apparently he conceived of this "check" as being achieved by the voluntary innervation of antagonistic muscles, a kind of control which we have all practised at times (but only, be it remarked, when we have very nearly "lost control" of ourselves). He reasoned that although such muscular antagonism does not erase the emotion, it may reduce it by eliminating some of the somatic reverberation of the emotional wave, an aspect of behavior which has great importance in his system. "It would thus appear that the will, operating through its proper instruments, the voluntary muscles, reaches the deep recession of emotion, and by stilling the diffused wave can silence the conscious state maintained by it."

Bain also supposed that conflicting action tendencies can and do struggle against each other within the brain, as well as in the limbs. He wrote: "We are not permitted to explore the seat of this struggle between two rival influences coursing through the same brain. We cannot tell the points where they meet, and neutralize each other; still we can see the broad distinction of character between the diffused excitement of an emotional wave, and the movements stimulated by the tendency of pain to work its own abatement, and of pleasure to work its own increase. . . . The same moving member may be urged by a plurality of impulses, as if flowing from different nervous centers, and when two of these oppose one another, we must needs term that the stronger which determines the actual result."

It is still not so different, really, from Plato's picture of the charioteer tugging at the reins of his unruly horse.

Another kind of inhibition, the suppression of one sensory experience by another, was also recognized by the ancient Greeks. One of the aphorisms of Hippocrates (No. 46), states that "Of two pains existing at the same time, but not in the same place, the stronger obscures the other." Aristotle, in his treatise *On the Senses and Sensibility*, presented a fairly extended discussion of the interaction of simultaneous stimulations, in which he not only spoke of the fact that "the stronger always tends to extrude the weaker," but also contended that "this greater should itself too be less distinctly perceptible than if it were alone," and pointed out that the outcome also depends on whether the two stimuli belong to the same sensory continuum or to different sense modalities. An additional complication which is introduced by the element of motivation is recognized in a passage of the *Nicomachean Ethics* (X, v): "People who are fond of flute-music cannot keep their attention to conversation or discourse when they hear the sound of a flute." Here, he was no longer thinking of the direct rivalry between the sensory stimulations, but of the fact that "the pleasure attendant on flute-playing destroys the working of conversation or discourse." This is a problem of volition with which the modern teen-ager at his homework still contends, as the printed page and recorded music vie for his attention.

Before leaving the ancient world, it is interesting to note that the holy men of India long ago possessed a theory of inhibition, as well as superlative skill in exercising it, in a form which we now call self-hypnosis. Warren's *Buddhism in Translations* (1896) gives a passage from *The Way of Purity*, a fourth-century commentary which tells how the priest attains "the trance of cessation" by a practiced passage through many preliminary stages of trance. In the last of these trances he enters the "realm of nothingness," but must arise from this to perform certain requisite duties, the most necessary of which is to reflect whether he is sure to live for the seven days of the final trance. Thereafter, "he enters the realm of neither perception nor yet non-perception; and having passed beyond one or two thoughts, he stops thinking and reaches cessation. . . . For the priest's progress in gradual cessation consists in an ascent through the eight attainments by the simultaneous use of both the quiescence and insight methods, and does not result from the trance of the realm of neither perception nor yet non-perception alone. Thus it is because of the priest's progress in cessation that beyond two thoughts the thoughts cease." In this final stage, there is "cessation of perception and sensation, bodily karma has ceased and become quieted, vocal karma has ceased and become quieted, mental karma has ceased and become quieted, but vitality has not become exhausted, natural heat has not subsided, and the senses have not broken up." These last phrases remind us of Brunton's definition: the Trance of Cessation meets the requirement that it is an arrest of function which is not a result of fatigue or paralysis.

The concept of inhibition appears in the writings of many of the pioneers of modern psychology. Hobbes utilized the Aristotelian notion of the mutual interference of sensory processes to explain both the limitation in the range of consciousness ("wherefore at one and the same time, we cannot by sense perceive more than one single object") and the "decay of sense" by which vivid sensations give way to the more pallid contents of imagination. However, in Hobbes we find also the beginnings of a distrust of inhibition, as somehow violating the mechanical principles by which he sought to explain mental activity. Hence he insists that "a vehement motion made by some one object in the organs of sense . . . deprives us of the sense of other phantasms, no otherwise than the sun deprives the rest of the stars of light, not by hindering their action, but by obscuring and hiding them with his excess of brightness." The fact that in dreams imagination can be as vivid as direct sensory experience is because "in sleep, the passages being shut up, external action doth not at all disturb or hinder internal motion." Hobbes also anticipated the attempt to explain inhibition in terms of the refractory phase in the nerve fiber, saying that when the nerves "which are common to all of the senses . . . are vehemently stirred by a strong action from some one object, they are, by reason of the contumacy which the motion, they have already, gives them against the reception of all other motion, made the less fit to receive any other impression from whatsoever other objects, to what sense soever those objects belong" (*De Corpore*, xxv, 6, 7).

Descartes mentioned sensory inhibition only in passing, but used it to provide an analogy for the even more interesting voluntary inhibition of movement.

Just as the soul, in making itself very attentive to something else, can prevent itself from hearing a slight sound or feeling a small pain, but cannot in the same way prevent itself from hearing thunder or feeling a fire burning the hand, so it can easily overcome the lesser passions, but not the stronger and more violent ones, except after the agitation of the blood and the animal spirits has subsided. The most the will can do while this agitation is in full force is not to consent to its effects, and to restrain some of the movements to which it disposes the body. For example, if anger makes us raise our hand to strike, our will can usually hold it back; if fear incites us to run away, our will can stop us, and so on with the other passions (Descartes, 1650, Art. 46).

Notice that Descartes' acceptance of the notion of act inhibition is linked with his doctrine of interactionism. That is, he did not describe inhibition as a process within the framework of that purely mechanical activity by which he explained animal behavior and most human movement, but as one manifestation of the soul's influence over the body. Elsewhere, he gave an account of what he conceived to be the mechanism for reciprocal action of antagonistic muscles, in which he assumed that animal spirits which inflate the muscles shuttle back and forth, from one to the other, through narrow tubes, so that the contraction of one muscle is necessarily accompanied by relaxation of its antagonist. However, inhibition plays no part in this process, for "the sole cause of one muscle's contracting rather than the one opposed to it is that it receives a slightly larger amount of animal spirits from the brain" (*Treatise on Passions*, Art. 11). That is, one muscle (or rather the spirits then present within one muscle) is excited more strongly than the other. The process is therefore excitatory in all its phases. Nevertheless, Sherrington (1951) has credited Descartes with introducing the concept of inhibition into physiological discussion, by this recognition of the need for reciprocal influence between antagonists.

Locke (1690), in his chapter "The Idea of Power," declared it "evident, that we find in ourselves a power to begin or forbear, continue or end several thoughts of our minds, and motions of our bodies, barely by the choice or preference of the mind." Locke, unlike Hobbes or Descartes, was deliberately nonphysiological in his method, and therefore he does not trouble himself as to how a forbearance might be effected, although he states, in a passage added in the second, 1694 edition, that "sitting still, or holding one's peace, when walking or speaking are proposed, though mere forbearances, requiring as much the determination of the will, and being as often weighty in their consequences, as the contrary actions, may, on that consideration, well enough pass for actions too."

Objection to this view was raised by Tucker, one of the most neglected men in the history of psychology, in *The Light of Nature Pursued* (1765). He declared: "What we call a forbearance I apprehend to be generally a choice of some other action." This seems a rather clear rejection of any notion of inhibitory action; yet a few pages on, turning his attention to the problem of how the slender nerves can contain the forces needed to produce powerful muscular exertions, Tucker designs a disinhibitory model, and even anticipates the modern argument that convulsive behavior demonstrates the existence of inhibitory controls! He writes:

> That there is another force within us besides our own, capable of acting upon the muscles, we may be convinced by convulsive motions, wherein the mind has no concern, nor volition any share, yet they sometimes imitate, and generally exceed the vigour of our voluntary actions. Perhaps there lies a mighty weight of some subtile fluid thrown from our animal circulation, constantly against the orifices of our nerves, but prevented from entering by certain little sliding valves kindly provided by nature for our use: the mind then has nothing more to do than draw aside the valves, and in rushes the torrent. The mind in this case works like the miller of an overshot mill—he has shoots lying over every one of his wheels, stopped by flash-boards at their upper ends, against which the water lies bearing always ready to drive the wheels whenever it can find a passage: so the miller, by drawing a little board, which any child might pull up with a finger, turns the stream upon this wheel or that as he pleases. . . . So some foulness of our juices may work under the valves, keeping them open whether we will or no: or the boiling of a fever may stretch them beyond their natural width, and produce convulsions stronger than anything the mind can effect by her volition (Tucker, 1765, I, p. 32).

Tucker was sufficiently pleased with this hypothesis to extend it, in his next chapter, to the sphere of the imagination. "Perhaps nature may have furnished us with valves too here, to serve us for stoppers. . . . Our own proper action, the action of our mind, extends no further than to opening the valves," thus regulating the currents of imagination.

Cabanis is another sadly neglected author, whose essay *Sur les Rapports du Physique et du Morale de l'Homme* has the distinction of being probably the most important work of the French enlightenment which has never appeared in English translation. In this work, the Cartesian dualism is replaced by a pragmatic and quite modern conception of mind-body relationships, in which the concept of correlation replaces that of causality. In the following passages, which describe the complexity of interaction among all bodily organs, he clearly implies the need for inhibitory as well as excitatory influences among them.

In this uninterrupted sequence of impressions; of determinations, of functions, of various movements, both internal and external, all of the organs act and react with one another: they communicate their states to one another, excite and repress one another, reinforce and balance one another, and mutually restrain one another. . . . If one thinks in this way of all of the important bodily functions, one will say that each one is tied to all of the others by more or less direct relationships, that they must mutually excite and support one another; that, in consequence, they form a circle in which life turns, maintained by this reciprocity of influences. . . . Therefore we can no longer have any difficulty in stating the true meaning of the expression, *the influence of the mental on the physical:* we clearly see that it designates this very influence of the cerebral system, as the organ of thought and of will over the other organs whose activity, by its sympathetic action, it is able to excite, to suspend, and even to pervert. It is this; it can be nothing more than this (Cabanis, 1802, II, pp. 415, 416, 431).

In Cabanis, also, one finds what is perhaps the first intimation of the drainage theory of inhibition, which appears again in the writings of Volkmann, of Spencer, of William James, of Sigmund Freud, and finally as a fully developed theory in the physiological psychology of William McDougall. In the course of a discussion in which Cabanis inisisted that the role of the nerves in sensibility is more than the merely passive transmission of impressions, he wrote:

Let us mention here that sensibility behaves like a fluid which has a fixed total quantity, and which, whenever it flows in greater abundance into some of its canals, is proportionately diminished in others. This becomes very apparent in all of the violent states, but above all in states of ecstasy, in which the brain and some other sympathetic organs enjoy the ultimate degree of energy and activity, while the faculties of sensation and of movement, while life, in a word, seems to have completely abandoned the rest of the body. . . . It is by taking advantage of this physical disposition that the charlatans of all kinds and in all countries have worked most of their miracles. . . . This is the true magic wand by which Mesmer sometimes stopped habitual pains . . . (1802, I, p. 127 f.).

The doctrine of inhibition received its most intensive development not in the hands of any physiologically oriented psychologist, but in the frankly metaphysical system of Herbart (1816, 1824). In Herbart's day, most German psychology was preoccupied with speculative discourse on the nature of the soul, while English psychology had developed association theory on an empirical, though not an experimental, basis. Herbart's great interest in pedagogy led him to respect the results obtained by the associationists; but he was not ready to give up the concept of the soul as an active entity, and to replace it with an ego which the skeptical Hume (1739) had described as merely "a bundle or collection of different perceptions . . . in a perpetual flux and movement." It was this on its surface, Herbart conceded; but he contended that metaphysics could penetrate below such surface phenomena, to reveal their necessary preconditions. He accepted the heart of the Leibnitzian position: that these experiences constitute activities of the soul, and not passive states imposed on it from without. For Herbart, as for Leibnitz, an idea is a striving for apperception, that is, for conscious representation. Herbart added that any striving presupposes a contrary resistance, and therefore we can deduce the existence of opposing forces that are not directly experienced. Any explanatory account of psychological events must deal with the resistances, or inhibitions, to which the striving of conscious ideas is opposed. Herbart also accepted the Leibnitzian doctrine that the soul, whose essence is thinking, thinks constantly, since otherwise its existence would be interrupted. Hence, thinking and consciousness are not identical. On these foundations, Herbart erected a theory of mental process which was explanatory and not merely descriptive—one in which the mental contents were active forces, not passive outcomes. He found the secret of the resistances in the competitive struggle of the ideas against each other, to enter consciousness and to remain there. Thus he dealt with ideas as Aristotle had once dealt with sensory processes, starting with the same simple assumption that the stronger will suppress the weaker, but will itself undergo some diminution in the process, and going on to formulate the hypothetical results of interaction among many ideas of different strengths and different degrees of compatibility. He escaped the need for a faculty of will, since he endowed each idea with its own motive force. He also ingeniously explained the creative surprises which take place in conscious experience, which seem so inexplicable under any theory of recall by positive associative bonds. Ideas which have been inhibited to the point that they do not rise above the threshold of consciousness, nevertheless persist as strivings for conscious representation. To return to consciousness, they need not wait for the assistance offered by some idea with which they have been associated: such a striving may become conscious because the ideas which had been inhibiting it must turn some part of their own force against some new idea which enters consciousness, and threatens to inhibit *them.* Since the degree to which one idea inhibits another depends in part on how opposite or incompatible they are, there is in this scheme abundant provision for a highly dynamic interplay, in which even a weak new idea may trigger the disinhibition of a much stronger idea which is not obviously related to it, and with which it has never previously been associated. Herbart represented these relationships in ingenious mathematical formulations which provided an important impetus toward the development of a quantitative psychology. Our interest, however, is to look upon his system as an early attempt at a "mathematical model" of behavior. From this point of view, we shall see later that the formulations which have so often been condemned as devoid of any basis in reality have an extraordinary "fit" to a great mass of empirical physiological and behavioral data.

The first experimental account of inhibition was given by Charles Bell (1823)—in connection with a discussion of the muscles of the eye. In describing the functions of the fourth cervical nerve, he said that it "is entirely given to one muscle, the superior oblique," and "if we suppose that the influence of the fourth nerve is, on certain occasions, to cause a relaxation of the muscle to which it goes, the eyeball must then be rolled upwards." Anticipating the objections of his readers, he appended the following footnote:

The nerves have been considered so generally as instruments for stimulating the muscles, without thought of their activity in the opposite capacity, that some additional illustration may be necessary here. Through the nerves is established the connection between the muscles, not only that connection by means of which muscles combine to an effort, but also that relation between the classes of muscles by which the one relaxes and the other contracts. I appended a weight to a tendon of an extensor muscle, which gently stretched it and drew out the muscle, and I found that the contraction of the opponent flexor was attended with a descent of the weight, which indicated the relaxation of the extensor. To establish this connection between two classes of muscles, whether they are grouped together as in the limbs, or scattered widely as the muscles of respiration, there must be particular and appropriate nerves to form this double bond to cause them to conspire in relaxation as well as to combine in contraction. If such a relationship be established, through the distribution of the nerves, between the muscles of the eyelids and the superior oblique muscles of the eyeball, the one will relax while the other contracts (Bell, 1823, p. 295 f.).

Take note that although Bell had a clear concept of inhibition, he still lacked a name for the phenomenon. Notice also that he inclined to an hypothesis of special inhibitory nerves—an hypothesis which was to be vigorously pursued after the discovery of such nerves in the autonomic system, but one which was to prove a blind alley insofar as the voluntary musculature of vertebrates was concerned.

Since Bell was a highly regarded author, one might have supposed that this passage would have stimulated additional experimentation along the same lines. However, there is no evidence that it ever received a truly perceptive reading before it fell under the eyes of Charles Sherrington. Sherrington (1906) improved the experiment by performing it on a living animal instead of a nerve-muscle preparation. He simply severed the attachments of the flexor muscles, so that the knee hung loose; then he stimulated the flexors and found that, though they could produce no movements of the knee, there was a deepened relaxation of the extensors.

In 1838, Volkmann described the vagal inhibition of a frog's heart. This event, which attracted little interest at the time, is recorded in every historical review of inhibition, but of even greater interest to us is the fact that in an earlier article published in that same year he indicated an awareness of the need for something like an inhibitory process in the control of voluntary movement. He penetrated clearly into an issue which is still the source of much confusion.

It is easy to see how the will is able to prevent a reflex movement from taking place. Of two opposed stimuli, the stronger is victorious; hence the convulsive movements of laughter due to tickling do not take place, if the will not to laugh is stronger than the tickling stimulation which tends to produce laughter. It is much more difficult to give a satisfactory physiological explanation of the influence of attention. If a man lost in thought is stimulated to startle by a light touch, but another, who sees the stimulus coming, is not, it is inappropriate to assert that the latter is not startled because he overcomes the stimulus to involuntary movement by the power of his will. For the attentive person, the light touch does not represent the slightest stimulus to reflex movement, and since he does not experience such a stimulus, he cannot be fighting it with volition. The question is rather why the stimulus to movement . . . does not exercise any exciting influence on the motor fibers in the attentive person? (Volkmann, 1838a, p. 32 f.).

He meets this question with a drainage hypothesis: that perhaps the effect of attention has been to heighten the conductivity of certain afferent nerves, and that these act "like lightning rods" to draw off excitation which might otherwise follow another path, to incite voluntary movement. However:

Whether this attempt at explanation is correct or not, the fact seems beyond doubt that the strength of reflex movements can be impeded by the influence of psychic forces. By this it is not meant that decerebration favors reflex movements by removing psychic influences, but on the contrary it is more probable that still other, unknown causes come into play. The tendency of the nervous principle to jump from one fiber to another is indeed so great in the decerebrate amphibian, that a wholly extraordinary psychic development of power would be needed, if this tendency were to be overcome, in the mutilated animal, solely by the action of the soul (Volkmann, 1838a, p. 34).

Despite such now-obsolete phrases as "the influence of psychic forces" and "the action of the soul," the essential point is clear: the suppression of one neural event by another does not come about because the stronger *overrides* the weaker, but because "unknown causes" counteract or *diminish* the excessive excitability of certain neural pathways.

In another article, Volkmann (1838b) discussed the cervical nerves of the frog, and stated with emphasis: "Nothing is more remarkable *than the influence of the vagus on the movement of the heart.*" Using the primitive electrophysiology of the time, he stimulated the vagus of a frog, about 15 minutes after its death, by opening and closing a key in the circuit from a voltaic pile. He observed that the heart beat was weakened, and some of the beats were missed altogether, but that subsequently the pulse regained its former strength and consistency. He repeated this observation at intervals on the same animal, obtaining the same result four times. However, he does not mention any possible relationship between this phenomenon and the suppression of voluntary movements of the limbs, which had been discussed in the previous article.

The vagal inhibition of the heart was reported again, in 1845, by the brothers E. H. Weber (well known to psychologists for his work on the sense of touch, from which Fechner was to deduce "*Weber's Law*") and the somewhat younger E. F. W. Weber. Perhaps the intermediate brother, W. E., a distinguished physicist, advised with them on the source of their stimulating current. This was not a voltaic pile (as erroneously stated by Brazier [1959a, p. 36]), but a generating apparatus which consisted of two coils which were rotated manually, by a belt and pulley arrangement, in the field of a permanent magnet. By use of commutators they obtained a direct though inconstant current, whose strength varied with the speed of rotation. (The apparatus is illustrated in Ed. Weber, 1846.) They state that strong stimulation from this source quickly stopped the heart, but the beat would be resumed a short time after cessation of the stimulation. When the rotation of the machine was less vigorous, the heart beat was weakened and slowed, but not stopped. They make special note that when the heart is stopped, it is in a state of relaxation, not of contraction—that is, in terms of Brunton's later definition, the heart is not paralyzed, but has its function abolished. They state that the same effect was obtained with the rabbit.

This report, unlike the earlier description of the same phenomenon by Volkmann, received a good deal of attention; but the reception was primarily skeptical or even hostile. No one questioned the facts reported. But almost everyone was prepared to question the interpretation that the impulses which traversed the vagus could, at their terminus, exert an inhibitory effect. The distrust of inhibition, even in the face of repeated experimental demonstration, was to last a long time. In 1899, Meltzer wrote with full justification: ". . . the phenomenon of inhibition is distrusted in physiology, (and) had to fight on general grounds at every step for the establishment of any new fact." We saw the root of this distrust in Hobbes' insistence that one sensory process could not "hinder" another, but could only obscure its effect as the sun obscures the stars, by outshining them. The reluctance to admit that any stimulation could subdue excitation, as well as provoke it, received an important doctrinal basis in the eighteenth century, when Haller (1755) distinguished between the irritability or contractility of muscles, on the one hand, and the sensibility of nervous and other tissue on the other. This doctrine of irritability was a major episode in the long struggle to free physiology from mystical concepts of a life force, and it is also the root from which the modern doctrine of stimulus and response has blossomed. Haller said that muscular contraction was the expression of a *vis insita,* an inherent force, in contrast to the animal spirits which were previously supposed to bring the power of reactivity into otherwise inert tissues. Following Haller, almost every physiologist in what we may today call the developing materialist tradition (although most, like Haller, would have rejected the designation "materialist" as one of opprobrium) looked upon this doctrine of irritability as one of the foundation stones of his science, because it made the responses of living tissue explicable in terms of the characteristics inherent in the tissues themselves, rather than referrable to an "extra" contributed by the action of some mysterious life force of external origin. So great was the prestige of this doctrine, that toward the end of the eighteenth century, in Erasmus Darwin's *Zoonomia, or the Laws of Organic Life* (1794), it is given a status comparable to that of Newton's principle of gravitation. Darwin wrote: "The fibres which constitute the muscles and the organs of sense possess a power of contraction. The circumstances attending the exertion of this power of *contraction* constitute the laws of animal motion, as the circumstances attending the exertion of the power of *attraction* constitute the laws of modern of inanimate matter."

Then he described sensation, volition, and association as secondary forms of motion, arising out of irritative motion. For example: "That exertion or change of the sensorium, which is caused by the appulses of external bodies, either simply subsides, or is succeeded by sensation, or it produces fibrous motion; it is termed irritation, and irritative motions are themselves contractions of the muscular fibres, or of the organs of sense, that are immediately consequent to this exertion or change of the sensorium."

Of each of the other forms of animal motion, Darwin likewise stated that it "either simply subsides" or gives rise to one of the other forms. Since the principle of conservation of energy had not yet been stated in all-embracing form, Erasmus Darwin, less cautious than Hobbes, could permit the irritative motion to waste itself in "simply subsiding," but he left no room for any supposition that the direct effect of a stimulus could be to negate contraction, rather than to provoke it.

By 1845, when the Webers made their report, it was already believed that the nervous impulse itself was an electric current, and it was simply unthinkable that such an electric impulse, reaching a tissue which had the distinctive characteristic of irritability, could produce an inhibitory effect. How could electricity, this quickening imponderable fluid which seemed at last to provide the long-sought physical substitute for animal spirits, exert a depressant rather than a stimulating influence? How could a muscle, whose special quality it was to respond by contraction, become flaccid as a result of stimulation?

In 1847, Helmholtz enunciated the principle of the conservation of energy in sweeping terms which left no doubt that it must embrace the physiological as well as the physical realm. Thus he extended the doctrine of the ancients—that something could not arise out of nothing—by just as effectively excluding the possibility that nothing could arise out of something, whether by a process of "simple subsidence" or in any other way. In 1848, duBois-Reymond triumphantly proclaimed that by his experiments he had in fact proved that the nervous principle is identical with electricity.

These advances were far more exciting than any demonstration of inhibition could be. To many physiologists, it seemed that to admit the concept of inhibition was to abandon the principles underlying the progress of their science, from Haller to duBois-Reymond.

A plausible explanation of the inhibitory effect, which would leave the principle of irritability unweakened, was urgently needed. One such explanation was offered by Schiff (1849), who argued that the rhythm of heart action was due to very rapid fatigue of responding elements in the heart, a kind of intermittent exhaustion, and that the effect of vagal stimulation was to make this exhaustion continuous. A quarter of a century passed before this hypothesis, which is not unlike the later theory of Wedensky, was reluctantly abandoned by its author (Schiff, 1873). Another widely accepted explanation was that suggested by Brown-Séquard (1853), who argued that the cause of cardiac deceleration was undoubtedly vasoconstriction of the coronary arteries. That is, the stimulation did after all result in muscular contraction, quite as expected, but the contraction of the arterial muscles expelled from the heart the blood which was the natural stimulus to the heart's contraction, and thus a slowing of the heartbeat was an indirect consequence. These theories could hardly be called satisfactory, but they sufficed to lay the ghost of inhibition, so that it need no longer disturb the orderly dreams of physiologists.

The ghost rose again when Pflüger (1857) demonstrated that intestinal peristalsis is inhibited by the splanchnic nerve. He surmised that the inhibitory fibers were "somehow able to disturb" the innervation of motor ganglia. Then Bernard (1858) showed that a branch of the facial nerve actually caused *dilation* of blood vessels in the submaxillary gland, and this discredited Brown-Séquard's theory that vasoconstriction is the cause of cardiac deceleration. In 1862, Rosenthal described the inhibition of respiration by stimulation of the upper laryngeal nerve, Eckhard demonstrated that the action of the erectile nerves is inhibitory (see page 42), and Goltz was moved to exclaim (as quoted by Meltzer, 1899) "Let us resist the flood of inhibitory nerves!"

The foregoing is background. But in 1862 there also occurred another event, which was to have a great though long-delayed impact on the history of psychology. In the laboratory of Claude Bernard, in Paris, a young Russian physiologist, Ivan Sechenov, demonstrated the inhibition of a spinal reflex by structures in the brain stem of the frog. The whole problem of inhibition had been raised, one might say, to a higher level.

SECHENOV AND ANSTIE 2

Sechenov's discovery of central inhibition was no accident. But it was preceded, as most individual achievements are, by a series of fortunate events which created the opportunity for it. Few scientists have biographies so fascinating as that of Sechenov, and in which there is such evident interaction between the events of the laboratory and conditions in the surrounding social milieu. Because this book appears in the centennial year of Sechenov's epoch-making masterpieces, we take leave to embellish it with a few paragraphs on the life of this quite remarkable man. He was a younger son in a provincial family of very modest means. His father owned some land, but his mother had been an unschooled peasant girl; and this is doubtless the beginning of Sechenov's later interest, not merely in the education of the working classes, but particularly in the education of women. It was the older brother who suggested to their widowed mother, out of wisdom gained by a tour of duty in the army, that a good way to provide for Ivan's future would be to send him to a military engineering school, where tuition would be free. Thus Sechenov received his opportunity for education under conditions rather similar to those that enabled Helmholtz, and many other gifted young Germans of modest means, to study medicine, on condition that they agree to serve as army doctors for a term of years after graduation. (Helmholtz was released from this obligation after several years as an Army surgeon, when his scientific genius had been demonstrated.)

At the engineering school, the brighter students were permitted to complete their degrees, but those in the lower half of the class, at the end of the second year, were commissioned as junior officers and packed off to their military duties. Sechenov was an industrious student who stood near the top of his class, but he was also a very proud young man. He dared to show open disrespect for one of his duller classmates, the braggart son of the school commandant—behavior hardly to be tolerated in a poor student without family. Therefore, at the end of the second year Sechenov's studies were interrupted and he was assigned as instructor to the military school in Kiev.

As it turned out, this was fortunate for science. The qualities of this brilliant and earnest young man, who was by disposition so unsuited to a military career, soon made him a welcome guest in the home of a cultured family in that provincial city, where he often sought refuge from the barracks life. A part of this home's attraction was the daughter, a young widow, surely fitted by her personality and her endowments to become the heroine of a Russian novel. She opened for the young officer new horizons of interest, the chiaroscuro world of the mid-century Russian intelligentsia, in which the dark shadows of the present were pierced by bright shafts of hope for the future. We can imagine her singing the following song, as did the heroine in Chernyshevsky's still unwritten novel, *What Is to Be Done?* (which was indeed to be published in the same year as Sechenov's own great work, *The Reflexes of the Brain*):

> Nous voulons pour tous les hommes
> Science et destins meilleurs.
> Étudions, travaillons,
> La force est à qui saura; . . .
> Qu'elle vienne, la science
> Qui nous affranchira tous![1]

Doubtless the still boyish Sechenov was smitten by love, but this unnamed heroine of science had a nobler role to play: to inspire the ardent genius with a passion for humanistic science. Soon

[1] I find the last two lines in yellowed notes, based on I know not what edition. They do not appear in the English translation listed among the references. Perhaps the censor had eliminated them from the original printing of the novel.

Sechenov had resigned his commission and was off to St. Petersburg, this time to study medicine, living on a pittance which enabled him to eat meat twice a week and to drink tea once a month (Sechenov, 1907).

As a medical student, Sechenov was clearly brilliant. When he took his degree in 1856 he also earned a scholarship which enabled him to travel abroad for two years to complete his education. Before following him there, we must read the theses which he stated in his dissertation. The topic was the medical treatment of alcoholism, a subject of lively concern to those who hoped for better things from the Russian peasant. How surprising, then, to read these theses (Sechenov, Pavlov, & Wedensky, 1952, I, p. 133), which show that his mind was already coping with a much broader problem:

"2. All movements known in physiology as voluntary are reflex movements in the strictest sense of the word.

"3. The outstanding feature of the normal activity of the brain (as expressed outwardly in the form of movement) is the disproportion between excitation and effect (movement).

"4. The reflex activity of the brain is more extensive than that of the spinal cord.

"5. There are no nerves which suppress movement."

During the next two years Sechenov studied abroad, chiefly under Karl Ludwig in Vienna and under DuBois-Reymond in Berlin. He returned to Russia in 1858, and immediately attracted favorable attention to himself by a course of lectures on animal electricity, the first to be given in Russia, enlivened in the contemporary German manner with demonstrations accompanying the lectures. In this period, the liberal Sechenov must certainly have been a regular reader of Chernyshevsky's journal *Sovremenik* (*The Contemporary*). He must have been familiar with Chernyshevsky's (1860) essay, "The anthropological principle in philosophy," in which it is stated that modern science views man as a unitary being, and sees no more essential difference between mental and physical orders of events than between the different qualities of inanimate objects. Of the year in which that essay appeared, Sechenov himself has written as follows, in his autobiography (1907): "1860 is memorable, I think, to everyone who lived then in Petersburg. Everyone knew that the great act of emancipation of millions of serfs would soon be performed, and everyone waited trembling for its proclamation. . . . New problems, new demands on life were born in literature and in society; but in this year the general mood was quiet and tense, expectant without any outbursts, like before a great festival."

It must have been shortly after the proclamation that Sechenov left for Paris, for a period of study and research in the laboratory of Claude Bernard. In his heart he had hope; in his mind he still carried the problem which he had formulated five years earlier: "The outstanding feature of the normal activity of the brain is the disproportion between excitation and effect."

How does one investigate the reasons for a lack of correspondence between stimulating events and cerebral reflexes? It was still all too true, as Bain had remarked, that "we are not permitted" to explore the sites where rival influences meet in the brain, and neutralize each other. However, it had been known for a long time that the spinal reflexes of the decerebrate frog were stronger than those of the intact animal. Most physiologists accepted the explanation that with so much nervous tissue removed, any given excitation would be less diffused, more concentrated in purely spinal channels, and hence evoke a stronger response. However (Sechenov tells us), Weber had already speculated that this fact was somehow connected with our ability sometimes to exercise voluntary control over involuntary acts, such as coughing. It was to this idea of Weber's that Sechenov returned, and not to the simple problem of reflex excitability. What he saw was that in the decerebrate frog there was a regular correspondence between excitation and effect, so that a stronger stimulus always evoked a stronger and swifter response, while in the intact animal it would sometimes happen that the response to a strong stimulus would be slight, or the response to a weak stimulus would be exaggerated. In the intact frog, in other words, there was some of that "disproportion between excitation and effect" which was the distinguishing mark of the brain's activity.

Sechenov decided to measure reflex excitability in terms of latency, using a procedure which had been developed by Türck. This was to dip the frog's leg into a weak acid solution, and to count the number of metronome beats until the frog's leg was lifted in the reflex act of defensive withdrawal. It was a measure of reflex readiness, rather than strength of response. Sechenov performed this experiment under a variety of conditions, systematically transecting the brain, the midbrain, and the spinal cord at several different levels, sometimes successively on the same animal, and noticing also the effect of stimulating the nerves at the point of the transection either with paper wads which had been soaked in a solution of common salt, or with a weak electric current. (The protocols printed in his report were based on experiments in which the salt solution had been used, but years later, in replying to criticisms, he stated that both methods had given similar results.) He observed that it was only transection at the lower levels which would result in stronger reflexes, whereas a cut through the cerebrum would always result in weaker reflexes. The most pronounced effect was produced by cutting through the roots of the optic nerves at the level of the third ventricle. Not only did this cut, in itself, result in stronger reflex excitability, but stimulation of the cut end of the neuraxis with salt-soaked paper immediately reversed the effect, suppressing the reflex. Because of the animals' quiet demeanor, Sechenov argued that the inhibition could not be a consequence of the depressing influence of pain. Control experiments showed that it was not due to loss of blood during the operation. That it was not due to overexcitation or fatigue of the mechanisms involved appeared from the fact that the effect was instantaneous, not preceded by any brief period of movement. All these observations led Sechenov to conclude that certain midbrain structures, at the level of the optic nerves, contained centers which normally inhibit spinal reflex activity. For convenience, let us designate as *Sechenov's principle* the hypothesis *that the brain stem includes structures which exercise tonic inhibitory influence on other portions of the nervous system.*

On his homeward journey, Sechenov visited his old friends and former teachers in Vienna and Berlin. He conquered their skepticism with successful demonstrations of his experiment, and rejoiced in its impact and in their generous praise. He knew that he had achieved a result of tremendous importance. By showing that inhibition took place within the central nervous system, he had opened the way to an understanding of higher nervous processes. All the while, he must have been working feverishly on the implications of his finding, for within a few months after his return home, at the latest, the manuscript of *The Reflexes of the Brain* must have been ready for the printer. Chernyshevsky's *Sovremenik* was the obvious medium for its publication.

However, the censors intervened. They declared that although Sechenov's thoroughly deterministic treatment of the mind was perhaps not immoral in itself, it would endanger the morals of readers without adequate scientific preparation. Therefore, the work appeared in the *Medical Bulletin* (*Medizinskii Vestnik*), in 1863. The matter was embarrassing to the Ministry of Education, and the police censorship was relaxed. A pamphlet edition was printed in 1864, but the ban was soon reimposed. Eventually it was lifted again, and a new edition was printed in 1870. Pavlov and Bechterev both have testified to the fact that the book was a subject of lively interest to the university students of their day. Whatever its political intent, no one can doubt that it had revolutionary implications for psychology.

Our principal interest is in the application which Sechenov made of his finding of central inhibition. It is obvious that he would use it to resolve the contradiction between theoretical determinism and the unpredictability of behavior in practice. But by the manner in which he did this, he also laid the foundation for a totally new kind of psychology, for he asserted that thought, far from being something above action, was in fact something less.

It will be remembered that in one of the theses in his medical dissertation in 1856 he asserted that all voluntary movements must be regarded as reflex (see page 28). This assertion reappears in *The Reflexes* in the following form: "All mental states are developed in the same manner as reflex actions. Thus all the conscious movements following from these acts and which are ordinarily called voluntary are reflex, in the strict sense of the word."

The next thesis referred to the "disproportion between excitation and effect" which is characteristic of cerebral activity. *The Reflexes* explained this thesis in the following way: "At the same time as, by the frequent repetition of associated reflex actions, man learns to group his movements, he also acquires (and always in reflex manner) the faculty of checking them. From this results an innumerable multitude of phenomena, in which the mental activity remains without external expression—in the state of thought, intention, desire, etc.

. . . Among psychic reflex actions there are many in which the last term—the movement—is inhibited."

And thus at last to this oft-quoted sentence: "Thought is a mental reflex reduced to its first two-thirds." It is important to recognize that the inhibitory powers which effect this reduction have been described as subject to improvement by training, and that such training, in both the emotional and the intellectual spheres, is regarded as at least as important as the development of associative bonds.

Sechenov was aware that one of the weaknesses in his position was the fact that his sweeping generalizations about human mental processes were based on an experiment with frogs. So, using somewhat less drastic procedures, he put himself in the frog's place, to test if his own reflex response to acid stimulation could be inhibited by introducing competitive stimulation, at a higher level. He dipped his finger, like the frog's leg, into an acid bath, but what he timed was not the latency of reflex withdrawal, but the latency of the burning acid sensation. Instead of being decerebrated, he was tickled by an assistant. (The choice of an assistant is crucial, since habituation would interfere with the experiment. Since Sechenov, ordinarily very ready to give credits, omits the name of the assistant, we may amuse ourselves with supposing that this role was assigned to the future Mme. Sechenov, who was one of his early students. At any rate, we suggest the scene to any future dramatist of his life.) The results were according to prediction, whether or not he made voluntary efforts to control the somatic response to the tickling (Sechenov, 1935, pp. 171 f.).

One of Sechenov's students, in an experiment patterned on his master's classic work, discovered that reflex excitability is increased when the frog's midbrain is stimulated electrically (Sechenov & Pashutin, 1865). Sechenov says that "in this experiment, we observe exactly the same phenomenon as when a man is tickled unexpectedly: the frog responds to our touch by starting with all its body. If, on the other hand, the brain is not stimulated, the frog often remains quiet when touched" (Sechenov, 1935, p. 276). Thus, Sechenov must be acknowledged not only as the pioneer in the study of inhibition as a factor in adaptive behavior, but also as having first made, with Pashutin, the discovery of the arousal function of certain brain stem structures. There is a clear parallel between these discoveries and those of Magoun and his coworkers (Magoun & Rhines, 1946; Rhines & Magoun, 1946; Moruzzi & Magoun, 1949), which, as we shall see in later chapters, have led to such startling developments in contemporary neurophysiology.

In 1870 Sechenov wrote an essay with the title, *Who must investigate the problems of psychology, and why.* He asserted that the task was one for physiologists alone. Nevertheless he did not concentrate his own efforts on those tasks, finding other problems to engage them. He did important research on the absorption of gases by the blood, and this naturally led him into studies of fatigue. He lectured before audiences of workers on the physiology of work, in support of the movement for the eight-hour day. Indeed, he was always ready to act in support of what he believed. When women were excluded from classes at the university, he lectured without recompense in special classes organized for them. When the Ministry of Education refused to permit the appointment of Metchnikov, a Jew, Sechenov resigned his position in Moscow as a protest, and taught for the next few years in the voluntary "exile" of Odessa. He continued scientifically active until the very end of his century, earning well the title which history was to bestow upon him: "father of Russian physiology."

Among Sechenov's students (and the successor to the chair that Sechenov vacated by his resignation) was Wedensky, whose contributions we shall consider in the next chapter. His work also had great influence on the thinking of Pavlov and Bekhterev, both of whom were members of that student generation which was so zealously protected from *The Reflexes of the Brain* by the czar's censors.

Almost simultaneous with *The Reflexes of the Brain* appeared a remarkable book by an English physician named Anstie. Apparently motivated more by his concern about the misuse of "stimulants" in medical practice than by interest in the nervous system as such, Anstie opened up a new and insightful approach to the problem of inhibition. Drawing primarily on his experience in the administration of chloroform, and on observation of the behavioral phenomena accompanying intoxication by hashish and by alcohol, he came to the conclusion that the mental excitement induced by these means "ought not to be called stimulation at all; that they are, in fact, the results of a partial and highly peculiar kind of paralysis of the brain." Anstie's name is all but forgotten, but "Anstie's principle," as Hughlings Jackson often referred to it, has been of lasting influence, although credit for it is usually given to Jackson himself.

In *Stimulants and Narcotics* (1864), Anstie questioned the then widespread practice of assuming that "every rapidly increased manifestation of mental activity from an external cause," or any marked increase in secretion, or in the force or rate of heart beat, or in any other bodily function, is the result of "the action of a stimulus." One example of an increased function which is not dependent on increased stimulation is taken from the work of Claude Bernard and Brown-Séquard, namely, that sectioning of the sympathetic nerve results in increased secretion. But Anstie finds his principal arguments in clinical observations, and we cannot resist the temptation to quote at length from this book, which will be accessible to few of our readers, and which has suffered such undeserved neglect.

The faculties of the mind are not homogeneous, nor such as are necessarily put in motion all at the same time, or by the same causes. On the contrary, nothing is more certain than that a natural opposition exists between the reason and the will on the one hand, and the emotions and the appetites on the other. . . . The early phenomena of alcoholic intoxication usually wear an appearance at first sight much resembling excitement. But on analyzing the symptoms we are at no loss to perceive that it is the emotional and appetitive part of the mind which is in action, while the intellect, on the contrary, is directly enfeebled. There is no exception to this rule, that in proportion to the degree in which the lower and more animal nature protrudes itself in the actions and words of a drunken person, the less of intellectual activity does he display. It is at least possible, then, that the violent outbreak of the passions is due, not to any stimulation of them but to the removal of the check ordinarily imposed by reason and will. . . .

The simplest explanation may be found in the supposition that, in the absence of any extraordinary circumstances, the apparent exaltation of certain faculties should be ascribed rather to the removal of controlling influences, than to positive stimulation of the faculties themselves, or of the physical machinery by which they work. . . . Something of the nature of paralysis, though it might be partial, has always appeared to me to characterise the action of large doses of opium. . . . and it would seem reasonable to account for the apparent increase of intellectual force, and of emotion, on the supposition that other activities are suspended, and their interference removed. For that would be a violent and improbable theory which should suggest that one portion of the nervous system was excited, and another paralysed, at the same time and by the same agent (Anstie, 1864, pp. 78 ff.).

Anstie was impressed by the fact that there is a regular sequence in the process of intoxication and recovery, or in the behavioral aspects attending the loss of consciousness under chloroform anesthesia, and its gradual recovery during the process of awakening.

The clue to a right appreciation of the successive phenomena is this: that the feelings ordinarily suppressed by voluntary effort, or observed by the impressions of actual life, are displayed, by the removal of their customary veils, *in the order of their concealment*. . . . On the whole, we may say of inebriation . . . that its essence consists in the destruction of the capacity of the brain for retaining or recalling moral and prudential impressions, and also for any kind of continuous intellectual labor; and that the apparent *excitement* of the emotions and desires is, in truth, but the unveiling of the lower part of our nature, which is more or less ready, in each of us, to spring into action when the customary checks are removed (Anstie, 1864, pp. 187 f., 190).

In short, the analysis of the phenomena produced by the above-named narcotics, and by others, would lead us to the conclusion that different agents of this class paralyze the brain in different ways, unveiling, in varying order and capricious combination, various antecedent impressions which have been made upon the mind through the brain. That there is anything "creative" about this process I cannot believe; notwithstanding the opinion of so able an observer as De Quincey. Whatever may be the nature of the dreams which occur in a state of health, a point on which I express no opinion, it appears to me demonstrable, in the clearest way, that the delirium of narcosis, and the delirium seen in various forms of disease, is the immediate consequence of the destruction, for the time at any rate, of the brain's capacity for performing some of its highest functions. Such phenomena universally occur in the midst of a general prostration of the powers of the nervous system, and are strictly comparable to the similar phenomena which terrify some children, because the latter have a weak and imperfectly developed nervous system (Anstie, 1864, pp. 199 f.).

Making some allowance for Victorian moralization, and recognizing the influence of Plato (whose rider and noble steed had such trouble in controlling the unruly horse which completed the team), these passages must still stand as an extraordinary example of insightful analysis of behavior, anticipating much that we have since learned about the cortical inhibition of emotion, about the hierarchic organization of behavior in the nervous system, and the role of maturation in acquisition of control.

Anstie also recognized that sensory inhibition is not, as had been supposed, merely a matter of interference of rival afferent processes. Referring to his personal experience as well as to the testimony of his patients, he stated that the pain of neuralgia tends to increase with fatigue, and from this he concluded that increased sensibility comes with a reduction of nervous energy, rather than its increase. Therefore, he argued, it is evident that pain is being inhibited during periods when the higher levels of the nervous system are working with full vigor.

Anstie's contribution might have been completely lost if it had not come to the attention of Hughlings Jackson, who discerned in it a means for understanding some of the puzzling aspects of epileptic seizures. Probably Jackson was unaware of Anstie's book until some years later. In 1869, five years after the appearance of *Stimulants and Narcotics,* we find that Jackson had begun to think about the organization of levels in the nervous system in an evolutionary sense, as he began to formulate his ideas on what was to become known as the principle of encephalization, but there was still no mention of inhibitory controls:

> The conclusion I have arrived at from study of cases of disease is, that the higher centers are evolved *out of* the lower—receiving intercalations as they ascend from the spinal cord to the cerebrum. The higher center re-represents more specially the impressions and movements already represented generally in the one below it. The co-ordinations are continually being reco-ordinated; for example, those of the pons and medulla are reco-ordinated in the cerebrum. There are in the lower center sensori-motor processes for very *general* purposes, but in their *higher* representatives for the more special (Jackson, 1958, I, p. 107).

In 1875, however, he had decided that in order to explain post-epileptic automatism, it would be necessary to assume the interruption of a control normally exercised by higher levels over the lower:

> I think it probable that there is a transitory epileptic paroxysm in every case of mental automatism. . . . I am fully aware, and freely admit, that occasionally no signs of a prior fit are *discoverable*. . . . I believe there is in such cases, during the paroxysm an internal discharge too slight to cause obvious external effects, but strong enough to put out of use for a time more or less of the highest nervous centers. The mental automatism results, I consider, from over-action of lower nervous centers, because the highest or controlling centers have been thus put out of use. . . . In other words, there is (1) loss of control *permitting* (2) increased automatic action (Jackson, 1958, I, p. 122 f.).

This insight has evidently been gained with the help of Anstie, for to this passage Jackson adds the following footnote: "This principle of over-action of lower centers as a consequence of loss of control from inaction of higher centers was stated by Anstie in his *Stimulants and Narcotics*."

In 1884, in his famous Croonian lectures, Jackson brought the two principles of encephalization and released function together in a single picture. After acknowledging his debt both to Spencer and to Anstie, he said:

> The doctrine of evolution implies the passage from the most organized to the least organized, or, in other terms, from the most general to the most special. Roughly, we say that there is a gradual "adding on" of the more and more special, a continual adding on of new organizations. But this "adding on" is at the same time a "keeping down." The higher nervous arrangements evolved out of the lower keep down those lower, just as a government evolved out of a nation controls as well as directs that nation. If this be a process of evolution, then the reverse process of dissolution is not only a "taking off" of the higher, but it is at the same time a "letting go" of the lower. . . . Another way of stating the general principle involved (Anstie's principle), is that the over-activity in epileptic mania and in the other cases mentioned, is not caused, but is permitted; on cutting across the pneumogastric, the heart is not caused to go faster, but is permitted to go faster. In other words, the lower level of evolution is not "goaded into activity," but is "let go" (Jackson, 1958, II, p. 58 f.).

That Jackson's interpretation was correct in its essentials is attested by modern authorities (Gastaut and Fischer-Williams, 1959). But Anstie's principle has immensely broader implications. Just as Sechenov boldly sketched the outlines for an objective psychology of the higher thought processes, so Anstie provided the foundation for our contemporary understanding of the evocation of instinctive and emotional behavior in man and animals. Coping with different problems, working and thinking in very different ways, each hit upon the fact that inhibition is an essential key to the understanding of behavior.

EVIDENCE ACCUMULATES 3

This chapter will summarize varying aspects of the research and discussion on the subject of inhibition for about forty years following the pioneering contributions of Sechenov and Anstie, including the opening years of the twentieth century and the appearance of Sherrington's monumental monograph on *The Integrative Action of the Nervous System.* The chapter will be somewhat discontinuous, because a full sequential account of the conflicting trends would be too voluminous. [Historical reviews of inhibition include those by Meltzer (1899), Hering (1902), and Howell (1925)].

The interest stirred by Sechenov's paper led to a great deal of experimental and theoretical activity. Other instances of inhibition were discovered; but these at first concerned mostly visceral processes, where it could be demonstrated that the inhibitory innervation was carried by peripheral nerves belonging to the autonomic nervous system. An exception was Goltz's demonstration (1869) that a pinch on the leg would inhibit the croak reflex in the decerebrate frog—a reflex which could otherwise be produced with such unfailing certainty by a gentle stroke on the back that Goltz playfully offered to provide a chorus of frogs for any performance of Aristophanes' play, and to guarantee that they would all croak in unison at exactly the right moments.

The doctrine of inhibitory centers, as proposed by Sechenov, was not popular, and became less so as time passed, even before physiologists began to express dissatisfaction with the concept of nervous centers in general. All sorts of efforts were made to find other explanations. Although Sechenov had explicitly rejected the possibility that there were inhibitory nerves to voluntary muscles, analogous to the inhibitory nerves of the viscera, most workers preferred "inhibitory nerves" to "inhibitory centers." However, the failure to discover such nerves became another factor encouraging the skeptics. When, in 1887, Biedermann found such nerves in the crayfish claw, this only added to the confusion, insofar as his discovery revived the search for nonexisting skeletal inhibitory nerves in vertebrates.

There was a fairly steady succession of theoretical efforts to explain how inhibition is possible, without violating the assumption that the nerve impulse is basically an excitatory phenomenon. Cyon (1871), also a Russian, appealed to the wave nature of the nervous impulse, and hypothesized that two such waves might cancel each other out. Wundt was among those who pointed out that the nervous impulse is not a "wave" in the sense required for such an effect to occur. Without abandoning his theory as applied to the circulatory system, Cyon (1874) conceded that it would not explain the Sechenov phenomenon. But he claimed that since the latter only demonstrated increased reflex latency, rather than reduction in reflex strength, it was not truly inhibitory. In any event, he felt sure that there could be "neither special centers for inhibition, nor special fibers which conduct these inhibitory influences." Interference theories continued to be popular with those who rejected the concept of inhibitory centers.

Wundt (1871) himself advanced another theory of inhibition which tried to escape the implication that there were special neural structures which exercised inhibitory effects. His theory was based on a series of experiments in which he recorded the muscular response to a test stimulus of constant strength, occurring at various intervals subsequent to an initial stimulus to the motor nerve. He emphasized that these experiments were not conducted on nerve-muscle preparations, but on the living organism (the frog) in which the circulatory system was intact. The "inhibitory" effects which he described were such as would have been interpreted later in terms of the refractory phase. However, they led him to argue for a concept of inhibition as something which takes place within the nerve cell. It is an intracellular, rather than an intercellular, theory of inhibition. At that time, the nervous system was thought to be a reticular system of continuous fibers, with cell bodies occurring here and there in the network. Synapses in the central nervous system had not yet been postulated, much less discovered. Wundt believed that the "work" of the cell was of two kinds, positive and negative. Positive work, which released warmth and other energy, including excitatory effects, depended on the dissolution of complex molecules; negative work consisted in the reconstitution of such molecules. Both processes go on simultaneously in all parts of the cell, the first being the basis of excitatory and the second of inhibitory effects. However, this inhibition consists merely in an intracellular resistance which must be overcome by any outside influence which tends to excite the cell, that is, to release its energy through "positive molecular work."

Wundt's theory of inhibition was incorporated in the first edition of his *Grundzüge der physiologischen Psychologie* (1874), the book which proclaimed the "new science" of physiological psychology. Here he pointed out that in most instances of stimulation there is a simultaneous increase of both the excitatory and the inhibitory effects, and "The entire process of excitation is therefore dependent at every moment on a mutual interaction of excitation and inhibition." He also hypothesized that stimuli which reach the central region of a ganglion cell have predominantly inhibitory effects, while those reaching the peripheral regions have predominantly excitatory effects. Hence no special apparatus for inhibition and excitation need be assumed. Wundt's theory of inhibition played no essential part in the early development of his psychological system, but we shall see in Chapter 8 that it had an important part to play in his later development of that system.

Wundt's intracellular theory of inhibition is in many respects similar to that which was put forward by Hering (1888) in his famous address *On the Theory of the Processes in Living Substances.* At that time, it was generally believed that living protoplasm consisted of giant molecules which underwent a continuous process of dissolution and reconstitution. Accordingly, Hering postulated that in all living substances there is an opposition between simultaneous processes of assimilation and dissimilation. The normal state of the tissue is one in which the two processes go forward in a balanced manner. However, either process may be accelerated or decelerated by special conditions, leading to a variety of disequilibrated states. The typical response to stimulation is a rapid expenditure of energy, called excitation, which is dissimilatory. Obviously, this must be balanced in the long run by an equal excess of assimilation—what Wundt called "the recovery of the work expended." If the physiological state of the cell is such that this recovery phase takes place quickly rather than slowly, the effect will usually be inhibitory. Hering was shrewd enough to see that the electrical phenomena were only signs of the essential chemical processes, and not their essence. In 1899, in another address *On the Theory of Nervous Action,* he emphasized again that a nerve cell, or any cell, must not be thought of as having only one way of responding; and he pointed for proof to the fact that the same cell, depending on its momentary physiological state, may respond to the same stimulation either by excitation or by inhibition. In England a similar theory was advanced, with some experimental support, by Gaskell (1886). The same general approach was taken also by Max Verworn (1895), who said that stimuli could produce either an intensification of life processes, which is excitation, or a slowing down of such processes, which results in a paralysis or inhibition. Still later, Ladd and Woodworth (1911) suggested, without specific reference to these earlier theories, that perhaps each neuron "has two opposite modes of response, positive and negative, corresponding to excitation and inhibition. It may in this case give either response to a stimulus, but more particularly according to its own condition as determined by preceding stimuli and responses. Each positive response is followed by a negative phase, and each negative response by a back swing toward a positive phase."

A very informative review of the early research on inhibition was written by Brunton (1874). After a discussion of vagal inhibition of the heart, Brunton points out that it is characteristic of the circulatory system generally that the muscular walls of the blood vessels are maintained in a state of tonic contraction, which is relaxed by inhibitory central innervation. He refers in particular to the work of Eckhard (1862), as showing that erection of the penis is due to relaxation of this tonus by inhibitory innervation through the *nervi erigentes,* which permits blood to pour into the relaxed vessels and distend them. A brief mention of Sechenov's finding of inhibitory centers in the optic lobes of the frog is followed by an extended discussion of efforts to establish the existence of cerebral inhibitory centers in the higher animals. Brunton mentioned the claim of Simonoff (1866) that electrical stimulation of the brain reduced spinal reflexes in dogs—with stimulation of the frontal lobes leading to the most marked inhibitory effect—and related this to the fact that Ferrier, in his explorations of the motor effects of faradic stimulation of the brain, obtained no response from stimulation of the frontal lobes. He said that he himself tried to duplicate Simonoff's work without success, but was still continuing these efforts.[1] On the other hand he related that McKendrick (1874) did have some success in similar experiments, and observed in particular "that the convulsions which occur in pigeons immediately after decapitation may be arrested by the application of a faradic current to the upper part of the spinal cord." He also reproduced a clinical note by Crichton Browne, reporting the case of a patient suffering from encephalitis. Browne first noted that "Tickling the soles of the feet and pricking the toes produced no movement whatever. This is a most interesting observation. It seems to prove that nerve currents set in motion by irritation of the brain or of some of its convolutions transmitted down the cord may inhibit reflex action." Then a few days later, after unconsciousness had set in, "reflex action as determined by pricking and pinching returned. After death the brain was found disorganised by erysipelatous changes." Brunton commented that "In this case excessive inhibition seems to have been produced by excitement of the cerebral centres through inflammation and to have ceased when these centres became disorganised."

Based on his review of the literature, Brunton argued that inhibitory centers such as those which Sechenov found in the brain

[1] Siminoff's technique is of considerable interest, because it comes so close to the modern technique of implanted electrodes. He inserted two steel sewing needles through the skull, and in order to be able to do this with ease, he did most of his work with dogs less than one month old. Then he attached wires to the needles, which, he says, were sufficiently secure so that they generally did not move during the experiment.

stem probably also exist throughout the spinal cord and also in the cerebrum. Even this, however, is not enough to explain all of the experimental phenomena, and he found it necessary to assume that the effect of the higher centers is often to inhibit the lower inhibitory centers.

> In the instances of inhibition already given, we have seen the action of muscles voluntary and involuntary, and of glands arrested by the influence of nerves, but there is another kind of inhibition no less important and still more complicated. This may be termed inhibition of inhibition, or inhibition of inhibitory centres as distinguished from the inhibition of motor centres which we have hitherto been considering. At present our notions of nervous action seem to be getting as involved as the Ptolemaic system of astronomy, and just as epicycles became heaped upon cycles so nerve centres are being added to nerve centres. And yet, clumsy though the system may be, it serves at present a useful purpose, and may give us real aid until a better is discovered (Brunton, 1874, p. 203).

This is in fact a fair approximation to the situation as we understand it today, complicated, but only as living organisms are complicated. The principle of "inhibition of inhibition," or disinhibition, was to be stated anew years later by Pavlov, who regarded it as one of the most important characteristics of nervous activity. However, in recognition of Brunton's priority, we shall designate this as *Brunton's principle: In the intact organism the release of an inhibition is usually brought about by inhibition of the inhibition, that is, by disinhibition.* In one of his illustrations of this principle, Brunton returns to the example of erection of the penis.

> We have already seen that the normal vaso-motor action of the ganglia in the penis may be arrested by inhibitory centres in the cord, so that the vessels dilate when these centres are stimulated by means of afferent nerves. But these inhibitory centres are themselves checked by means of irritation applied to certain other afferent nerves, and the vaso-motor ganglia are then allowed to act undisturbed. Thus the dilatation of the vessels in the penis of a dog, whose spinal cord has been divided, may be at once stopped and the organ restored to its normal condition by pinching the foot of the animal or irritating the scrotum or anal region by a faradic current (Brunton, 1874, p. 203 f.).

Perhaps Brunton expected his Victorian readers to recognize without reminder that sometimes in the human, with spinal cord undivided, cerebral inhibitions might effect the disinhibitory loss of penile erection. At any rate, some pages later he went on to say:

> The effect of a stimulus arising from the periphery of the body, and acting upon a nerve centre, may be inhibited by a stimulus from the ideational centres. Thus the sobs and tears which naturally follow a fall or blow in a child a few years old will often be stopped by the idea that tears are unmanly. . . . But the stimulus arising from the ideational centre probably does not act directly on the motor and emotional centres, but only through the medium of some inhibitory apparatus. If this be so, the nature of the actions performed by any individual on the application of a stimulus to the periphery . . . will depend to a considerable extent on the development and power of the inhibitory apparatus through which one centre may influence another (Brunton, 1874, p. 219).

This remarkable article ends with a brief discussion of the effects of various drugs, including alcohol, nicotine, hashish, etc., on the inhibitory centers. Brunton gives special attention to the fact that the same drug frequently has opposite effects in small and large doses, and he ends with this prophetic statement: "It is not impossible that we may be able at some future period so to employ remedies as to alter for the better the moral character of individuals, and greatly diminish the prevalence of crime."

Reliance on nerve "centers" became less and less popular as time passed, and before long Brunton (1883) abandoned his Ptolemaic theory for what he thought to be a more parsimonious explanation. He offered a theory of the same general type as that which had first been suggested by Cyon, one in which inhibition is to be regarded as a result of interference between different sets of nerve impulses. He started out from a fact already noted in the earlier article, that in the phenomenon of tickling there is convulsive response to very light tactile stimulation, but that this violent response can be immediately inhibited by a firm contact, that is (as he viewed it), by more intense stimulation of the same kind. Hence, he argued, it is neither the amount nor the kind of excitation which is decisive, but something about the relationship among excitatory impulses. He found a further clue in the effects of drugs, and specifically in the reversal of the effect which may be observed when a dose is increased. He hypothesized that the influence of a drug is usually to slow the transmission of the nerve impulse, without stopping it, and if this causes an inhibitory rather than an excitatory outcome it is probably due to a change in the temporal relationship of impulses arriving at given centers. He emphasized that nerve impulses probably travel at different speeds in different fibers, and hence any condition which influences the rate of conduction unequally in different fibers may, by upsetting the normal time relationships, change exciting into inhibiting interactions.

In 1876 Ferrier's important book, *The Functions of the Brain* appeared. This book was influential in establishing the view, which was so widely accepted for the next fifty years, that the frontal lobes of the cerebral hemispheres are the seat of the intellectual functions. Ferrier's theory was in agreement with the views being expressed at the same time by Hitzig, whose pioneering work on the discovery of the motor areas Ferrier was helping to amplify by his own experiments. However, Ferrier's arguments are of particular interest to us because, following the line of argument already presented by Brunton, he looked upon the frontal lobes as having predominantly inhibitory functions. It is for this reason, his friend Brunton had hinted, that he was unable to produce motor effects in this area, and it is precisely for this reason that he regarded it as the seat of the intellect. In Chapter 8 we shall look at Ferrier's psychological theories in some detail. Here, we shall mention only that he anticipated the Watsonian theory that thinking is suppressed speech, he emphasized the role of inhibition in attention, and he described the part that it played in overcoming infantile impulsiveness. It was this high estimate of the importance of inhibition which led him to conclude that "the centers of inhibition . . . constitute the organic basis of all the higher intellectual faculties. And in proportion to their development we should expect a corresponding intellectual power." Here he quotes with approval Bain's statement that "A great profusion of remembered images, ideas, or notions, avails little for practical ends without the power of arrest or selection, which in its origin is purely voluntary." Then Ferrier tied all this in with the conclusion for which his book has been particularly remembered—the importance of the frontal lobes.

In proportion to the development of the faculty of attention are the intellectual and reflective powers manifested. This is in accordance with the anatomical development of the frontal lobes of the brain, and we have various experimental and pathological data for localizing in these the centers of inhibition, the physiological substrata of this psychological faculty. It has already been shown that electrical irritation of the antero-frontal lobes causes no motor manifestations, a fact which, though a negative one, is consistent with the view that, though not actually motor, they are inhibitory-motor, and expend their energy in inducing internal changes in the centers of actual motor execution (Ferrier, 1876, p. 287 f.).

Ultimately a crowbar thrust through the brain of an unschooled laborer, and Lashley's more orderly ablations of cerebral cortex in university-trained rats, provided some of the most persuasive data which led to abandonment of Ferrier's hypothesis. More recently, it has been found that prefrontal surgery does interfere with the performance of delayed response tasks (e.g., Weiskrantz et al., 1960) and so we are wondering once again whether there may not be much truth in Ferrier's argument that the prefrontal lobes are essential for some of the higher intellectual functions, because they are the seat of important inhibitory capacities.

Possibly the most important single contribution to the experimental literature of inhibition, in the period between the work of Sechenov and that of Sherrington, was the demonstration of cortical inhibition by Bubnoff and Heidenhain, in 1881. At the University of Breslau, in Silesia, close to the border of Russian Poland, the distinguished German physiologist Rudolf Heidenhain had a steady stream of Russian students. One of these was Wedensky, of whom anon. Another was to be Pavlov. Between these came Bubnoff, whom we remember only as a name linked with Heidenhain's in this important study.

The problem with which Bubnoff and Heidenhain were immediately concerned was not inhibition, but the physiological nature of hypnosis.[2] They wanted to produce in their experimental animals the kind of cerebral depression which they thought must be characteristic of the hypnotic state, and they thought that they had succeeded in doing this by putting their dogs under morphine narcosis. Their electrical procedure consisted in recording movements of the

[2] G. Stanley Hall (1923) tells the following anecdote of his student days in Germany: "There was much interest in hypnotism and I visited Breslau to see Heidenhain's remarkable methods and results. At one time he passed down a line of soldiers giving each a glass marble to hold up and gaze at in a fixed way, as the result of which nearly a third became more or less cataleptic."

limbs in response to electrical stimulation of the motor cortex. Because of their interest in hypnosis they made observations at various depths of narcosis, and they noticed that reflex excitability did not decrease progressively with increasing narcotization. On the contrary, it increased at first, under light narcotization, and then decreased sharply under heavier dosage. They also observed that if the cortical stimulation was weak, then an added sensory stimulation, such as a light stroking of the paw, would retard the response, whereas if the cortical stimulus was strong, the same peripheral stimulation would accelerate it. They particularly observed that in the narcotized state all muscular responses tended to be tonic, that is, unduly prolonged. Nevertheless, a light stroke on the paw, or a light tap on the nose, might cause a sudden complete relaxation. Struck by the fact that the effect of a relatively strong cortical stimulus could thus be set aside by a very weak peripheral stimulus, they wondered whether a weak cortical stimulus might have the same effect. "The test gave a positive answer: if a lasting contraction of the experimental muscle was evoked in any manner, whether by strong electrical stimulation of the cortical center for the foreleg, or by reflex means, it could be interrupted by much weaker stimulation of the *same* cortical point, either completely at the very first stimulation, or stepwise by repeated stimulations" (Bubnoff & Heidenhain, 1881).

They concluded that one possible interpretation of these observations was that both excitatory and inhibitory cells were located at the same point in the cortex, the former being more responsive to strong stimulation, the latter to weak stimulation. They stated the following hypothesis:

> Under normal conditions, it seems, every central excitation finds or produces in the excited center conditions which, as soon as the stimulation is over, prepare a prompt end to the excitation, or more correctly, reduce it to the point where it is below the threshold value. If such a precise limitation of the central stimulation conditions, whether motor or sensory, is absent, so that every central excitation only subsides slowly in the course of time, then neither would our movements be exactly determinable according to our desires with respect to time, nor would our sensations and perceptions correspond to the temporal course of the

external impressions which evoke them. [That is, we would be troubled by a confusing medley of positive after-images.]

This consideration leads to the conception that in central activity there must be, along with the process which we call excitation, another process to be reckoned with, which works to dampen the excitation that has been begun (Bubnoff & Heidenhain, 1881, p. 188).

Thus Bubnoff and Heidenhain introduced a new motif into the discussions of inhibition, by recognizing the necessity for a braking process in the brain, not merely to serve the execution of voluntary cessation of movement or suppression of tendencies to movement, but in order to permit efficient performance of movements generally, and also to permit a proper succession of perceptual images without undue interference from one to the next. They reasoned that the effect of morphine was to upset the normal relationship between the excitatory and inhibitory processes, to the disadvantage of the latter, and this resulted in abnormally prolonged responses, tonic rather than phasic contractions. They pointed out that this can explain why there is an increased tendency to epileptic seizures, from the spreading of cortical excitation, under narcosis. With respect to hypnosis, the problem on which they started, they concluded that hypnotic phenomena are probably dependent on an "enormous sinking" of the inhibitory processes which normally accompany central excitations. They were quite positive about the fact that the inhibitory process is definitely antiexcitatory, and not merely a cessation of the excitatory process. This deduction, *that every cortical excitation tends to arouse a local inhibitory process which has the function of limiting the excitation,* we shall in later discussions refer to as Bubnoff and Heidenhain's principle, or more briefly, as *Heidenhain's principle.*

In this same series of experiments, Bubnoff and Heidenhain also observed the phenomenon of cortical facilitation. They reported that "in a certain stage of morphine narcosis, a subliminal stimulus which would be ineffective by itself, has a powerful effect if just before its application to the motor apparatus there is a very light tactile stimulation of the skin of certain body parts." To perform this experiment, the minimal cortical stimulus requisite for a motor response is first determined, while the animal is sleeping quietly, and the inductorium is adjusted to give a lower, below-threshold shock. The paw is then stroked lightly and, allowing sufficient time to avoid any summation effect, the previously subliminal cortical stimulus is then applied, and found to be effective. Stimulation of the belly or chest on the same side as the paw have a similar, but weaker effect; peripheral stimulation on the other side of the body is without effect.

Essentially the same facilitation phenomenon which had been described by Bubnoff and Heidenhain was again described in the same journal, in the following year, by Sigmund Exner. However, Exner (1882) not only described the phenomenon, but also gave it a catching name. He thought of the facilitating stimulus as somehow lowering the threshold of excitability for the reflex path, thus "opening the road" or "smoothing the way" for the stimulus to follow. The German language offers a single expressive word for this concept: *Bahnung*. The word caught on, and for a long time was current in the physiological literature of every language. Indeed, one wonders whether more modern thinking, or the anti-Teutonism engendered by two major wars has been more responsible for the fact that it has given way, in French and in English, to the less colorful *facilitation*.

Exner himself, as we shall see in a later chapter, looked upon inhibition and facilitation, *Hemmung und Bahnung*, as two equally important principles of nervous action. In general, he wrote, "the play of excitations in the cortex is constantly under the simultaneous influence of inhibitions and facilitations. The momentary state of each individual fiber depends on which of the two antagonistic effects has the upper hand in respect to it." These lines were written in 1894, as part of a psychological treatise in which he also distinguished between two kinds of attention, based upon these two processes. However, many of those who were still reluctant to accept the concept of inhibition looked hopefully to *Bahnung* for explanation of all the vagaries of the brain's behavior.

It was in the midst of a study of *Bahnung* or facilitation that Bowditch and Warren (1890) discovered another striking instance of inhibition. They were studying the facilitation of the knee jerk by voluntary muscular effort. At a signal, their subjects were to clench their fists, and the extent of the knee jerk with and without this preliminary facilitation was compared. To their surprise, they discovered that if the signal for hand-clenching preceded the tap on the tendon by more than about four-tenths of a second, the reflex response was diminished rather than increased. This finding and others of the same general sort encouraged some physiologists to believe that inhibition and facilitation were essentially the same phenomenon, the difference depending only on very fine differences in the timing of nervous impulses at points of confluence in the nervous system.

Wedensky, the student of both Sechenov and Heidenhain, succeeded to the chair which Sechenov resigned in protest against an act of anti-Semitism, and became himself the founder of what is now generally designated in Russia as the Wedensky-Ukhtomsky school. He is probably the outstanding example of a physiologist who saw in inhibition not merely an important problem, but the central problem of physiological theory. His contributions to the subject range over a long period of years. The demonstration of "Wedensky inhibition" was first performed in 1886, but the definitive statement of his views, on which the following account is largely based, is the monograph *Excitation, Inhibition, and Narcosis* (1903).

Wedensky's important early contributions were based on an ingenious use of the telephone, itself one of the new wonders of the age. It was not yet possible to record a rapid succession of nerve impulses, but Wedensky found that if he "listened in" on the nerve's activity, it was easy to distinguish between the steady note of a healthily functioning nerve whose rate of discharge kept pace with the rhythm of the inductorium being used to stimulate it, and the irregular noise of a nerve in which the conduction of excitation could not be maintained at this frequency. Others before him had noticed that although a narcotized section of nerve was not directly stimulable, it might nevertheless transmit an excitation which had been initiated in a healthy sector of nerve. Conduction in the nerve was studied indirectly, by observing the contractions in a nerve-muscle preparation, and by this method it appeared that the nerve's ability to conduct was not gradually reduced, but was extinguished suddenly and completely as the narcosis took effect. Wedensky confirmed these results, but he also used his telephone technique to detect activity in the final stretch of nerve, following the narcotized sector. He discovered that before the narcotized sector ceased to conduct excitation, as evidenced by failure of the muscle to contract, it passed through a transitional stage of defective conduction. As long as the nerve was capable of following the frequency of stimulation from the inductorium, the action current passing through Wedensky's earphones gave a clear musical tone, but when it could no longer maintain that frequency, the tone was replaced by a "hollow sound," accompanied by confused noises. Investigating further, Wedensky discovered that this transitional stage was followed by a "paradoxical stage" of deeper narcotization, in which the nerve was capable of transmitting weak excitations, although strong excitations were blocked by the narcosis. This fact had escaped the attention of previous investigators, because it had been the regular practice to use only the minimal stimulus which was needed to produce a response. Furthermore, at a time when the narcotized sector was still stimulable, as evidenced by tonic contraction of the muscle to steady stimulation, the introduction of an *additional* stimulation at an earlier point caused a reduction in the strength of the muscular contraction, that is, an inhibition.

In seeking an explanation for these phenomena, Wedensky found that he could bring about the paradoxical stage by other means than narcotization, and he therefore decided to designate it by a new name, *parabiosis*. He conceived of parabiosis as a kind of local, nonpropagating excitation, which constitutes a morbid but reversible condition, and one which might be brought about by many different forms of stimulation. Like any excitation, it has the effect of preventing response to other stimulation, including that which would ordinarily evoke propagating excitation, that is, a nervous discharge. In other words, the parabiotic tissue cannot respond, because it is already in a state of excitation, but since this excited state does not propagate itself, it of course does not lead to a muscular response. The inability of the nerve to follow the rhythm of stimulation in the early, transitional stage is considered to be due to interference between the newly arriving stimulation and the local, "hidden" excitation already taking place in the parabiotic (narcotized) sector. This description of the inhibitory state as a morbid state is in contrast to the Hering-Gaskell theory, which described inhibition as a restorative or assimilative phase in the nerve's metabolism.

Wedensky felt that he had proved his theory when he could produce a like effect by the use of stimulation alone, without the use of a narcotic. This can be done by stimulating a single nerve fiber with two electrodes, at different points. The first impulse is given by the peripheral electrode, that is, the one nearer the muscle, and results in an initial twitch. The first impulse from the central electrode is timed to fall in the relative refractory phase of the nerve, which follows that first effective discharge. This second, central impulse is therefore able to produce an abortive, but not an effective excitation; without evoking any response of the muscle, it does renew the refractory phase of the nerve. If the rhythm of stimulation from both electrodes is such that each successive shock from one falls within the relative refractory phase produced by the previous shock from the other, the effect is to maintain the state of parabiosis. This phenomenon has come to be called "Wedensky inhibition." It leads Wedensky to this conclusion: "It is possible to regard inhibition as a narcosis which is evoked by purely physiological factors—by arriving impulses—and one which therefore disappears immediately when they are removed." He defined the functional *lability* of tissues as their ability to follow the time sequence of stimulation. (In this concept he antedated Lapicque's notion of chronaxy, and although it is probable that Lapicque developed the idea independently, he did subsequently acknowledge that there was every reason for him to have been familiar with an article on lability which Wedensky had published in a French journal.) Wedensky emphasized that the nerve cell and the terminal apparatus have lower lability than the nerve fiber, and it is therefore relatively easy to induce parabiosis at one of those points, by a frequency of stimulation beyond that to which they can successfully respond.

At the Third International Congress of Psychology, Wedensky (1897) described contralateral motor inhibition in the frog. He stated that when motor points were stimulated simultaneously in both hemispheres, the stimulation of the point for flexion of a given limb in one hemisphere would raise the threshold for the corresponding point, and lower the threshold for the antagonist, in the opposite hemisphere. Later, Hering (the younger) and Sherrington (1897) described the same phenomenon in the monkey, without reference to Wedensky's work—an oversight for which Wedensky subsequently chided them because, he said, Hering had been present listening to his report in Munich.

Wedensky's work gave added impetus to the movement away from reliance on special inhibitory nerves[3] and inhibitory centers, in favor of the explanation of inhibition as a general process which might occur in any nerve cell. Lucas (1911) attempted to formulate a general theory of inhibition based upon it, in which he tried to explain all inhibition as an aspect of the refractory phase. However, he abandoned this theory when the all-or-none character of the nerve impulse under normal conditions was shown (1917). Most physiologists outside of Russia have long been disposed to dismiss Wedensky inhibition as a curious artifact which is unrelated to the inhibitions which actually occur in behavior. For the Wedensky-Ukhtomsky school, parabiosis is a basic theoretical principle of prime importance. Furthermore, it is possible that the readiness of Russian physiologists generally, including Pavlov, to acknowledge the importance of inhibition, is largely a result of the prominence given to this topic by Wedensky and his followers. Pavlov's designation of "paradoxical" and "ultraparadoxical" states reflects Wedensky's influence. His students include not only Ukhtomsky, but also Beritov, who has been especially outspoken in his criticism of Pavlov's theories. The work of both these men will be considered in Chapter 10.

In 1888, Charles Mercier wrote a book titled *The Nervous System and the Mind,* in which the inhibitory functions of the nervous system were emphasized. Mercier (1888a) also presented his views to a meeting of the Neurological Society in London, where Hughlings Jackson and J. McKeen Cattell were two members of a distinguished list of discussants whose remarks have been preserved in an addendum to Mercier's paper. Mercier declared that inhibition is an essential and ever-present aspect of nervous functioning, and that

[3] He himself pointed out that although he made no mention of inhibitory nerves in describing cortical inhibition in the frog, the distinguished Hermann gave an account of this experiment, in his *Textbook of Physiology,* in which he assumed that inhibitory nerves were involved.

"every nerve center is normally subject to inhibitory influence imposed upon it from without," since otherwise a center once stimulated would continue to discharge without stop. While this may be an overstatement, it is certainly true, as Bubnoff and Heidenhain had already surmised and as Sherrington was to demonstrate, that efficient motor control is dependent on inhibitory limitation of the after-discharge from excited cells. But whereas Bubnoff and Heidenhain had pointed to the need of a local inhibitory process, perhaps arising from the cell's own characteristics, Mercier considered that this influence would be exercised at every level by higher centers. When Cattell objected to the apparent endlessness of this chain, Mercier added that the highest centers would be subject to the inhibitory effects from the general mass of cells surrounding them. As one illustration of the need for inhibition, he spoke of the confusion which would result from an endless stream of orders given by an officer to his subordinates, each new order being issued before the previous order could be carried out. The aptness of this illustration has since been shown by the example of Klüver's (1933) monkey, its inhibitory capacity reduced by bilateral prefrontal lobectomy, accepting one grape after another as it was offered, and dropping each as the next was offered, without ever getting any grapes into its mouth.

William James, about the same time, reached a similar conclusion. He said that "in a nervous system ideally reduced to the fewest possible terms," any muscular contraction would be self-maintaining. Hence, *"we should all be cataleptics and never stop a muscular contraction once begun, were it not that other processes simultaneously going on inhibit the contraction. Inhibition is therefore not an occasional accident; it is an essential and unremitting element of our cerebral life"* (1890, II, p. 583). James mentions the coincidence of this conclusion with that which had been reached by Mercier, "by a different path of reasoning."

James then developed in some detail the idea of neural drainage as the basis for learning, concluding with the illustrative explanation of how the burnt child learns to avoid the flame: "S^2 [the burn], having been stimulated immediately after S^1 [the sight of the flame], drained the latter, and now S^1 discharges into S^2 before the discharge of M^1 [grasping] has had time to occur. . . . The result is an inhibition of M^1, or an overtaking of it before it is completed, by M^2 [withdrawing]."

An interesting footnote underscores the essential role of inhibition in the learning process as thus conceived: "This brain-scheme seems oddly enough to give a certain basis of reality to those hideously fabulous performances of the Herbartian *Vorstellungen.* Herbart says that when one idea is inhibited by another it fuses with that other and thereafter helps it to ascend into consciousness. Inhibition is thus the basis of association in both schemes, for the 'draining' of which the text speaks is tantamount to an inhibition of the activity of the cells which are drained, which inhibition makes the inhibited revive the inhibiter on later occasions" (1890, II, p. 585).

This drainage theory was subsequently elaborated by William McDougall (1903, 1905). McDougall emphasized that "*Inhibition appears always as the negative or complementary result of a process of increased excitation in some other part.* This fact suggests that inhibition is essentially the result of a competition, and many psychologists have given expression to this conception in some such vague phrase as: The mind has only a limited quantity of energy, which will not suffice for the simultaneous maintenance of two mental processes" (1903). McDougall defined the energy available to nerve cells as *neurin,* and hypothesized that all nerve cells draw upon one common source of such energy, which is constantly being generated by the afferent neurons, and is seeking "escape by the paths of least resistance into motor neurons, and so into the muscles. The higher-level paths are brought into activity only when the store of neurin attains a certain potential or head of pressure, which degree of pressure is an essential condition of attentive consciousness. And only one of these higher-level paths can be active at any one moment, because any one of them is capable of carrying off the whole surplus of neurin; when, then, any combination of causes reduces the resistance of any other path to a lower point than that of the path active at any moment, the current shifts from one to the other, just as the opening of a new and shorter channel causes the stream to flow wholly in the new channel, leaving in the old river bed only stagnant pools of water" (1903).

McDougall's drainage theory was never seriously regarded by

physiologists, although the psychologist Flugel (1933) has called it "almost beyond doubt, the most successful neurological theory that has ever been propounded." McDougall himself applied it, as Flugel states, "to a great variety of phenomena at all levels of the nervous system: the reciprocal inhibitions of the spinal level, inhibitions on the sensory level . . . , the mutual inhibitions of instincts, and finally many well-known features of the 'attention process.' The theory seems to fit admirably, too, with the 'displacement' and 'sublimation' doctrines of the psychoanalysts and also (as McDougall himself has pointed out . . .) with the phenomenon of the conditioned reflex as demonstrated by Pavlov." This last is least surprising, since it took its start, as we have noted, from a Jamesian theory of sensori-motor associative learning. For all this breadth of application, it is certainly no more than a superficially successful analogy, having little relation to the true nature of nervous activity.

It would be an error to suppose, from this incomplete survey of positive experimental findings and theoretical speculation, that there must have been at least a growing conviction among physiologists in general that inhibition was a real and important phenomenon, which would have to be dealt with directly before we could have any adequate understanding of the nervous control of behavior. It is well to remember that at all times the skeptical detractors were more numerous, and never lacking in prestige. We shall offer only a small sample of these negative opinions.

Perhaps the commonest interpretation was in terms of presumed fatigue of nerve centers. One eminent advocate of this theory was Goltz, who showed that a decerebrate frog would never croak spontaneously, would do so unfailingly if gently stroked on its back, but could be inhibited from doing so by any strong stimulus such as strong pressure on a foot; he explained the inhibition as probably due to the fact that the centers involved in the reflex were fatigued by the intense stimulation thus provided (1869).

In 1877, George Henry Lewes doubtless expressed a majority opinion when he dismissed the notion of inhibition in his book, *The Physical Basis of Mind,* in this manner: "The Law of Arrest is only another aspect of the Law of Discharge, and may be regarded as the conflict of excitations." He ridiculed the notion of special inhibitory centers: "Indeed, if the action of arrest be, as I maintain, only another aspect of the action of discharge, the result of the conflict of forces, to say that all centers have the property of excitation, is to say that all have the properties of discharge and arrest: the discharge is only the resultant of the conflict along the line of least resistance, the arrest is the result of the conflict along the line of greatest resistance."

Another rather interesting skeptical note was contributed a few years later, by Alexander James (1881). He replicated a portion of Sechenov's experiment, with refinement of technique which permitted him to confirm that when the brain stem had been transected at the optic lobes, the frog would not only kick faster, but also stronger. But he could not accept the doctrine of inhibitory centers as a plausible explanation, and offered instead a "concentration theory"—that the increased intensity of reflex contraction in the decerebrate frog is simply a consequence of "the mechanical effect of the prevention of passage of nerve force to the optic lobes and cerebrum." To support his argument, James pointed out that the phenomena of hypnotism "have been explained as being due to a like concentration and consequent intensification of nervous force." Even the concentration of attention in study, and the elimination of waste motion in learning to walk, were offered as examples of the effect of concentrating nervous force. In the intact animal, he says, "the effects of a peripheral stimulus are carried in part to the motor centers in the cord and in part to the brain, in the former resulting in motion, in the latter in sensation. In the decapitated animal, on the other hand, the nerve channels leading to the brain are cut out, and hence the effects of a peripheral stimulus are manifested in motion alone." This is the argument advanced not long before by Ferrier, turned to another purpose. Where Ferrier had said that the inhibition of movement facilitates thinking, because the nervous energy is not dissipated in motor channels, Alexander James says that the physical removal of the brain will facilitate spinal reflexes, because the nervous energy can no longer be diffused into those all too numerous cerebral pathways. Perhaps neither had advanced very far beyond Erasmus Darwin, who thought that the irritative motions might waste themselves by "simply subsiding."

The painstaking work reported by Bubnoff and Heidenhain (1881) was dismissed by Munk (1890) on the grounds that all such inhibitory effects are really due either to fatigue of the nerve elements involved, or to opposing action of the antagonistic muscles. The latter argument was based on work done by his student Schlösser (1880), who had found that when pain inhibited Goltz's croak reflex in frogs, there was an accompanying constriction of the vocal apparatus. Munk even argued that the early domination of reflexes is overcome in the mature organism because we learn to check the reflex movements by innervation of their antagonists. Heidenhain (1881) admitted that some reflexes, such as coughs or sneezes, may be checked in this manner, but if this were the general mechanism of reflex inhibition it would show itself in a general increase of muscular tension, which is not the case. He also pointed to the fact that it is possible to achieve a voluntary relaxation of the involuntary tonus of postural and facial muscles, and in these cases there can be "no question of antagonistic muscles." This controversy is now obsolete (although Beritov in 1948 was still citing Schlösser's work to the same purpose!), but it expresses a perennial attitude which is still with us—the view that the inhibition of one act can always be regarded as equivalent to the excitation of an opposite tendency. In a later chapter, in a discussion of conflict, we shall try to show that it is essential from a psychological point of view to distinguish between conflictful behavior, in which there is real interference among divergent response tendencies, and the selection of one possible response by the exclusion of other responses through a process of conflictless inhibition.

Waller (1892) expressed the opinion that since there did not seem to be any inhibitory nerves to skeletal vertebrate muscles, it was still "premature and hazardous" to extend the notion of inhibition to the voluntary control of those motions.

Soury (1899) devoted an immense tome of almost 2000 quarto pages to the central nervous system. In it he declared that "every action of arrest is basically nothing but an action of retardation, and this effect of retardation does not derive from a special function of the nervous system, such as that of the pretended inhibitory centers, but from the passage of a nervous current across several ganglia or nuclear relays." Specifically, he stated that the lack of response from electrical stimulation of the prefrontal area is merely due to the fact that the effects are remote, "always more or less slowed up by the number and above all by the complexity of the nuclear relays which are interposed, more or less realizing the physiological conditions of what is called arrest or inhibition, which is basically nothing but retardation."

Jacques Loeb, the paragon of hard-headed thinkers, necessarily rejected the concept of inhibition in his *Comparative Physiology of the Brain* (1900), because it did not fit his schematic theoretical view of the nervous system as organized entirely on a segmental basis, with the nervous elements within each segment serving only as indifferent conductors for the peripheral organs. He is unwilling to recognize any sort of "control" exercised by one segment over another. Near one end of the comparative scale, he refuses to acknowledge that the ceaseless locomotion which follows removal of the supraesophageal ganglia in a worm is an indication that these ganglia normally exercise an inhibitory influence; he prefers to assume that this effect is due to an interruption of hypothetical stimulation from the digestive tract to the motor segments, which ordinarily causes the intact animal to rest. (It is hard to see how this hypothesis does more than replace one kind of inhibition with another.) At the other end of the scale, he is willing to concede to the human brain no higher function than associative memory.

After the discovery of the refractory phase, Verworn (1910) changed his mind about inhibition and declared: "Recent investigations have established with certainty that these processes of inhibition are only very special forms of fatigue and exhaustion processes, which consist of momentary *developments of a relative refractory phase.* The ganglia are made refractory by the inhibiting stimulus, their excitability is reduced to a certain degree, so that another immediately subsequent stimulus has no effect on them." Then, invited to deliver the Silliman Lectures at Yale—that is, to take the same platform from which Sherrington, a few years earlier, had delivered the memorable talks whose content we shall soon consider at length—Verworn chose as his topic *Irritability* (1913). He argued that "inhibition is . . . a relative fatigue, which is conditioned, as is true of every fatigue, by a lengthening of the refractory period following a relative deficiency of oxygen. The processes of inhibition are simply and solely an expression of a refractory period persisting as a result of dissimilatory excitating stimuli." He explained reciprocal inhibition of antagonistic muscles as due to the fact that the stimulus which reached one muscle with strength to excite it, reached the antagonist in weaker form, and although strong stimuli summate, a series of very weak stimuli brings about a refractory state without evoking response.

In Italy, in 1895, Fano had demonstrated that removal of the frontal lobe shortened the reaction time of a leg to faradic stimulation of the skin, and that electrical stimulation of that area for five minutes prior to the stimulation of the skin would lengthen the reaction time. This was in essence a replication of Sechenov's experiment at a higher level. Oddi (1895) depressed contractions of the gastrocnemius to direct faradic stimulation of the motor nerve by stimulation of the contralateral pre-frontal lobe. Polimanti, in 1906, observed circus movements in dogs as a result of unilateral frontal lesions, and attributed them to loss of inhibitory influence. But Bianchi, who reports all these facts in his book *The Mechanism of the Brain* (1922), and who outdoes Ferrier in attributing important intellectual functions to the frontal lobes, is not only unwilling to acknowledge that the frontal lobes have a special inhibitory function, but explains all inhibition as merely a subtractive effect from the algebraic summing of contrary impulses, or from loss of nervous energy which is being consumed in another process. He dismisses Hering and Sherrington's results as "due to the fact that the potential in the area belonging to the antagonistic group of muscles becomes diminished during excitation of the other area." In general, "this phenomenon of inhibition may be regarded as regulated by physical laws analogous to those which regulate the flow of liquids in closed tubes or electric currents in conducting wires."

Thus we see that over and over again, leading physiologists, although they could not question the reality of inhibitory effects, persisted in interpreting them as consequences of fatigue, depletion, or interference arising from interactions among excitatory impulses. The complaint which Meltzer voiced in 1899 is valid for all of the 100-year period from the first public pronouncement of inhibition, in 1845, until the epoch-making article by Magoun and Rhines in 1946: "The phenomenon of inhibition is distrusted in physiology, and had to fight on general grounds at every step for the establishment of any new fact. . . ."

The work of the nineteenth century on the role of inhibition in the performance of reflex acts came to a splendid climax in the research of Sherrington, and the theoretical synthesis achieved by him at the beginning of the twentieth. Almost sixty years have elapsed since he delivered at Yale the series of lectures on *The Integrative Action of the Nervous System.* There are few comprehensive scientific works of that period which can still be read with so much profit, and with so little need for emendation in the light of later work. The importance of his contribution to our understanding of the mechanisms of posture and locomotion is universally acknowledged. However, the emphasis which he gave to the process of inhibition, as a process distinct from excitation, has been obscured by the use of the phrase "reciprocal innervation"—too often read as if it implied no more than reciprocal excitation—to designate the manner in which antagonistic reflexes which are cooperative elements in the same behavior, such as walking or scratching or directing the eye toward a visual stimulus, limit one another.

Sherrington's earliest publication, in which he was the junior author, was an anatomical description of the brain of one of Goltz's decerebrate dogs. Goltz had succeeded in keeping such animals alive for long periods, and his observations of their behavior (including the "sham rage" syndrome, to which we shall return in a later chapter) showed that subcerebral mechanisms are adequate not only for the basic life processes, but also for a variety of unlearned ways of relating to the environment. Another important influence on the direction of Sherrington's thought was the statement of the neurone theory by Waldeyer in 1891, based largely on Cajal's work only two years earlier. Until then, the delay involved in the transmission of nervous impulses from receptors to effectors, beyond the time required for the impulse to traverse an equal length of nerve fiber, was thought to be occasioned by resistance within the cell bodies. Now it became evident that the delay might occur in the gap between the connecting fibers. Sherrington, in 1897, introduced the word *synapse* to designate that gap.

In *The Integrative Action of the Nervous System,* Sherrington showed that the distinguishing features of reflex-arc conduction, as contrasted with nerve-trunk conduction, are consequences of the interposition of synapses. Some of the characteristics mentioned by him are increased latency, summation of subliminal stimuli, and characteristic rhythm. The increased latency of the reflex arc indicates that a time-consuming process is taking place at the synapse. The fact that a series of stimuli, no one of which is strong enough to evoke a response, can summate to effectiveness (a fact first demonstrated by Sechenov), shows that the effect of a stimulus can somehow be stored up for a brief period of time, which is not possible in the nerve trunk. The phenomenon of summation is essential to permit that the reflex arc shall have its own characteristic rhythm, since discharges in the terminal element of the arc need not conform to the rhythm of stimulation. However, something more than summation is involved in the determination of rhythm, for it is not possible to accelerate the rhythm of scratching, for example, by increasing the intensity of stimulation. The rhythm is a reflection of the fact that the nervous system is making a choice, directing the excitation now into one final path, now into another. Sherrington joins Heidenhain and Mercier in the conclusion that this control cannot take place without an active process of inhibition, which he locates at the synapse. "If resting paths all lie open to conduction, prevention of confusion must depend not on the path excited being the only one open for conduction, but on its excitation being accompanied by inhibition of others that, did they enter into action, would detrimentally confuse the issue of events."

Sherrington describes two important pathological states: decerebrate rigidity and strychnine paralysis. In decerebrate rigidity the extensors are tensed, and the flexors relaxed. In a four-footed animal, this corresponds to an exaggeration of the standing posture. It is a state which results from the continuous exercise of midbrain inhibitions, when cerebral inhibitions have been eliminated. It constitutes a standard tonic background for the activity of a waking animal. Strychnine rigidity, on the other hand, is a tonic rigidity of all skeletal muscles, both extensors and flexors. Sherrington emphasized that it cannot result from a general lowering of the threshold of excitation for all of the muscles, because no increase in the intensity of stimulation can produce the same result as a very small quantity of strychnine. Therefore he infers that strychnine somehow converts spinal inhibition into spinal excitation. (We know now that it blocks inhibitory synapses, thus permitting excitatory innervation of all the muscles at once.)

The behavior of walking and the behavior of scratching are two natively organized patterns of response which employ the same muscles in different ways, though both involve reciprocal innervation of antagonistic muscles. One misses the point of Sherrington's research if one looks at each of these response patterns by itself, as consisting of reciprocating reflexes which evoke and inhibit one another by turns when some external incitement sets them going. What Sherrington demonstrated is, rather, that postural tonus is the resultant of the interaction of reciprocating reflexes which are under continuous restraint from many sources, and that locomotion on the one hand, and scratching on the other, are two of the behaviors which can result when those inhibitions are modified appropriately. Walking and scratching, as elucidated by Sherrington, are two special cases of Anstie's principle.

Furthermore, the reciprocal simultaneous excitation and inhibition of antagonistic muscles is undoubtedly a feature of voluntary acts, and not only of unlearned motor patterns. This appears from the fact that, at a given stage of narcosis, it is possible to demonstrate that stimulation of the motor cortex can lead to muscular relaxation, as well as to muscular contraction. (This was shown by Sherrington and Hering, in their experiments with monkeys, in 1897.) The point from which the relaxation of a given muscle can be obtained, under these conditions, is the same one from which the contraction of the antagonistic muscle is ordinarily elicited. In other words, whenever muscles are paired as antagonists, the stimulation of a given point in the motor cortex leads simultaneously to contraction of one muscle of the pair, and to relaxation of the antagonist. Under normal conditions, the contraction is the more prominent effect, but in the proper stage of narcosis, the inhibitory effect becomes evident.

Nor did Sherrington limit the application of his results to behavior which involves anatagonistic muscles. He explicitly stated that the relationships which exist between antagonists only represents a broadly distributed but special case "of the general principle of the mutual interaction of reflexes that impinge upon the same common path." He continued: "The same principle extended to the reaction of the great arcs arising in the projicient receptor organs of the head . . . operates with more multiplex shifts of the conductive pattern. Releasing forces acting on the brain from moment to moment shut out from activity whole regions of the nervous system, as they conversely call vast other regions into play. *The resultant singleness of action from moment to moment is a keystone in the construction of the individual whose unity it is the specific office of the nervous system to perfect.* The interference of unlike reflexes and the alliance of like reflexes in their action upon their common paths seem to lie at the very root of the great psychical process of 'attention.' "

In thus stating that attention is dependent on cortical inhibition, which serves to "shut out from activity whole regions of the nervous system," Sherrington was in agreement with views then being expressed by many psychologists (and those views were in harmony with today's research). But his generalization can be applied still more widely, for example, to the use of the hands in manipulation, or of the vocal organs to utter the many sounds of speech. In these activities, "multiplex shifts of the conductive pattern" are needed to select not one of two antagonistic responses, but one of literally innumerable incompatible response possibilities.

Perhaps it is permissible at this point to intimate the nature of an hypothesis which will engage our attention in later chapters of this book: that the most general method of behavioral choice is precisely by the modulation of inhibitions, and not by the excitation of specific acts. The system of brakes in a complex organism is fully as complex as the system of its reaction mechanisms. Long ago Bain (1855) wrote, without thought of neural inhibition, that "The nervous system may be compared to an organ with bellows constantly charged, and ready to be let off in any direction, according to the particular keys that are touched." Such a mechanism cannot function without its stops. The control of behavior is indeed like the playing of an organ—each act, involving many muscles, is like a musical chord which rises with the measured lifting of a coordinated set of inhibitory stops.

A COMPARATIVE SURVEY 4

The Need for Inhibition. The concept of inhibition was developed primarily in the course of research on the vertebrate nervous system. However, even the frog has a rather highly developed brain, compared with that of a snail or a lobster, not to mention the diffuse nerve-net of the jellyfish, for example. The latter part of the nineteenth century witnessed a good deal of research on the behavior of the lower animals. This research was motivated at first by the desire of the Darwinians (e.g., Lubbock, Romanes) to demonstrate the continuity of intelligence through the entire range of the animal kingdom, and later by the effort of the extreme objectivist group, including such men as Loeb, Beer, Bethe, Bohn, and Uexküll, to concentrate their research on animals with simple behavior patterns, which might reasonably be expected to yield to their efforts at physicochemical analysis. These studies revealed many examples of inhibition in invertebrate organisms. In the present chapter we shall try to view some of these in a phylogenetic perspective, which will help us to understand why the development of inhibition was inevitable, and what role it must play in the behavior of higher animals.

We shall begin our survey by examining the behavior of an "organism" which is very simple and fully understandable, for the reason that it is designed and built by man. This is Grey Walter's mechanical model of elementary reflex behavior, which he has whimsically called *M. speculatrix* (Walter, 1953). If one tries to design a machine which, like a living organism, utilizes the same effectors to attain different ends under different conditions, one will quickly discover that any such mechanism which relies solely upon excitatory processes for the instigation of the responses is necessarily inefficient, since it must involve wasteful conflict of the effector systems. This defect is not present in *M. speculatrix,* but it is symptomatic of the second-class status of the concept of inhibition that it receives no mention in Walter's capsule description of his machine as "a model of elementary reflex behavior [which] contains only two functional elements: two receptors, two nerve cells, two effectors." It also contains two relays, for circuit interruption, without which it would scarcely be able to behave as intended by its maker, that is, to display positive light-seeking behavior *and* the ability to circumvent obstacles which it encounters in this quest.

Somewhat superficially described, *M. speculatrix* operates as follows. It has one effector which consists of the driving wheels, and another effector which is a rotating verticle spindle on which both the steering wheel and the light-sensitive cell which serves as one of the receptors are mounted. Both effectors are motor driven, and the only "excitation" they receive is the current of the batteries on which they operate; this current is subject to certain interruptions. When a weak light enters the photocell, it causes a "transient interruption" of scanning, that is, of the rotation of the spindle on which the photocell is mounted. A strong light causes "steady inhibition" of the scanning operation. Since the steering wheel is mounted on the same spindle, pointed in the same direction as the photocell, the effect of these inhibitions is to bring the cell gradually "on beam." The second receptor is a bumper-ring. Whenever an obstacle is encountered, the movement of the bumper-ring interrupts the sensitivity to light. As a result, the machine is no longer stimulus-bound, and therefore it can escape the fascination of the light toward which it had been moving long enough to effect a change of direction. This maneuver will be repeated as often as necessary until the obstacle has been circumvented. The responses of this light-seeking "organism" are not in any sense excited by the light or by any other external stimulus. The machine is inwardly driven, but it is so constructed that one of its effectors is inhibited by one of its receptors; and this inhibition can be inhibited in turn

—so that the effector is disinhibited—by stimulation of the other receptor. It is the appropriateness of these inhibitions which gives direction and an appearance of intelligence to what otherwise would be aimless wandering.

Let us compare the behavior of *M. speculatrix* with that of a paramecium, a living creature which has approach and avoidance patterns not unlike those of Walter's model. Its effectors consist of the myriad tiny cilia whose steady beat, under nonthreatening circumstances, at once propels it through the water and drives a stream bearing minute nutritive particles into its oral cavity. If a paramecium comes into contact with some solid object, or enters a region of suddenly higher acidity, the beat of the cilia is immediately reversed and intensified, and the same bodily asymmetry which gives a gentle spiral twist to its forward navigation now determines an abrupt change of direction, after which the forward-swimming pattern is resumed on the new course. It is not impossible that the reverse lash is accomplished by some mechanism which, by its vigor, overcomes the continuing tendency of the cilia to perform their gentler swimming-ingesting action. If that is the case, it is one of those rare instances in which nature has had less foresight than a human engineer would have under like circumstances. Such an arrangement would be wasteful of energy, and hence less adaptive than a mechanism, of whatever sort, which would *arrest* the swimming activity at the very moment when it initiates the reversal, rather than permitting the two actions to oppose each other. For efficient action, the two reaction patterns, which utilize the same effectors, should be mutually inhibitory and not merely antagonistic.

That the paramecium does possess some sort of inhibitory mechanism is shown by the fact that it does not swim ceaselessly, but also displays a thigmotactic response, by which it sometimes adheres to solid objects. In this response, "the cilia in contact with the solid remain stiff and immobile as if anchoring the animal to the spot, while the cilia over the rest of the body keep moving, although with diminished vigor" (Holmes, 1911). This reaction is readily given to a bit of cotton wool placed in the water, and is not to be interpreted as an evidence of fatigue.

Interesting as it would be to know whether the reaction patterns of the paramecium are mutually inhibitory, we shall have to content ourselves now with the observation that *if* such an arrangement existed, it would have survival value.

The one-celled paramecium has a problem, and we have seen how a similar problem was solved by *M. speculatrix*. We must inquire whether nature has followed a similar plan for the coordination of receptor and effector mechanisms in complex, differentiated organisms, and what part the nervous system plays in such a plan. A nervous apparatus is not simply a means for the communication of excitations between differentiated receptor and effector cells. One very important function of a nervous apparatus is to provide an arrangement whereby, when the same organism has multiple response potentialities, one of these can be activated without simultaneously activating the others. If the several response systems are to be coordinated, and not independent, inhibition is required.

To illustrate this need, let us look at an example of inhibition in human behavior—an example no less vivid for having been provided by G. H. Lewes (1877), who had a wholly skeptical attitude toward the concept of neural inhibition. Said Lewes: "The boy when first learning to write is unable to prevent the simultaneous motions of tongue and legs, which are ludicrously irrelevant to the purpose of writing; but he learns to keep all of his organs in subjection, and only the eyes and the hands active." This same need to *differentiate* each response from others of which the organism is capable exists in all behavior. The performance of an unlearned response requires not only that there be a native organization of the necessary exciting pathways, but also that other responses which might be excited by the same stimulation be natively inhibited. It is the thesis of this chapter that the *necessity* for inhibition of this sort underlies the evolutionary development out of which came, at last, the ability of the English schoolboy to keep his tongue quiet inside his cheek, while writing his lesson. With every increase in the organism's sensitivity to stimulation of any sort, with every increase in the effectiveness of the nervous system as an apparatus linking together all parts of the behaving organism, with every increase in the variety of behaviors available to the organism, this need for inhibitory limitation of responsiveness becomes greater. But the need exists from the very beginnings of such complication, and hence the *first* steps toward variability in behavior *must* be accompanied by the beginnings of inhibitory control over inappropriate response.

Inhibition in the Invertebrates. Koshtoyants (1957) considers that the beginnings of inhibition must be recognized in the suppression of the functional activity of certain protozoa. As an example, he cites the fact that under certain environmental conditions the amoeba retracts its pseudopodia and becomes temporarily inexcitable, a form of response which appears to be protective. Perhaps a clearer example can be taken from the behavior of the stentor, a trumpet-shaped protozoan which swims about by ciliary action much like the paramecium, but more often attaches itself to some solid object by the narrow base of its stalk. If the object to which it is attached is lightly jarred, a stentor contracts its body, in what may be assumed to be a defensive withdrawal with some survival value. After a few such stimulations in fairly close sequence, it fails to contract. This loss of irritability after a series of responses is usually interpreted as an effect of fatigue, but we should not fail to note that such quick fatigue is itself adaptive, for without it the organism might be led, by some nondangerous repetitive stimulation, to waste its energies. Since the stentor, like the paramecium, is capable of many quick reversals of its swimming motion, we must wonder whether this "habituation" is to be explained by fatigue in the ordinary sense. Whatever its nature, it seems legitimate to regard it as meeting something of the need which is to be served later by specialized inhibitory structures.

The coelenterates are radially organized, multicellular organisms which have nervous tissue diffusely distributed in a so-called nerve-net, between the outer tissue which contains some specialized receptor spots and the inner muscular tissue. Hydra is a coelenterate which, in form and behavior, resembles the protozoan stentor in many respects. It usually attaches itself by its pedal stalk, and feeds by the action of the tentacles at its free end. If the object to which it is attached is tapped, it contracts defensively; but if the tapping is continued with rather short intervals, then "sooner or later, in spite of continuous stimulation, the Hydra slowly expands" (Wagner, quoted by Holmes, 1911). It will then usually remain normally expanded as long as the intensity of stimulation is not further increased. Thus the original defensive contraction is somehow suppressed by a process of habituation. It is unlikely that this effect is due merely to fatigue induced by the contraction itself, for when the intervals between the taps are somewhat longer, hydra can contract repeatedly, a fact which indicates that recovery from such fatigue is rapid. If stimulated more intensely, as by direct contact of a glass rod, the hydra may bend to one side and change its points of attachment, moving to a new location. This is a fairly complicated maneuver, probably involving some form of inhibition of the defensive contraction, which would be incompatible with it.

In the flatworms, the nerve-net is replaced by a synaptic system which consists of two nerve cords, with an agglomeration of cells forming a cephalic ganglion at the anterior end of each cord, and some nervous tissue connecting the two ganglia. Each cephalic ganglion is connected with a light-sensitive eyespot on its side of the head. The locomotion of the flatworm is by a contractile wave which starts at the anterior end and passes along the length of one side of the body, while another similar wave, which at any given point is in opposite phase, passes similarly down the other side of the body. The coordination of these two waves depends on the anterior ganglia. If the fibers connecting the ganglia are severed, the locomotor process disappears. But if one of the ganglia is then removed completely, the wave reappears on the uninjured side. This seems to indicate that the maintenance of the normal rhythm depends on inhibitory influences between the ganglia. That some inhibitory phenomena are present is indicated by the fact that the response to tactile stimulation of the head region is reversed by the application of strychnine.[1] Moore (1918) found that under normal conditions such stimulation causes the body of the worm to shorten, suppressing locomotion; with strychnine, tactile stimulation causes the worm's body to lengthen. It therefore seems highly probable that a true synaptic inhibitory process exists in the flatworm.

McConnell, Jacobson, and Kimble (1959) conditioned flatworms to give this shortening response to illumination, using an electric

[1] At several points in this chapter, in interpreting experimental results, we shall make use of the finding of Bradley, Easton, and Eccles (1953), that the overtly "exciting" effect of strychnine results from an interference with the process of synaptic inhibition. The way in which this takes place will be explained in the next chapter.

shock as the unconditioned stimulus. They then divided each animal approximately in half, fore and aft, and allowed four weeks for regeneration. After that long interval, relearning showed that there was very considerable and approximately equal retention of the habit by both halves. Control animals, first divided and then trained, were inferior to the original experimental group, showing that the surgery per se did not lead to swifter learning. Intact animals showed no greater retention than divided animals. It is noteworthy that in a few instances the conditioned response appeared on the first retraining trials of tail sections with regenerated heads, suggesting that the regenerated cephalic ganglia may have had the conditioned response "built in." These authors suggest (relying in part on Hovey's earlier work [1929]) that "the cephalic ganglia may be necessary for *acquisition* but not for *retention* of a conditioned response in the planarian." However this may be, it appears to us of crucial importance that, as mentioned in the preceding paragraph, the participation of synaptic inhibition in the shortening response of the flatworm has been demonstrated.

The mollusca, including the clams, the snails, and the octopus, have a much more highly developed nervous system; and in them inhibitory phenomena are conspicuously present, and no longer a matter of conjecture and inference. Snails possess many scattered ganglia, including a cerebral ganglion, pedal ganglia, and visceral ganglia. Jordan (1901) found that when the cerebral ganglion of *Aplysia limacina* is removed, leaving the pedal ganglia intact, there results an increased and ceaseless locomotion. The creatures are unable to eat, and waste their body substance in unending movement, until death overtakes them. If only one pedal ganglion is removed, a slow circus movement takes place. If a nerve which has been separated from its pedal ganglion is stimulated, the result is always a strong contraction, and the isolated muscle remains permanently contracted. Thus it appears that the influence of the nerve on the muscle is excitatory, but the pedal ganglion is at the same time the site of an inhibitory process, which is responsible for the rhythm of automatic movement; the cerebral ganglion, on the other hand, is the source of inhibition which interrupts this automatic movement. The total pattern is not dissimilar from that with which we are accustomed in the vertebrates, even including man, in whom restless activity is one of the symptoms of prefrontal brain injury. However, Jordan emphasized that the cerebral ganglion is not exclusively inhibitory, but is also the source of excitatory effects.

Jordan (1929) also described an interesting form of adaptive inhibitory response in this snail, which is also mediated by the pedal ganglia. *Aplysia limacina* has large parapodia and a relatively small foot, a combination which exposes it to the danger of being swept from its hold on the rocks by the strong surf, if the parapodia did not instantly relax "like a limp cloth," as soon as the current of moving water stimulates them. If the pedal ganglia are removed, this response is eliminated. The same response is not found in another species, *Aplysia depilans*, which inhabits the same surf-washed rocks, but which has a larger foot and smaller parapodia.

Although both the cerebral ganglion and the pedal ganglia are partly inhibitory and partly excitatory in their functions, Koshtoyants (1957) states that work he has done together with Smirnova and Popkova indicates that the functions of the visceral ganglion are entirely inhibitory. When this ganglion is stimulated in a variety of ways, whether mechanically, thermally, or electrically, and in varying intensities, the effect is always inhibitory.

The annelids, or true worms, are segmented animals with a ventral nerve chain. There are paired ganglia in each segment posterior to the head region, but the ganglia of several anterior segments merge together into specialized structures. The "brain" consists of a bilobed supraesophageal ganglion in the third segment, which is connected by a ring of nervous tissue with the subesophageal ganglion in the fourth segment, from which the ventral chain takes its origin. It is known that the intestine receives both excitatory and inhibitory nerves, the former being adrenergic, the latter cholinergic. (That is, different chemical transmitters activate the two sets of synapses, as explained in the next chapter.) Locomotion depends on reciprocating action of an internal layer of longitudinal muscles and an external layer of annular muscles, plus the grip of many tiny setae whose angle of placement is adjusted by the muscular activity so that the body can easily slide along the ground in the direction of movement, but not in the reverse direction. Beheaded, the earthworm and other annelids show the same increased tendency to forward locomotion which is characteristic of the snail without its cerebral ganglion or the dog without a cerebrum. Cut in half, either part of an annelid is capable of coordinated movement; hence it is obvious that the supraesophageal and subesophageal ganglia are not essential for locomotion. As a matter of fact, the two halves coordinate with each other if they are loosely connected with a loop of thread, the posterior part following the anterior part under its own power, but contracting in the same rhythm. Therefore it is evident that intersegmental coordination requires no more than the mechanical tug of one segment on the next, but this does not mean that the effect is purely excitatory. The earthworm is capable of moving backward as well as forward, a maneuver which requires that the setae be set differently into the ground, and just as mechanical stimulation of the anterior segments will check forward movement, so stimulation of the posterior end will check a backward movement in progress.

There are many different kinds of evidence that synaptic integration is essential to the earthworm's coordinated movement. Knowlton and Moore (1917) found that strychnine prevents locomotion by causing both sets of muscles to contract simultaneously, an effect which we now understand as due to blocking of normal inhibition. Holst (1932) showed that nervous conduction along the ventral cord is faster if peripheral nerves have been removed, which points to their involvement in some inhibitory feedback. On the basis of further experimental analysis, Holst (1933) also contends that each segment must contain both a "movement center" and an "inhibitory center." The movement center directly governs the alternating phases of the movement cycle, exciting and inhibiting annular and longitudinal muscles in turn, but it comes into action only when it is released from the control of the inhibitory center, and this requires disinhibitory stimulation from the adjacent segment. It is this trigger action which is provided, in normal locomotion, by the tug of the anterior parts.

The most interesting evidence for inhibition in the earthworm comes from its performance in the maze. Yerkes (1912) trained an earthworm in a simple T-maze, which offered the alternatives of electric shock or the comfort of a dark and mossy bed. When a position habit had been formed, the anterior ganglia were removed by cutting off the first five segments; the habit was well retained, but it disappeared after regeneration of a new head. Thus, whatever was "remembered" by the spinal ganglia was extinguished by the activity of the new brain. (It will be recalled that flatworms showed retention of conditioning after regeneration of the head segments.) Heck (1920) confirmed Yerkes' findings as to the docility of the intact earthworm. He also removed the supraesophageal ganglia of several worms, and established that this did not interfere with retention of a previously acquired habit, nor with acquisition of such a habit before a new ganglion was regenerated. However, he remarked that the operated worms gave the impression of "completely automatic" movement, and seemed to have lost much of the possibility for variation in behavior. He does not report on results after regeneration, nor did he attempt habit reversal in any of the operated animals. The possibility therefore exists that the brain may be needed to "unlearn" the habit, even though it is not needed for habit acquisition. At least, the "brainless" worm seems less spontaneous. The intact earthworm which is being trained in a T-maze shows a fairly strong tendency to various negative movements, such as backing up and turning around, and it alternates between left and right choices more often than would be expected from chance alone (Wayner & Zellner, 1958). These negative movements disappear when the supraesophageal ganglion is removed, and the alternation of choices becomes less than might be expected by chance. Possibly the supraesophageal ganglion has no part to play in the fixation of the turning habit, but its presence, and its association with the increased sensibility of the anterior tip, introduces a degree of response variability which is favorable to learning, and also favorable to extinction of learned responses which are no longer reinforced.

Both the anatomy and the physiology of the arthropod nervous system were intensively studied by Bethe (1897, 1897–1898). The members of this phylum, which includes crustaceans, insects, and arachnids, all possess a supraesophageal ganglion, a subesophageal ganglion, and a ventral nerve chain. However, associated with the development of complex, image-forming eyes and other elaborate sensory structures, the supraesophageal ganglion is differentiated into several parts, which are called the protocerebrum, the deutocerebrum, and, in the highest forms, a tritocerebrum. Bethe's behavioral studies included such varied members of this phylum as the crab, crayfish, bee, grasshopper, and water beetle, and they brought him to the general conclusion that "the brain of the arthropods is to be regarded as above all an organ for the inhibition of reflexes." The evidence for this conclusion lay not only in the almost invariable tendency of these animals to circular motion when the commissure had been cut on only one side, and their "almost continuous motion" when deprived of the supraesophageal ganglion, but also in the fact that most other reflexes could also be more readily evoked, and by stimuli ordinarily inadequate, in specimens without the supraesophageal ganglion. The crab, for example, would ceaselessly bring objects to its mouth, even pebbles and other inedible objects. It was still capable of rejecting these as food, for the acts of chewing and swallowing required additional chemical stimulation; but when food was in abundance it could not limit its eating, and might stuff its stomach literally to the point of bursting. When the price of an uncurbed appetite comes so high, the need for inhibition is indeed imperative! The annelids, which have nervous systems with the same general plan, can get along with very little cerebral inhibition because the sensory organs are relatively undeveloped; for the arthropods, with their greatly heightened sensitivity to environmental stimulation, and more differentiated ways of responding, cerebral inhibition has become indispensable.

Casselli (1899) provided an interesting confirmation of Bethe's work by another method. He evoked reflex bending of the lobster's tail by electrical stimulation at the spinal level, and was then able to inhibit such response by simultaneous electrical stimulation of the supraesophageal ganglion.

The death feint of insects can be shown in many cases to be an inhibitory effect of central innervation. Koshtoyants (1957) states that Schmidt, in 1913, found that in the walking stick, one of the phasmids, if the insect is decapitated while in the cataleptic state, the catalepsy continues only in that portion of the body which is united with the head, while the rest of the body immediately recovers its normal reflex activity. In this case, therefore, the death feint results from an intensification of the inhibitory influence of the cerebral ganglia on the peritoneal nerve chains. That is, not only is a steady normal inhibitory influence over locomotion exercised by the brain, but an additional reserve of inhibitory power, rather than a facilitatory innervation is evoked when an intense environmental stimulation of the head receptors provokes an unusually strong discharge to the lower center. In commenting on Schmidt's study, Koshtoyants (1957) points out that decapitation does not stop the cataleptic state in all insects, and where it does not, the immobility is generally of shorter duration. In these cases, he says, "removal of the head ganglia causes the immobility to appear more readily and to last longer." Here, it would seem, we are dealing with a subcerebral source of catalepsy, which is itself moderated by the cerebral ganglia. This is true in general of butterflies, in whom catalepsy is induced not by intense stimulation of the head receptors, but by pressure on the roots of the wings, which are connected to lower ganglia. However, Koshtoyants points out, in those butterflies in which immobility can be produced by very light pressure at these points, much stronger stimulation is required after removal of the head ganglia. This suggests that in those species in which catalepsy is induced only by relatively strong pressure on the roots of the wings, all of the inhibitory effect is produced by peritoneal ganglia, whereas in those in which a very light pressure suffices, the greater part of the inhibitory innervation has been delegated to the cerebral ganglia.

Roeder (1935) studied the sexual behavior of the praying mantis. Many authors had reported that the voracious female often eats the courting male. Roeder found that the male must indeed approach with extreme caution, stalking the females slowly, for if she detects him she will seize and devour him. Fortunately, the mantis is not unaccustomed to such slow movement, since normally he may remain stationary for hours or even days at a time. If the protocerebral ganglia are removed, the insect becomes "extremely restless" and the "slightest stimulus will initiate locomotion which lasts for long periods and leads to extreme fatigue" (Roeder, 1937). The copulatory pattern is inhibited by the subesophageal ganglion, and when this is removed, copulatory movements will go on endlessly, even without contact with the female. When perchance it happens that the male does fall victim to his intended mate, she invariably eats the head first of all, thus removing the subesophageal ganglion. This not only releases the copulatory movement, but also a curious sideward locomotion which tends to bring the male into copulatory position with the female still chewing at his head. By this oddly adaptive disinhibition, he atones for his error, not simply with his life, but by fulfilling his seminal mission!

Wagner made extensive studies, summarized by Koshtoyants, of inhibition in the learned behavior of bees. For example, if a bee is first trained to feed from a card of a given color, *A*, and is subsequently retrained to prefer another color, *B*, we may assume that this differentiation involves inhibition of the former preference for *A*. If the bee is then trained to prefer *C* in preference to *B*, this differentiation in turn involves the inhibition of the positive response to *B*. However, this has the effect of disinhibiting the response to *A*, so that if the bee is now offered the choice between *A* and *B*, *A* will be preferred. The next stage of training is a differentiation between *C* and *D*, the latter being chosen as positive stimulus. Hence *C* is inhibited, its effect on *B* is cancelled, and if confronted anew with the choice between *A* and *B*, the preference is for *B*.

A characteristic feature of the arthropods is the presence of inhibitory motor nerves, first discovered by Biedermann (1887, 1888) in the claw of the crayfish. The antagonistic muscles in the claws of a crab or a lobster consist of a relatively weak "opener" and a much stronger "closer," but each of these muscles receives both excitatory and inhibitory innervation. Inhibitory innervation has also been shown to play a part in the grasshopper's leap, which has been carefully studied by Hoyle (1958). He recorded the action current in the motor nerves while stimulating the antennae at the tip of the abdomen.

> We must suppose that grasshoppers exercise some discrimination among stimuli, else the enormous expenditure of energy required for their leaps would soon exhaust them. It seems that usually the animal "decides" to leap; in other words, its jump is not a simple reflex action but is controlled by a mechanism of inhibition. . . . Before the animal can jump, it must stop walking. The first impulse therefore inhibits the slow nerve fiber and puts it out of action. Next it excites the flexor muscles to draw the jumping legs into the cocked position. Thirdly, the sensory message, combined with others from the brain, acts on the fast jumping nerve fiber. The message may restrain this nerve, saying in effect: "Disregard this stimulus; it is irrelevant." Or it may warn: "Get

ready; if you receive another message like this one, act on it immediately, for it is really urgent." Now, when a second burst of impulses comes, the nerve fiber fires immediately. The grasshopper instantly rears up and takes off (Hoyle, 1958, p. 32 f.).

In this account, Hoyle explicitly recognizes that the capability of giving violent response to slight stimulation would be destructive if not joined with inhibitory control. (One may compare this with the memorable passage in Lange's *History of Materialism* (1873–1875), which describes the excited "leap" and the long subsequent chain of activity released when a merchant, who had been dozing comfortably in his armchair, was handed a dispatch reading: *Antwerp—Jonas & Co. bankrupt.* Doubtless Lange would have been less pessimistic about the possibility of explaining the merchant's "leap" from his armchair on purely physical grounds if he had been acquainted with the phenomena of neural inhibition.)

The echinoderms, a phylum which includes the sea anemone and the starfish, seem by their radial structure to be more primitive than the bilaterally symmetrical annelids and arthropods. However, biochemically they are more closely related to the vertebrates. Their locomotion, too, depends on the reciprocal innervation of two sets of musculature, the excitation of one group of muscles being simultaneous with the inhibition of the other group. Scheer (1948), describing the locomotion of the sand dollar, says that "evidently two groups of motor neurons are involved, one for the ampulla, and the other for the longitudinal muscles of the tube foot. These groups have different stimulation thresholds, and excitation of one group must involve simultaneous inhibition of the other." The tube foot is first pointed in the direction of locomotion, attached, bent through an arc, disattached, and retracted. Many tube feet perform this stepping pattern in coordination with each other, the coordination being effected by a nerve ring which possesses a "coordination center" for each of the five rays.

A distinctive pattern which has received a great deal of careful study is the righting response of the starfish. When the starfish is right side up, now one of the rays, now another, exercises dominance in establishing coordinated locomotion, depending on local conditions of stimulation. When the starfish is placed on its back, this coordination is lost, and the individual rays make rapid movements, as if each were trying to bring its undersurface into contact with the ground. A successful righting response requires that two adjacent rays continue to pull strongly, but that their activity shall inhibit the remaining rays, which are then passively pulled through the necessary somersault. Loeb (1900), Moore (1910), and others have shown how, when the nerve ring is cut at two or more points, the isolated rays continue vigorously active and thus impede the maneuver. Moore (1918) found that a small dose of strychnine also prevents the righting response, because all of the rays then arch backward simultaneously even in the intact animal. His interpretation was that the inhibition had been "converted into an excitation," but now we know that the inhibitory innervations were not "reversed," but selectively blocked.

Thus the locomotion of many invertebrates depends, as in the vertebrates, on alternating excitation and inhibition of opposing sets of muscles. It seems that locomotion is never based on the continuous action of any effector. It is always a rhythmic response, as in the ciliary beat of the paramecium, the alternating contraction and relaxation of the umbrella of the jellyfish, the antagonistic action of longitudinal and annular muscles in the earthworm, or the antagonism of flexors and extensors in the higher forms with articulated limbs. In the more primitive examples, the source of rhythm may be something analagous to refractory phase in a pace-setting mechanism. However, as the locomotor apparatus becomes more highly developed, and its separate parts achieve a degree of functional independence for other purposes, the integrating mechanism must also become more elaborate. Therefore in locomotion, which is such a prominent part of the animal's behavior, we see inhibitory capacity progressively developed. However, an equally important aspect of that development, but one to which less attention has been given, is the increasing role of cerebral inhibition which serves to suppress the locomotor response when necessary, in order to permit the more effective performance of other responses which may or may not involve some effectors of the locomotor system.

Inhibition in the Vertebrates. The vertebrates (including fish, amphibians, reptiles, birds, and mammals) are the principal representatives of the phylum *chordata*. These animals all have a dorsal nerve chain, that is, one which lies above rather than below the digestive tract. This central nervous system arises from the ectoderm, so that it is embryologically associated with receptor functions, with environmental relationships, rather than with effector functions as is generally the case in the lower phyla. Starting as a wrinkle of ectodermal tissue, its principal structures always remain enclosed in a neural tube. The arrangement has evidently been favorable to an increasing degree of cephalization, and hence also to that "unity of the organism" which finds its highest expression in primate individuality. This unity depends on a system of interrelationships such that conditions which influence the performance of any part of the behavioral repertoire will also influence the performance of all other parts. It is not difficult to find instances of such interaction in organisms at every level of evolution, but it is far from a universal rule of nature. As a universal dictum it is a metaphysical delusion, a last stronghold of vitalistic philosophy. Among the more complex invertebrates, and especially among the arthropods, separate parts of the behavioral apparatus seem sometimes to live an almost independent existence, so that with transection of the neuraxis, it is possible to have anterior and posterior parts of the organism engaged in quite different activities—mating and eating, for example. Yet without such transection, it is inconceivable to have such simultaneity of divergent actions; it is therefore evident that there must be mutual inhibition, since there is not an actual incompatibility of the parts.

Although organic unity is not a law of nature, it is an evolutionary tendency to attain and maintain such unity despite the increasing differentiation of the organism. This cannot be effected simply by a closer union of all the parts, because that would lead only to convulsive disaster if it were not accompanied by increasingly effective inhibitory controls. The vertebrate nervous system has been especially effective in maintaining, as Sherrington put it, that "*singleness of action from moment to moment* [*which*] *is a keystone in the construction of the individual whose unity it is the specific office of the nervous system to perfect.*"

In many fish, there is a giant Mauthner cell present in the medulla oblongata. This cell receives afferent innervation from the VIIIth (auditory) nerve and sends a motor axon to a muscle which causes a sideward flip of the tail fin. Retzlaff (1957) found that stimulation of the VIIIth nerve would uniformly lead to the tail flip, but it proved to be impossible to cause both Mauthner cells to discharge, and thus to contract the muscles on both sides of the tail fin, by simultaneously stimulating the nerves on both sides. In fact, he found that strong simultaneous stimulation of both nerves tended to produce rhythmically alternating movements of the tail, rather than to evoke simultaneous contractions of antagonists. He discovered that the afferent fibers terminated in synapses on the dendrites and cell body of the homolateral Mauthner cell, and on the axon hillock of the contralateral Mauthner cell. In further investigation, Retzlaff and Fontaine (1960) discovered that each of the motor axons gave off a collateral which then terminated in a ring around the base of the axon on the contralateral cell. If the cells were frozen and then stained immediately after the VIIIth nerve had been stimulated on one side, it was found that the cell body on the stimulated side stained darker, and that on the other side stained lighter, than in control (unstimulated) fish, indicating that contrary chemical processes had been taking place in the two cells. Here we see the evidence of an intricate mechanism to insure an absence of conflict for the fish—at least in the motor act of flipping its tail.

A very different kind of inhibition appears in the behavior described by Limbaugh (1961) in a discussion of "cleaning symbiosis." Many fish avail themselves of the sanitation service which is offered by the Pederson shrimp, a tiny and conspicuously colored animal which lives in association with the sea anemone.

> When a fish approaches, the shrimp will whip its long antennae and sway its body back and forth. If the fish is interested, it will swim directly to the shrimp and stop an inch or two away. The fish usually presents its head or a gill cover for cleaning, but if it is bothered by something out of the ordinary, such as an injury near its tail, it presents itself tail first. The shrimp swims or crawls forward, climbs aboard and walks rapidly over the fish, checking irregularities, tugging at parasites with its claws and cleaning injured areas. The fish remains almost motionless during this inspection and allows the shrimp to make minor incisions in order to get at subcutaneous parasites. As the shrimp approaches the gill covers, the fish opens each one in turn and allows the shrimp to enter and forage among the gills. The shrimp is even permitted to enter and leave the fish's mouth cavity. Local fishes quickly learn the location of

these shrimp. They line up or crowd around for their turn and often wait to be cleaned when the shrimp has retired into the hole beside the anemone (Limbaugh, p. 42).

It should be obvious to the reader that the fish cannot "stop an inch or two away," present itself "tail first," open its gill covers "in turn," suffer the shrimp to enter and leave its mouth, and wait for service (even without keeping track of its proper turn), without exercising a variety of inhibitory controls.

A number of vertebrate forms have been the objects of investigations directed toward discovering correlations between the appearance of unlearned response patterns and the maturation of nervous structures. The results represent an interesting supplement to those obtained by surgical procedures, in which the function of a structure is assessed by observing the effects of its removal. In embryological studies, we wait for nature to fit the new part into place, or to render it functional, and observe what change takes place in behavior.

Based on his observations of amblystoma, Coghill (1930) declared that mass reactions involving the trunk and tending to spread to the whole body appear before discrete movements of individual limbs. He argued that local reflexes are not the primary building blocks of behavior, but rather have to be differentiated out of the mass reaction. Thus, his account of the ontological development of behavior is not unlike Lewes' description of the schoolboy's early efforts at writing. This generalization has found supporters and opponents, both in sufficient number so that it seems reasonable to conclude that it is a correct description of the development of some behavior sequences in some animals, but not a valid generalization for all vertebrate behavior. Minkowski's (1928) descriptions of discrete reflex responses in the human fetus seem not to fit Coghill's conception, but Hooker (1943) believes that his own observations of similar material can legitimately be described as conforming to it. However, Carmichael (1946b) points out that observations of the human fetus are never made under good experimental conditions, since some degree of anoxia is almost inevitable, and that even under the better conditions which prevail in experimentation with fetuses of subhuman mammals it is risky to base negative conclusions on what we do not see. However, Carmichael's observations of embryo guinea pigs, and those of Barcroft and Barron (1937) on the development of behavior in fetal sheep, were performed under especially careful experimental controls, to avoid either the shock effects of separation from the mother or the effects of anesthesia administered to the mother.

Carmichael is quite positive in his statement that discrete local reflexes, and also discrete reflex movements of the neck or of a distant limb, appear before any general mass responsiveness to external stimulation. Carmichael operated with a systematic chart of stimulation points, prepared in advance, which were to be tested in embryos exposed at predetermined ages. Out of this careful methodology there appeared a picture of comparable precision in the maturation of behavior, with highly predictable relationships between points of stimulation and responding parts. In evaluating his observations, we must give some weight to the fact that their trend is opposite to the expectation with which he undertook his work, forcing him, as he has noted, to abandon an initial disbelief in the existence of fairly complex unlearned patterns of response. The views of Coghill and of Carmichael seem to assign different functions to the developing inhibitory functions: in one case, there is an initial general irritability which must be channeled into discrete paths, a process requiring inhibition of rival paths which originally were active simultaneously; in the other case, as the many discrete reflexes appear, they must be integrated into functional patterns of behavior, in a process which involves many reciprocal inhibitions among the reflexes themselves. Certainly, neural inhibition does perform both of these functions, and therefore we can readily accept the idea that both processes go on, in some species one being more prominent, and in some the other.

Although there is a steady advance in the availability of functional response mechanisms in the course of embryological development, it has also been observed that somewhere in the course of the mammalian embryonic development there is an actual decline in the frequency of spontaneous movements, which cannot be ascribed to changed environmental influences. Hooker found such a change in the human fetus at about sixteen weeks, and Barcroft (1938) places it at the fiftieth day for the fetus of the sheep, which has a gestation period of 144 days. Koshtoyants cites the opinion of Volokhov, that the process of establishing specialized reflex arcs in the fetus—that is, the differentiation of which Coghill spoke—is due to a limitation of the previous unrestrained spread of excitation through the nervous system, and the appearance of an ability to concentrate excitation along certain pathways by inhibiting its progress along others.

Barcroft provides not only a vivid picture of the behavioral change, but also convincing evidence as to how it comes about.

> As the days pass between the 40th and the 50th, the movements become not only more purposeful and concrete but also more easy to elicit. By the 49th day the foetus is so lively that it is difficult to manipulate it at all without consequent slight movements taking place, each followed by a rhythm. The result is that rhythmic movement scarcely ceases, and the foetus presents the general appearance of an ordinary animal breathing naturally. . . .
>
> We have now, at the 50th day, reached a very definite period in the lifetime of the sheep foetus; so far every new development has been in the direction of greater activity, but now the embryo enters upon a new era. This era is signalized by two things:
>
> 1. The foetus becomes quiescent. . . .
> 2. Asphyxia tends to bring back the picture as it was at the end of the earlier period . . . (Barcroft, 1938, pp. 26, 28).

Barcroft and Barron (1937) were able to section the central nervous system of the fetus in utero, without checking the normal growth. About ten days after this surgery, they would remove it for study.

> The results were quite convincing; a foetus of say 70 days which had reached the quiescent stage reverted to the general condition of a 50-day foetus when its central nervous system was completely transected just above the region of the red nucleus. If tapped it would immediately respond by stretching itself out and maintaining its limbs in this extended picture for a time. Indeed I have seen one such foetus exhibit the complete picture of a person who, after getting up from an unsatisfactory night, stretches and yawns. . . . It would seem that the quiescence which overcomes the activities of the foetus after the 50th day is really due to the development of an inhibitory mechanism higher than the position of the section, and its seems that this mechanism is more susceptible to asphyxia than those below it (Barcroft, 1938, p. 31).

With lower sections, the movements which are restored are found to have a much more jerky form. We shall see in Chapter 6 that the smoothing of motion is an essential function of inhibitions mediated by some subcortical structures involved in the control of movement.

Maturational development is prolonged in the human child, to the point that its locomotor apparatus is not ready to function for about a year after birth. We may therefore include as an example of embryological investigation a summary statement on the reflex response of the toes to stimulation of the sole of the foot, as it is observed not only before birth, but also in childhood and maturity. For this, we quote Carmichael:

> Minkowski showed that the first response to stimulation of the sole of the foot is probably an independent effector response that follows the direct stimulation of the muscles through the thin skin. The reaction does not involve neural elements. The next level of reaction in a foetus of 3 to 4 months is believed to involve connections in the spinal cord. This response shows a dorsal flexion of the toes. As the central nervous system continues to mature in the midfetal period, connections in the midbrain become effective, and the pattern of response changes again: the big toe is often extended while the other toes flex. As still higher centers become functional in late fetal life, the response becomes variable, sometimes showing a spreading of the toes. With the development, ordinarily after birth, of cortical dominance, the typical Babinski reflex (big-toe extension and flexion of other toes) disappears and is replaced by the adult plantar reflex (the contraction of all toes). In adults the presence of the Babinski reflex is sometimes indicative of a lesion of the pyramidal tracts of the brain and spinal cord (Carmichael, 1951, p. 288).

In pathological senility, we may add, or just before death, as the higher centers fail, the Babinski reflex reappears, to give final proof that the structures responsible for it have remained functional during all the years when this pattern of reflex response has been suppressed by inhibitory controls.

It is not possible to extend this chapter to include a survey of the many instances of unlearned behavior in higher vertebrates which seem to depend on disinhibitory release. Instead, we shall merely mention the contributions of two investigators whose work is doubtless already well known to most of our readers. Bard and his associates (see Bard, 1950) have shown that the neural mechanism of control over rage behavior includes at least two stages of inhibition, that is, that the rage pattern which is organized at a diencephalic level is inhibited by the amygdaloid cortex, and that release of the pattern normally implies disinhibition from higher levels.[2] The same general pattern of organization is suggested by Tinbergen (1951) for all sorts of unlearned behavior. Characteristically, he says, such behavior is triggered by what he calls "internal release mechanism" which operate on standing inhibitions. There is a clear parallel between these views and Sherrington's analysis of locomotion and posture, in which spinal reflexes are integrated at midbrain levels, but are subject to still higher inhibitory controls of cortical origin. These examples can serve to complete our comparative survey. Chapter 6 will give a more detailed view of the role of inhibition in the behavior of mammals. Meanwhile, we shall turn first to a consideration of inhibition as a synaptic process.

[2] New support for this interpretation comes from the work of Egger and Flynn (1962), who succeeded in suppressing hypothalamic rage behavior by amygdaloid stimulation.

SYNAPTIC INHIBITION 5

It was one of the great achievements of Sherrington to have pointed (1906) to the synaptic membrane as the probable seat of the inhibitory process, and subsequently (1925) to have shown that there is a "central inhibitory state" (c.i.s.) which has many of the same characteristics as the central excitatory state (c.e.s.) which he had previously defined—characteristics which could only be understood as synaptic phenomena. Sherrington's hypothesis has now been established beyond all doubt by an accumulation of knowledge which justifies the definition of inhibition (page 9) as "an event which begins with the release of an inhibitory transmitter substance by the activated neuron, the effect of which is to prevent, or tend to prevent, the discharge of another neuron." It is this type of event which we assume to be the antecedent of each and every phenomenon which is described as an "inhibition" in this book, except in quotations from noncontemporary authors. To avoid misunderstanding, let us point to two exceptions to this statement—each is of the nature of an exception which tends to prove the rule. First, it is not intended to deny the possibility that overt activities may sometimes be obstructed by a conflict of excitatory tendencies, or of muscular contractions in antagonistic muscles; but in the interests of clarity it is better that such phenomena be designated as instances of *suppression,* or by some synonym of suppression, and that the word *inhibition* be reserved to designate the effects of synaptic events of the type described. Second, it must of course be recognized that the inhibitory effects of the transmitter substances, which are neurohumors, may be mimicked in whole or in part by certain drugs, and influenced by similar hormones which may be produced elsewhere in the body.

It is the main task of this chapter to summarize present knowledge on the nature of synaptic inhibition. The latter part of the chapter will introduce the problems of the relationship between synaptic inhibition and the action of drugs on the central nervous system, and of the implications of the chemical theory of transmission for our understanding of behavior. Much of what follows is written in dependence on excellent reviews by Eccles (1953, 1959), to whom we owe much of our present knowledge of the nervous impulse generally and of the synaptic process in particular, and by Grundfest (1959a, 1959b, 1960a, 1960b), who is another leading exponent of this theory of inhibition. (The reader who desires closer acquaintance with current problems in this area may turn to Florey, 1961b.)

The outer surface of each cell, including its axon and dendrites, and the surfaces which they present to other contiguous cells at synaptic junctions, is a very thin membrane, with a thickness of about 50 angstrom units. (That is about one five-millionth of an inch, or about one-tenth of the length of a light wave in the blue-green band of the visible spectrum.) Like any cellular membrane, it has pores which are too small even for detection by the electron microscope. These pores permit diffusion processes by which the cell maintains its metabolism with the outside medium, but they must be small enough to limit these diffusion processes so that the cell can maintain differential concentrations of certain chemicals. The pores have not been measured in nerve cells, but it has recently been determined that the pores of red blood cells have a diameter of about 7 angstroms, which provides a corridor just about wide enough for one water molecule to jostle past another, and they appear to be spaced at least 200 angstroms apart, on the average (Goldstein & Solomon, 1960). Selective diffusion of ions can cause an electrical potential to exist between the two surfaces of a cell membrane. In what is called the resting state of the neuron, the strength of this potential is about 50 to 80 millivolts, the inner surface being negatively charged with respect to the outer. Somehow, the cell maintains a considerable excess of positive sodium ions on the outer surface. It also maintains cross-membrane gradients in the distribution of potassium and chlorine ions; but these are less marked, and tend to lessen rather than to increase the polarization, since there is a somewhat higher concentration of positive potassium ions inside the membrane, and of negative chlorine ions outside. The fact that the potassium and chlorine gradients are weaker than the sodium gradient does not make them less important, for we shall soon see that the existence of these opposed gradients, in the resting state of the neuron, is an essential condition for the occurrence of neural inhibition. This "resting state" is an equilibrium between active processes: on the one hand there is the constant tendency of these electrochemical gradients to run "downhill" across the membrane, and on the other hand there is some unknown cellular process, which is often referred to as an "ion pump," which maintains the gradients. The effectiveness of the pump depends on the ease of diffusion through the membrane: if the membrane becomes suddenly permeable to all sorts of ions, the "pump" will be unable to maintain the potential difference, and the membrane will become depolarized.

The nerve impulse which traverses the axon is—as Bernstein (1902) correctly surmised—a temporary abolition of a pre-existing state of polarization. This depolarization can be initiated at any point where the permeability of the membrane is suddenly increased by any local influence. Such an initial rupture can be precipitated in many ways: by mechanical stimulation, by chemical agents, by an electric current, etc. The condition spreads rapidly in all directions, but it is of very brief duration at any one point because it is self-limiting, due to the fact that the swift rush of ions through the breach results in a brief period of hyperpolarization. The consequence is the "absolute refractory phase," which insures that the wave of depolarization which spreads progressively along the length of the neuron cannot turn about and sweep back again. There is a slightly longer period of relative refractory phase during which the pump reestablishes the "resting" potential. If a continuous record is being made of the electrical activity of the neuron at any point, the passage of the wave of depolarization appears as a sharp upward spike followed by a dip below the level of the resting potential. In any given neuron the height of the spike is remarkably constant, for the strength of this response depends on the sudden release of the resting potential, that is to say on an inherent characteristic of the neuron itself, and not at all on the type or strength of the stimulus applied to the nerve, once that stimulus has passed the critical level needed to precipitate a discharge. This phenomenon is referred to as the "all-or-none" action of the nerve cell. One might say that the nerve membrane "inhibits" the movement of ions, and that the nerve impulse results from a temporary interruption of this function, a kind of "disinhibition."

The transmission of an impulse from one neuron to another takes place only at a synapse, that is, a point where the membranes lie close together although there is no structural joining of the cells. The word synapse was suggested by Sherrington in 1897, at a time when it was still a matter of controversy whether nerve fibers were continuous from cell to cell, as maintained by Golgi, or discontinuous, as maintained by Cajal. Before the discovery of the synapse, all discontinuities in the movement of the nerve impulse were presumed to take place in the cell bodies scattered along what appeared to be continuous nerve fibers. It was assumed that the cell body was the site for summation and interaction of impulses, that it offered a resistance which could sometimes check them (as in Wundt's early theory of inhibition), and that it was responsible for initiation of new impulses based on incoming stimulation and on its own physiological state. The discovery of the synapse did not enforce any essential change in these views, although it was obvious that a new kind of resistance had been introduced into the system of connections. It was still assumed that the normal physiological stimulus to the discharge of one neuron is an electrical impulse received from another, and the synaptic structure of the nervous system was simply interpreted to mean that nature had anticipated the electrical engineer in the invention of condensors in which a series of weak charges could be accumulated to form one charge strong enough to jump the gap. The synapse, instead of the cell body, became accepted as the site of interactions and summations; but the realization that what happened at the synapse had to be explained as a chemical rather than as an electrical phenomenon gained ground slowly.

We shall not attempt to review all the important steps leading up to the present understanding of synaptic transmission, but we shall mention a few outstanding events which also have special bearing on our general subject of inhibition. (For a fuller account, see Minz, 1955.) When Claude Bernard (1857) discovered that curare produced a motor and not a sensory paralysis, he interpreted the effect as differential poisoning of the motor nerves—a fact which he regarded (1858a, 1864) as verification of Haller's distinction between irritative and sensitive functions. Despite his insightful characterization of toxic substances as delicate physiological instruments which are capable of dissecting out the functional properties of the living organism, he did not surmise that the effect of curare was not on either nerve or muscle as such, but on the process of transmission from one to the other. The greater part of a century was to pass before it became possible to envisage this effect as we now understand it, as due to the competition of curare, whose active principle is a quarternary ammonium ion, with acetylcholine for receptor sites in the neuromuscular synapse. Important support for a chemical theory of nervous transmission came from the research of Langley, Dale, Cannon, and others, on the pharmacological properties of acetylcholine and epinephrine (adrenalin), which could produce the same effects on various organs as those resulting from sympathetic and parasympathetic innervation. In 1921, Loewi produced the first direct proof of chemical transmission by demonstrating that when the heart of a frog is stimulated by the vagus nerve, the liquid in which it is immersed is enriched with some substance (he called it vagus-stuff) which can inhibit the action of another heart, just as the vagus innervation itself does. Samoilov (1924) showed that changes in temperature exert much greater influence on the speed of the transmission process than on conduction within the nerve axon, and he concluded from the nature of this dependence on temperature that a chemical reaction was involved. In an evolutionary sense, he said, the nervous system only provides a swifter means of transport for the humoral influence which is the the primitive basis for coordination among the cells of the body. This was in agreement with Cannon's (1927) work on homeostasis, in which the coordinative effects of adrenal secretions were emphasized. Cannon and Rosenblueth (1937) recognized the difficulty of explaining the medley of visceral effects as resulting from the action of a single neurohormone, and advanced the hypothesis that two forms of "sympathin," one excitatory and one inhibitory, were produced in the effector cells. At that time it was not known that the adrenal secretion included norepinephrine as well as epinephrine, and that it was the former which would be discovered to be the transmitter at peripheral sympathetic synapses. In 1933, Dale proposed that instead of Langley's classification of the autonomic nervous system into sympathetic and parasympathetic divisions, it would be better to speak of adrenergic and cholinergic nerves, a classification which is almost but not entirely parallel, and which of course is applicable also outside the autonomic system. By the early 30's there was an accumulation of much circumstantial evidence, and a small amount of questionable direct evidence, that acetylcholine and some epinephrine-like substance are the principal transmitters at peripheral synapses. Very little was known about how they obtain their effects, and the theory of electrical transmission still had strong support, particularly as regards central synapses. The more detailed study of the synaptic phenomenon had to await the startling development of microtechniques which has taken place within the past decade.

The electron microscope reveals the synapse as a sharply defined interneuronal space which is about 150 to 500 angstroms in width, although the width of any given synapse varies very little. On one side of the synapse, in the presynaptic neuron, it is sometimes possible to discern tiny vesicles which appear to be suited to the storage of small quantities of the transmitter substance, ready to be discharged into the synaptic space. Florey (1961a) points to the possibility that because of influences affecting these storage facilities, the synaptic activity may not have the same all-or-none character as the axonal impulse. On the other side, the postsynaptic or subsynaptic membrane lacks visible distinguishing features, but this is not surprising since, for reasons soon to be stated, it is probable that the special characteristics of the so-called receptor sites on which the transmitter takes effect are a matter of fine molecular structure which constitutes some kind of valving mechanism designed to alter the size of the pores through which the diffusion of ions takes place. Direct measurements of electrical potential in the subsynaptic membranes show that in the absence of a proper transmitter substance, electrical potentials considerably greater than those of the presynaptic nerve impulse are unable to leap the synapse, and cannot by themselves excite the subsynaptic neuron.

When transmission does take place, by chemical means, the resulting postsynaptic potentials (PSPs) are of two kinds, which make it possible to differentiate between two types of synapses: depolarizing and hyperpolarizing, which in their usual effects are, respectively, excitatory (with EPSPs) and inhibitory (with IPSPs). In depolarizing synapses, the effect of the transmitter on the receptor sites is to bring about a general increase in permeability of the membrane to all types of ions. As a consequence, the electrochemical gradients are locally abolished, and this phenomenon of depolarization tends to spread along the cell membrane, giving rise to the axonal impulse or nerve discharge. However, there are some synapses which, whether because of the special nature of the receptor sites or the nature of the transmitter substance, give rise to postsynaptic hyperpolarization. This is the result of a selective increase in permeability, presumably because the pores of the receptor sites are opened only sufficiently to allow ions of very small size to pass freely, while still impeding the passage of large ions. In this case, the potassium and chlorine gradients are quickly abolished, but the stronger sodium gradient remains in full force. Since the gradients for potassium and chlorine in the resting fiber are opposite in sign to the sodium gradient, the effect of removing them is to increase the net electrical polarization of the membrane. Thus, in the two types of synapses the immediate response of the subsynaptic membrane to the transmitter is similar in type, being in both cases an increase in the permeability of the membrane; and the very different final outcomes depend on a quantitative difference in this phenomenon. In excitatory synapses, the depolarizing effect tends to propagate along the membrane, that is, to set up an axonal nerve impulse. In inhibitory synapses, the hyperpolarizing PSP counteracts any simultaneous tendency to depolarization, and thus tends to quell any excitation.[1]

The question arises as to whether most cells possess both types of synapses, and here a distinction must be made between terminal synapses or discharging surfaces, on the one hand, and subsynaptic or receptor surfaces on the other. It seems quite likely, as Dale suggested, that any given neuron will produce only one transmitter substance, but of course it does not follow from this that it can terminate in only one kind of synapse. In crustaceans, where inhibition is peripheral, there are known instances in which the same motor cell has branches to two antagonistic muscles, so that by its discharge it simultaneously excites one and inhibits the other. A comparable situation has been discovered in the cardiac innervation of the snail. It therefore seems risky to assume, as Eccles does in face of these facts, that in vertebrates each cell will have only inhibitory or excitatory functions.

It is true, as Eccles states, that "conceptually, by this subdivision of nerve cells into excitatory and inhibitory types, a great simplification is introduced," but it seems to us that such conceptual simplification may be more hindrance than help in fitting the events of nervous activity to the very complex phenomena of behavior. Grundfest argues that since acetylcholine, at least, serves as transmitter for both exciting and inhibitory synapses, it is likely that the nature of a synapse is determined by the structure of the subsynaptic membrane, and this certainly suggests that many cells of the central nervous system will have both excitatory and inhibitory terminations. Eccles has presented evidence tending to prove that an inhibitory interneuron participates in every instance of inhibition at the spinal level, but Lloyd (1960) offers other experimental evidence in refutation of that position. Since their difference hangs upon niceties of experimental technique in which differences of less

[1] In some cells of the salivary gland only hyperpolarizing PSPs occur, but then it is a misnomer to call them inhibiting, since their effect is to evoke secretion. When both types of PSP occur in the same gland cell, their effect is probably not to excite and inhibit, respectively, but to induce the release of qualitatively different secretions. It is not difficult to reconcile this apparent contradiction with what has been said above, since the release of thick or thin saliva is not so different from the valving of large and small ions.

than one millisecond are crucial, this is a problem beyond our competence to consider. While the matter remains in dispute, we must at least not close our minds to the possibility that the same neurons exercise both excitatory and inhibitory functions.

As regards subsynaptic surfaces, the problem is simpler. There are probably many cells of the central nervous system which, like muscle fibers, produce only depolarizing PSPs. However, there are many others, and perhaps the majority, in which subsynaptic receptor surfaces of both kinds occur. In the latter case, the question whether a neuron will discharge or not is resolved by the cumulative effect of many local EPSPs and IPSPs, the outcome being influenced not only by their number and their strength, but also by their spatial distribution. It is probable that even without such antagonism, actual discharge never occurs except as a result of the summation of many excitatory receptor sites. It should be remembered that the typical cortical neuron is covered with literally thousands of synapses, and its dendrites spread into an area occupied by thousands of other neurons (Sholl, 1956). It is known that some of the hyperpolarizing synapses on spinal motoneurons are those of inhibitory interneurons which are excited by collateral branches of the axon from the motoneuron itself. That a similar situation exists in the cerebral cortex, to provide one basis for "Heidenhain inhibition," is extremely probable (Purpura, 1960). Even when a great many excitatory synapses have been activated, the hyperpolarizing effect of a much smaller number of inhibitory synapses may reduce the polarizing effect below the critical level necessary to induce neuronal discharge, or may prevent the wave of depolarization from reaching the axon.

The theory of chemical transmission of nerve impulses, the validity of which may now be said to have been established beyond question, leads to a radically new conception of nervous control, in which the neurons are regarded as specialized glandular cells, producing neurohumors which serve at central synapses to influence one another, and at peripheral synapses to influence other bodily organs. It is therefore no longer a matter of surprise that one of the known transmitter substances, norepinephrine, should also be the product of an endocrine gland, nor that the neurohumors secreted in the hypothalamic area take effect, not only on immediately adjacent neuronal elements, but also on the pituitary glands which are situated at the base of the brain. By replacing electrical transmission by chemical transmission, we have not merely replaced one form of stimulation by another. We have replaced an undifferentiated source of excitation by a class of stimulating agents which can have many different effects. It now makes no more sense to talk about "nervous excitation" than it would to talk about "endocrine secretion," without distinguishing between the different effects of thyroid, adrenal secretions, anterior and posterior pituitary secretions, etc. The psychologist who believes that his theories need not be influenced by advances in neurophysiology should ask himself how his theories of emotion would fare if he only knew that "glands secrete," and had never learned that they secrete different substances.

Indeed, we are now able to understand why, time and again, pharmacology has given important insights into major problems of neurophysiology. It will be remembered that the title of Anstie's neglected book was *Stimulants and Narcotics*, and that his insight into the principle of release came from his initial interest in drug effects. Claude Bernard's study of the flaccid paralysis induced by curare initiated study of neuromuscular transmission. The contrast between this and the spastic paralysis induced by strychnine, a closely related compound, will soon draw our attention. Heidenhain, Wedensky, Sherrington, and many other investigators have had to emphasize that the inhibitory effects they witnessed were clearly apparent only at "a certain stage of narcotization." It is convenient at this point to summarize certain facts and suppositions concerning chemical transmitters and the effects of drugs at synapses, although we shall postpone a fuller discussion of drug effects on behavior until a later chapter.

Only two substances, acetylcholine (ACh) and norepinephrine are definitely known to act as synaptic transmitters in the vertebrate nervous system, but there is very good evidence that serotonin (5-hydroxytryptomine, or 5-HT for short) is a third transmitter, a fairly strong body of opinion that gamma-aminobutyric acid (GABA) is a fourth, and general agreement on the likelihood that others remain to be discovered, while the claims of several other substances are pushed by their discoverers. Florey (1961a) says that "the assumption of a small number of transmitter substances is not based on evidence but rather on the admittedly strong argument that not many compounds could qualify as transmitter agents."

Acetylcholine is the transmitter at skeletal neuromuscular synapses, at peripheral synapses of parasympathetic effector nerves, at sympathetic ganglia, and possibly in the majority of central synapses, including those of the spinal cord. It seems unlikely that it is the only cerebral transmitter, despite the fact that it can function in inhibitory as well as excitatory synapses. Feldberg and Vogt (1948) suggested that it is probably the transmitter only at alternate synapses in the central system, and that a variety of different transmitters are involved in the intervening synapses.

Norepinephrine is the transmitter at peripheral synapses of sympathetic effector nerves, and at many central synapses in the hypothalamus, and probably also in other areas of the brain which are concerned more with visceral than with skeletal action.

GABA is another natural substance which is found in higher concentrations in the brain than in other organs—it produces both excitatory and inhibitory effects when administered. Furthermore, when the metabolic process by which it is synthesized in the brain is prevented from taking place, convulsions result, which suggests that it is involved in inhibitions necessary to maintain normal levels of excitation in the brain. Koelle (1959), after reviewing the evidence with respect to this and a number of other proposed transmitter substances, concludes that "GABA appears to be a promising candidate for the role of a central inhibitory transmitter." On the other hand, Grunfest believes that it gains its effects by a tendency to inactivate excitatory synapses, rather than by activating inhibitory synapses. A recent symposium (Roberts, 1960) produced much evidence of the importance of GABA in neural functioning.

Serotonin received its name at a time when it had not yet been identified, but was being sought as a vasoconstrictor substance which evidently assisted in the clotting of blood. After it had been isolated and analyzed, it was found to be present in the brain, where it has especially high concentrations in the hypothalamus and other parts of the "visceral brain," but is absent from the corpus striatum and the cerebellum, that is, from structures which are mostly concerned with posture. It has been suggested that serotonin serves as a transmitter at hypothalamic centers, where it tends to activate the parasympathetic system. Brodie and Shore (1957) offer evidence that there is a serotonergic system, similar to the cholinergic and adrenergic systems.

Less evidence is available regarding other proposed transmitters. There is reason to suppose that some substance different from any of those yet identified is active in the cerebellar cortex. It would be surprising, in view of the specificity which is now being attained in the action of drugs on different parts of the central nervous system, if research in the next decade does not confirm the suspicion that some of this specificity depends on special characteristics in different nervous structures. Purpura (1959) suggests that the naturally occurring, synaptically active amino-acids probably include not only inhibitory and excitatory transmitters, but also "anti-excitatory and anti-inhibitory transmitters which compete at receptor surfaces with their excitatory and inhibitory counterparts."

Indeed, investigation of the influence of drugs on various processes and the further investigation of natural synaptic transmitters must now proceed hand in hand, each advance in one of these fields shaping hypotheses for the other. Few fields now have such close interdisciplinary interdependence as pharmacology and neurophysiology. The metabolism of a transmitter, as well as its mode of operation in the synapse, provides many opportunities for varied drug effects.

Each transmitter substance must be synthesized, stored, released when needed, and destroyed following its use, preferably in some manner which permits its economical resynthesis. This metabolic cycle is well understood for both acetylcholine and epinephrine (and of course norepinephrine, which is actually one step ahead of epinephrine in the cycle of synthesis). Each stage in the cycle presents some opportunity for a distinctive effect to be produced by some drug which prevents or facilitates that particular phase. Thus, for example, the enzyme cholinesterase plays an essential part in nervous activity by its destruction of acetylcholine, tending thus to terminate the effect produced at the synapse by release of the transmitter. Anticholinesterase agents interfere with this process, and thus tend to prolong excitations. Other drugs may themselves tend to combine with the transmitter, thus reducing its effectiveness. A drug which has a chemical structure similar to that of the transmitter in certain respects may be able to mimic its action at the synapse. Another drug, whose structure is only slightly different, may be able to mimic the transmitter only partially, and the behavioral effect may be quite the opposite, because the drug now occupies the receptor site and thus blocks the access of the natural transmitter to it, but it cannot actually activate the site into creating a postsynaptic potential.

One very important instance of such an effect is provided by strychnine, a drug which has long been regarded as a powerful nervous excitant. Bradley, Easton, and Eccles (1953) show that what strychnine actually does is to set up a selective blockade of inhibitory synapses. The dramatic result of this impairment of inhibitory power—spastic paralysis on the spinal level, convulsions on the cortical level, which may be initiated by quite mild intensities of visual or auditory stimulation—demonstrates the crucial importance of inhibition to normal functioning of the nervous system. Knowledge of its mode of action has made strychnine an extremely valuable tool in the hands of the neurophysiologist, since the occurrence of convulsions or increased excitability in response to the local application of strychnine establishes a strong presumption, if not absolute proof, that inhibitory synapses are present at that point, and the violence of the reaction can be used to measure the relative proportion of synapses which are of this type. The blocking of the inhibitory synapses gives rise to a series of intermittent convulsions, the frequency of which depends on the speed of resynthesis, at the given site, of the supply of acetylcholine which is rapidly depleted by the convulsive activity. Where inhibitory synapses of this type are not present, there must be some other mechanism to prevent the needless depletion of acetylcholine.

Grundfest's schema of some of the ways in which drugs can act at synapses, shown in Table 1, is wholly consistent with Anstie's idea that "stimulants" are misnamed, because so often they gain their effects by the suppression of normal controls. To classify a drug as a "stimulant" or as a "depressant" on the basis of its overt effects tells us nothing about the nature of its action at the synapse. Thus, in the table, we see that overt excitatory effects may be produced by acetylcholine, which is a natural transmitter, or by metrazol,

TABLE 1. Mode of Action of Synaptic Drugs

Class of Drug	Type of Synapse Depolarizing	Type of Synapse Hyperpolarizing	Type of Compound	Overt Effect
Activators				
Nonselective	+	+	Acetylcholine Norepinephrine	Excitatory or Inhibitory
Selective (a)	+	0	Metrazol Picrotoxin	Excitatory
Selective (b)	0	+	?	Inhibitory
Inactivators				
Nonselective	+	+	D-tubocurarine	Inhibitory
Selective (a)	+	0	GABA	Inhibitory
Selective (b)	0	+	Strychnine	Excitatory

SOURCE: Based on Grundfest, *Inhibition in the Nervous System and Gamma-Aminobutyric Acid,* 1960a, pp. 47–65. By permission of Pergamon Press, Inc.

which is able to mimic it at excitatory but not at inhibitory synapses, or by strychnine, which is able to partly mimic it, and thus to blockade inhibitory synapses. Similarly, inhibitory effects may be produced by norepinephrine, by acetylcholine, by curare, which is able to block both types of synapses, and by GABA, which blocks only the excitatory synapses. The reader will remember that GABA has also been proposed as a central inhibitory transmitter. It is possible that it plays a blockading role in the cerebral cortex, and a transmitting role in the cerebellum, where inhibitory synapses of the kind that are blocked by strychnine do not occur. Reality has been simplified in this schema, for, as Grundfest points out, it is probable that the receptor sites in each major type of synapse include subtypes which are differentially responsive to different natural transmitters and hence also to different drugs.

Although at the present time the contradictory effects of very closely related substances present a confusing picture, it is likely that the analysis of these very contradictions will lead to increased understanding. For example, it has been observed that the pharmacological effects of a certain class of amino acids, each of which includes an amino group (NH_2) at one end of its molecule and a carboxyl group (CO_2H) at the other end, seems to depend on whether the carbon chain between these radicals is short or long. Although these acids have a depressant effect, another class of amino acids, which include two carboxyl groups in their structure, tend to have excitant effects. As an explanation for this double paradox, Curtis and Watkins (1960) suggest that an acid of the latter type represents a kind of three-pronged key which is capable of "opening" the pores of a depolarizing receptor surface, whereas the same receptor sites can be blocked (thus giving rise to depressant or inhibitory effects) by the acids which include only one carboxyl group; —the effectiveness of the blockade depends on the distance which separates this carboxyl group from the amino group of the same molecule. Whether this hypothesis proves to be correct or not, it is a good example of how the problem of the sharply differing effects of drugs with fairly similar structures will ultimately be solved.

The theory of chemical transmission of nerve impulses also makes us aware of a very important limitation in all of the experimental work which utilizes electrical stimulation of the brain (a limitation which must be kept in mind when interpreting the results of such stimulation). Except when single units are stimulated by microelectrodes, the effect of electrical stimulation must be to activate all units in the area indiscriminately. It is true that some of these units will have inhibitory terminations, nevertheless, the effects obtained by this diffuse activation cannot give a true picture of the function of any portion of the brain.

At best, we can expect excitatory effects from regions in which cells with excitatory terminations are preponderant, and inhibitory effects from regions in which cells with inhibitory terminations are preponderant. In the motor areas, as we know, it is sometimes possible to obtain either inhibitory or excitatory effects from the same point, depending on its state at the moment, which depends in part on the activity of the corresponding point in the opposite hemisphere. In general, however, we cannot hope to reproduce the effects of natural stimulation—which depend in part on the release of inhibitory neurohumors—by the application of an exclusively excitatory stimulus. The picture is one in which each region of the brain seems to give rise to some characteristic form of response when it is activated, whereas it is quite probable that in reality each region participates in control of at least two antagonistically related responses.

The fact that electrical stimulation of most areas of the cerebral cortex produces no detectable overt response raises a strong presumption that the effect of such nonphysiological stimulation tends on balance to be more inhibitory than excitatory. This is probably the reason for the paradoxical fact, brought out in Penfield and Roberts' (1959) account of cortical explorations performed with patients undergoing surgery for focal epilepsy, that direct stimulation in and near the speech area always leads to an arrest of speech rather than to any utterance. This is just what we should expect from nondifferentiated stimulation, on the assumption that control of speech rests on an interaction of excitatory and inhibitory innervations. This is probably also the reason for the confused situation in mapping functional areas of the hypothalamus, where a general parasympathetic dominance of the anterior hypothalamus and a general sympathetic dominance of the posterior hypothalamus are discernible, but points giving rise to opposite effects often seem to be intermingled.

We can anticipate that a much clearer picture of the localization of functions will arise, not only from the use of microelectrodes to stimulate single units and to record their activity, but still better from the use of natural transmitter substances applied in minute quantities. Several workers have already demonstrated the usefulness of this technique. For example, Grossman (1960) has reported that different behavioral effects are produced by the release of acetylcholine and norepinephrine at the same point in the hypothalamus. (See page 368 for a fuller discussion of this finding.) This provides a better approximation to physiological conditions of stimulation than has been achieved previously, and the results show the need for extreme caution in interpreting effects which have been attained by electrical stimulation.

Finally, we wish to allude briefly to the importance of the concept of synaptic inhibition for interpretation of the effects of the so-called psychoactive drugs. It is obvious from the facts which have been reviewed in this chapter that much of the specificity of drug effects has its basis in synaptic differentiation. As long as the process of nervous transmission was regarded as uniform, no possibility existed for understanding the nature of drug effects. Dale's (1933) distinction between cholinergic and adrenergic parts of the autonomic system was an important step in the development of pharmacology. And the more recent recognition that there are several different inhibitory transmitters active in the nervous system represents a still greater step, which opens up new perspectives for explanation of hitherto puzzling phenomena. To illustrate this, we shall give a brief statement of three recent hypotheses about the manner in which LSD-25 (*d*-lysergic acid diethylamide) attains its effects.

LSD-25 is used experimentally to create "model psychoses" in normal subjects, and it has also been used as an adjunct to psychotherapy (Abramson, 1960). It also produces abnormal behavior in spiders (Witt, 1954), in fish, and in snails (Abramson & Jarvik, 1955). One reason why this drug is especially interesting from a pharmacological point of view is that it is extremely potent, being effective in doses as small as those of a natural transmitter, a fact which certainly suggests that its influence on nervous processes is quite direct. To illustrate, the ordinary dose used to induce a model psychosis is only about one four-thousandth of the usual dose of chlorpromazine, a tranquilizer which counteracts its effects. Very minor changes in the structure of the drug are accompanied by an enormous loss in its potency. Evidently this molecule, though it is not a natural transmitter substance, is capable of exerting strong effects at the synapse. However, one paradoxical fact which must be accounted for by any theory of LSD-25 action is that its depressant effect on electrical response of the cortex, to stimulation of a corresponding point in the opposite hemisphere or some subcortical structure, is readily eliminated by the action of various sedative and tranquilizing drugs which, in themselves, have effects similar rather than opposite to those of LSD.

In brief, without entering into the details of experimental support, the three theories offered in explanation of the action of LSD-25 are as follows: 1) Purpura (1957) contends that "LSD-25 activates inhibitory postsynaptic receptors." 2) Marrazzi (1957a), who believes that in all types of synaptic action it is possible to discern an opposition between excitatory cholinergic and inhibitory adrenergic mechanisms, argues that LSD-25 is a powerful activator of the central adrenergic process, but it is very often blocked by drugs which, though they have much weaker effects, are able successfully to compete with it for possession of the receptor sites. 3) Brodie (1957), who hypothesizes antagonistic effects of adrenalin and serotonin, thinks it most likely that LSD-25 "acts by interfering with the normal depolarizing action of serotonin released at synaptic junctions. . . . [It] does not merely neutralize the effects of serotonin itself, as it does in the case of smooth muscle, but it actually induces the opposite effects. [This] suggests that in the brain stem there are two antagonistic systems, and if one is blocked the other is unmasked." (See also Shore & Brodie, 1957.)

We shall make no effort to appraise the respective merits of these three theories. This is a matter which is certainly beyond our competence, and which could not reasonably be attempted without considering many complex interactions with other drugs. However, looking at the theories as a group, it is obvious that the concept of synaptic inhibition is basic to all of them, and that this concept has not only opened up new perspectives for the analysis of drug effects, but that it also suggests a new approach to the problem of the nature of conflict among action tendencies. In the multitude of depolarizing and hyperpolarizing synapses which cover the surface of the typical central neuron, a variety of neurohumors, which are identical with or closely related to substances that also have essential functions in other parts of the body, contend for mastery. The experimental testing of theories like those which have just been stated will throw additional light on this process, but already it is clear that the failure to take note of qualitative differences in the synaptic process must prevent any proper appreciation of the role of the nervous system in control of behavior.

THE SCOPE OF INHIBITION 6

In the preceding chapters we have seen that inhibition, which was once no more than an embarrassing necessity, has at last become an understandable fact. Thus the old concept of a purely excitatory nervous system is obsolete, and it would be a great mistake to replace it with a makeshift which only grudgingly acknowledges that inhibition plays an incidental part here and there, where the fact is indisputable. It is clear that inhibition is an indispensable part of nervous activity, and we should expect to find it playing an essential part in every instance of nervous control.

One hundred years ago, the nervous system was regarded as a communications network in which strong impulses "reverberated" and weak impulses "subsided." After the invention of the telephone, it was natural to think of the brain as a center in which messages could be switched along relatively discrete paths, which might go from any part to any other part. However, we know by direct electrical recording that the brain is unceasingly active in all its parts, and that no one of the billions of units which compose it is quite inactive for more than a brief period. We also know that the sensitivity of the neural elements is such that the brain is, in Jung's phrase (1954) an "enormous synaptic powder barrel" which would explode in epileptic convulsion if it were not constantly restrained by inhibitory elements.

This fact had already been recognized in a degree by Heidenhain and by Mercier; it is implicit in Ashby's logical demonstration that a brain which is "fully joined" cannot function adaptively. If communication were the single basic principle underlying nervous organization, the result would be chaos. Therefore, as Ashby (1960) states, we must "dispose once for all of the idea, fostered in almost every book on the brain written in the last century, that the more communication there is within the brain the better." There can be no question that the tendency of nervous impulses to propagate themselves must constantly be held in check by inhibitory influences. What we wish to consider in this chapter is the extent and variety of such influences, as revealed by recent research.

Not all of the relevant neurophysiological research takes place *in vitro* or *in vivo.* In his *Design for a Brain,* Ashby demonstrated with mathematical tools that there must be two kinds of negative feedback in any "brain" which is capable of regulating behavior adaptively, that is, in a manner which "maintains the essential variables within physiological limits." This implies only that a trial-and-error modification of response takes place, in such a way that responses which are poorly adaptive in the immediate situation tend to be discontinued and those which are more successful in meeting the organism's needs tend to persist. To achieve this end, Ashby proves, it is necessary that there be two different feedback loops, one to deliver information about change in the environment, and the other to inform about the state of essential intraorganic variables which are influenced by the environment. In other words, the second loop brings the reports of success and failure which tend to discontinue some responses and to selectively confirm others. He also points out that this motivational feedback will work best as a "step function," so that its feedback is based on changes which pass certain critical levels rather than being continuous, for otherwise there would be a very wasteful incessant variability of behavior. For example, we all know from personal experience during illness that an excessive sensitivity to minute fluctuations of temperature does not help to attain a state of comfort.

Ashby summarizes his result as follows: "What has been deduced . . . is *necessary.* That is to say, *any* system that has essential variables with given limits, and that adapts by the process of testing various behaviors by how each affects ultimately the essential variables, must have a second feedback formally identical (isomorphic) with that described here. This deduction holds equally for brains living and mechanical" (1960, p. 85).

Figure 1 gives a schematic representation of Ashby's system of dual feedback. Following his presentation, the environment constitutes a link in each system. We feel it important to emphasize that the minimal requirement is only for negative feedback from each loop, that is, that the processes initiated by environmental feedback, both directly and indirectly by way of the "essential variables" which constitute the motivational state, must be able to limit the activity of the effector mechanisms, but need not be able to increase that activity. This point is of particular interest because positive

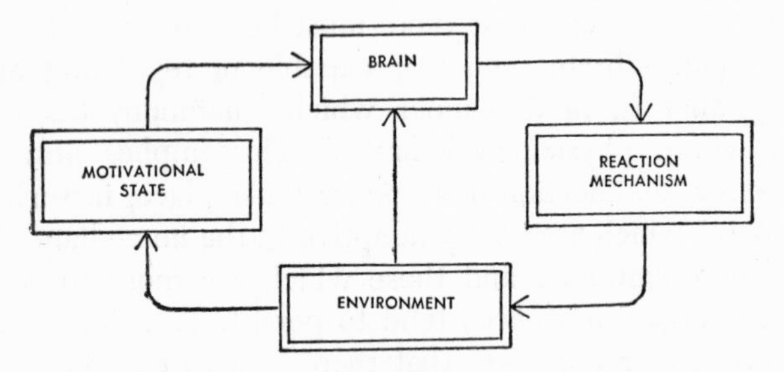

Figure 1. Double feedback: Ashby's minimal requirement for an adaptive nervous system.

feedback, from "rewarding" events which supposedly strengthen or reinforce processes under way, not only play some part in behavior, but commonly receive major emphasis in psychological theories. However, only the need for negative feedback is demonstrable a priori. If an organism is equipped to perform an adaptive response, without environmental prompting, the survival of the organism does not require that success be confirmed by positive feedback; when the response is maladaptive, it is essential that there be some negative feedback to provide a signal of the need for a different response.

Hence we can restate Ashby's conclusion in this form: a brain which is capable of adaptively regulating behavior must have at least two kinds of response-suppressing feedback. This does not exclude the possibility that positive, response-enhancing feedback may also come to play an important part in adaptive behavior, but it does mean that any system which relies exclusively upon positive feedback—and this is the kind of system which has been implicit in a great deal of S-R theorizing—is headed for a catastrophic breakdown. Nothing could be more maladaptive than an unmitigated repetition compulsion, and the organism burdened in this way

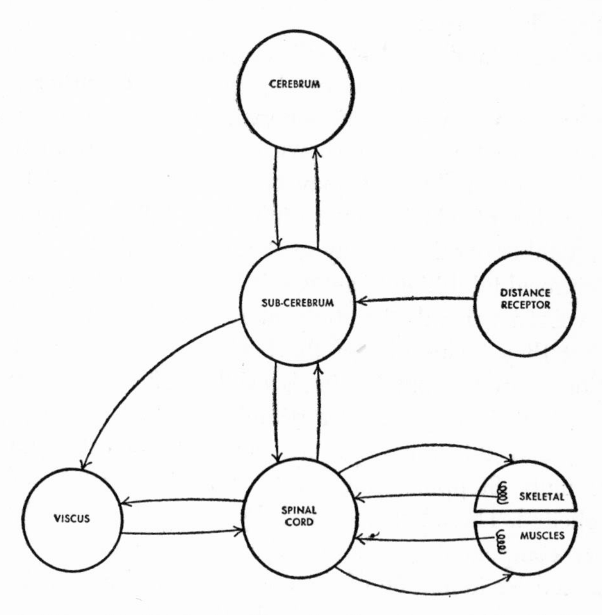

Figure 2. The basic schema for the nervous system of the vertebrates.

would not be saved by the fact that as a result of experienced satisfactions or reinforcements the repetition of some acts becomes even more compelling than that of others.

The minimal brain which is schematized in Figure 1 might be elaborated in many ways, but every useful elaboration would doubtless entail additional feedback loops. Figure 2 includes a number of such elaborations, which are chosen to conform to characteristics common to many animals: the effector apparatus is represented by two antagonistic muscles, within which the stretch receptors are also indicated; environmental feedback takes place in part by way of the head receptor; the motivational state is represented by a visceral organ which has antagonistic efferents; and three distinct levels of organization are shown in the nervous system. Any nervous system of this complexity will probably exhibit all of the varieties of inhibitory relationships which have already been described in earlier chapters. We shall review them briefly, in terms which apply to vertebrate behavior.

1. Peripheral inhibition of each visceral organ takes place by means of one of its efferents, that is, by means of either the sympathetic or the parasympathetic innervation. Since, in the diagram, the parasympathetic nerve is shown as descending from the intermediate level of the brain, it may be taken to represent the vagus nerve, branches of which exercise inhibitory influence on the heart and on a number of other widely scattered viscera.[1]

2. Reciprocal inhibition of antagonistic muscles takes place on the spinal level. In general, the study of reflexes in the spinal animal shows that they include all of the basic elements for posture and locomotion. Chronic spinal animals exhibit reflex flexion of all the joints of a limb in response to a stimulus applied to the surface of that limb, and this reflex pattern includes the extension of the opposite limb. Stepping movements, and the scratch reflex, can also be elicited. These balanced and rhythmic acts obviously include inhibitory components, such that the extension of any muscle is accompanied by inhibition of the antagonist in the same limb, and of the like muscle in the opposite limb. Furthermore, the disruption

[1] Why, one may speculate, have the vertebrates retained peripheral inhibition of the viscera, while perfecting central inhibition of the motor apparatus? Peripheral inhibition represents a modulating influence which does not check excitatory influences, but competes with them. Central inhibition, on the other hand, actually blocks excitation. Therefore if the heart, for example, were subject to central inhibition, we would be exposed to the danger of heart blocks of central origin. Similarly, paralyses which could affect respiration, intestinal function, and other vital processes, would be far more common than we find them. In short, the replacement of peripheral by central inhibition of basic life processes would have been maladaptive. On the other hand, central disinhibition of both sympathetic and parasympathetic innervation does exist, as we shall see later.

of this pattern and its replacement by the indiscriminate contraction of all muscles under strychninization shows how essential spinal inhibition is as the basis for posture and movement.

3. Spinal reflexes are inhibited by impulses descending from the intermediate brain. This phenomenon was discovered by Sechenov in the frog, but the rediscovery of the same phenomenon in higher mammals (Magoun & Rhines, 1946) proved to be an extremely important event in modern neurology. The important point is that in all vertebrates there are structures, intermediate between the segmental spinal structures and the cerebral hemispheres, which tend by their activity to inhibit the lower-level reflexes.

4. Reflex responses can also be inhibited if, just before the usually adequate stimulus is given, there is some other fairly strong stimulus. This is one type of inhibition which may be initiated by the head receptors. Another kind is illustrated by the influence of the labyrinths on postural reflexes, which are influenced by the position of the head; this necessarily includes inhibitory components, because it involves the relaxation of some extended limbs. Indeed, extreme positions of the head may even counteract decerebrate rigidity (Gernandt, 1959).

5. Despite the existence on the intermediate level of some mechanisms for inhibition of spinal reflexes, the decerebrate animal, in whom these mechanisms are still intact, suffers from a general rigidity due to the exaggeration of the postural tonus. Since Sherrington's work, it has been clear that this rigidity is due to the elimination of inhibitory influences normally descending from the cerebrum. Various hyperkinetic disturbances in humans (which we shall consider later in this chapter) represent analogous "release" phenomena. Another evidence of cortical inhibition is provided by the reciprocal influence of corresponding points in the motor areas of the two hemispheres, as demonstrated by Wedensky in the frog and by Hering and Sherrington in the monkey.

6. We must not neglect to mention the local inhibitory effect which was postulated by Bubnoff and Heidenhain as a normal consequence of excitation in any part of the nervous system, and which has the function of reducing after-discharge. Knowledge of the nature of synaptic inhibition enables us to see that this is not an

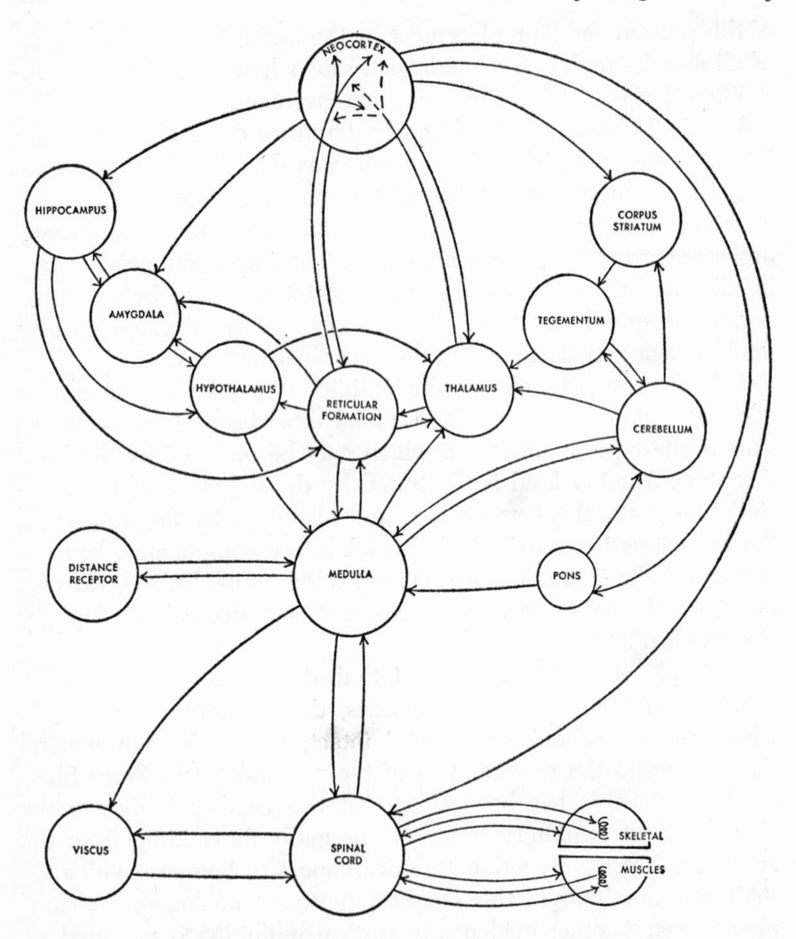

Figure 3. Some of the feedback circuits in the nervous system of a higher mammal.

intracellular effect, as they believed, but a consequence of feedback from neighboring cells, or in some cases from recurrent collaterals by means of which a discharging neuron may inhibit its own after-discharge.

None of these forms of inhibition as previously described performs the function of Ashby's second feedback, that is, none shows the necessary interaction between visceroception and environmentally directed behavior. The incapacity of spinal and decerebrate animals for adaptive behavior shows that in the higher verebrates such interaction takes place at relatively high levels. To illustrate this, and some additional kinds of inhibition, we need to introduce further elaborations into our schematic nervous system. Figure 3 is intended to depict the complexity of the mammalian brain only to the extent necessary to show how some of its numerous inhibitory controls are organized into great, multistaged loops which include overlapping sectors. We shall use it as a basis for discussion of three classes of inhibitory effects: those which (1) directly influence the motor mechanisms, (2) primarily influence the motivational background of behavior, and (3) bring about the suppression of sensory input and modify its perceptual elaboration.

1. *Inhibition of motor elements:* The impulses which enter the final common path to the skeletal muscles are modulated by inhibitions which take place in the spinal cord, the reticular formation of the brain stem, the cerebellum, the corpus striatum, and in several distinctive parts of cerebral cortex. All of these structures are necessary for the proper regulation of movement, and the efferent impulses from each of them are probably a balanced medley of excitatory and inhibitory influences. In reviewing their effects on behavior, it should be borne in mind that in some cases, and quite possibly in most, facilitation is only the external appearance of a process which is actually a disinhibition. On the other hand, a structure which appears to be inhibitory may be the source of excitatory impulses to other neurones which actually effect the inhibition. Whenever the peripheral muscular effect is taken as the evidence of inhibition, or of facilitation, we know only that the given structure participates in releasing such an effect, but we usually do not know if it is directly inhibitory or facilitatory, as the case may be. Since vigorous muscular action is possible with spinal mechanisms alone, the greatest economy of effort in regulating this activity from higher levels would not be gained by adding facilitations, to tip the balance one way or another as desired, but by introducing inhibitions and disinhibitions, which would produce the same effects.

We shall begin with the anterior pole of the cerebral cortex. Lesions in this area lead to overactivity and may also lead to extensor rigidity; therefore it is possible to conclude that this area exercises a direct or indirect inhibitory influence on locomotion generally. An interesting illustration of this is provided by G. M. French (1959a, 1959b), who observed the effects of ablation of Area 9, which is the frontal pole of the cortex, in monkeys. The animals had previously learned to press a bar to obtain food. The effect of the Area 9 lesions, which caused an extreme hypermotility, was to lower the bar-pressing scores markedly, whereas lesions in Area 6, a motor area, which more directly affects the use of the limbs for bar-pressing, had only a transient influence. The animals with Area 9 lesions were kept too busy moving about to give a consistent bar-pressing performance.

An important study of hypermotility following brain injury is that of Mettler and Mettler (1942). They found that extensive unilateral injury of the corpus striatum in cats leads to forced postures or circus movements, and bilateral injury has an effect which is so strong that the animals "struggle violently against any obstacle which bars the forward progression which they usually display. The whole impression created is one of peculiar perversity, . . . (but) reactions are more nearly uniform and predictable once one is familiar with the nature of the alteration of the behavior pattern. . . . Its incessant propulsive efforts bring it [the cat] into opposition with static obstacles against which it struggles blindly." The Mettlers reached the conclusion that "the striatum is an inhibitory mechanism, subject to cortical control and forming a significant link in the inhibitory path from the cortex to the motor neurone." They say that the striatum "appears to hold back those patterns of a primitive type, the so-called associative movements which are really what we encounter in the cursiveness and resistance to impressed movements which animals with bilateral lesions show."

Figure 3 shows that the striatum is a link in a circuit which also passes through the tegmentum, the thalamus, and the neocortex, and which provides opportunity for interaction with cerebellar and sensory impulses. Actually, the principal origin of this circuit in the cortex is in Area 4-S, that is, in one of the so-called suppressor strips; and its terminus is in Area 6, that is, in a motor area. We shall defer the discussion of the suppressor strips briefly, in order to first consider the effects of injury to the striatum and the tegmentum in humans.

Jung and Hassler (1960) describe a number of distinctive syndromes of hyperkinetic muscular disturbance, and they indicate the usual location of lesions responsible for each kind of disturbance. Three of these syndromes are described as usually associated with lesions in different structures of the corpus striatum. These are: the *choreic*, which is characterized by involuntary jerks at irregular intervals (caudate nucleus and putamen); the *athetoid*, which is marked by slower involuntary movements which are often described as "wormlike," leading to distorted extensions of the fingers and exaggerated facial expressions (pallidum); and the *dystonic*, in which the intention to make a discrete movement often leads to contraction of muscles which prevent the intended movement—that is, muscles which must be inhibited if the movement is to be performed—whereas the performance of many skilled acts which require complex muscular integrations may be accomplished without difficulty (putamen).

Syndromes associated with tegmental lesions are the *myoclonic*, which consists of a succession of quick, nonrhythmical contractions, leaping from muscle to muscle (red nucleus), and the *parkinsonian*, in which there is stiffness and generally increased muscular tonus rather than excessive movement (substantia niger).

Finally, the *ballistic* syndrome, in which violent tossing movements occur, arises from injuries of the subthalamic nucleus, which has connections to both the corpus striatum and the tegmentum.

The variety and specificity of these clinical disturbances, all of which have some form of hyperkinesis or hypertonus in common, shows that we are not dealing with a single source of generalized inhibition, but with a variety of inhibitory effects, which are normally disinhibited in various ways in order to provide smoothly functioning automatic or voluntary movements. The fact that hypermotility and exaggerated tonus occur so commonly as consequences of injury to motor apparatus shows us that the efficiency of this apparatus depends upon a system of steadily ongoing inhibitions at many levels. In other words, the overaction of the motor apparatus is not simply a danger which arises when an act is initiated, but one which would arise spontaneously, everywhere in the muscular system, if its responsiveness was not being dampened by these influences.

The inhibitory influences of the cerebellum have often been

demonstrated. It is known, for example, that the ataxia which accompanies cerebellar lesions is a result of overaction of the reflex righting reactions of vestibular origin. Moruzzi (1950) discusses many forms of cerebellar inhibition, including relief of decerebrate rigidity by stimulation of the cerebellum, which had been demonstrated by Sherrington and by Horsley, and the inhibition of movements arising from electrical stimulation of the motor cortex. These inhibitory functions do not take place in the cerebellum, but result from its action. Bremer (1925) discovered that strychnine does not abolish inhibitory functions of the cerebellum. This is consistent with the fact which Grundfest (1960a) points out, that hyperpolarizing synapses are rare in the cerebellum, in contrast to the situation in the cerebral cortex or in the spinal cord. However, fibers which originate in the cerebellum often terminate in inhibitory synapses, or serve to excite inhibitory neurons in other structures. Thus Moruzzi showed that the brain stem reticular formation serves as a relay for the cerebellar inhibition of spinal reflexes.

We turn back to the cerebral hemispheres, to consider the controversial question of the suppressor areas. There is a long history of dispute as to whether movements can be inhibited by stimulation of any part of the cerebral cortex. (See, for example, the mention of Simonoff's early claim, on page 43, and of Oddi's work, on page 61.) The problem was given a new aspect by Dusser de Barenne and his collaborators, using the technique of strychninography. Their results are summarized by McCulloch (1944). Their purpose was to trace intracortical pathways; the method was to apply strychnine to one spot of the cortex, while observing electrical activity in other parts. They found to their surprise that this activity often declined, and they mapped a series of "suppressor strips" which are so located as more or less to delimit major functional areas of the cerebral cortex. Feedback from the caudate nucleus was found to be essential to such "suppression" noted in the motor areas. Some of their findings are now dismissed as artifacts, but some truly inhibitory effects remain. J. D. French (1960) says that although many "objections are valid, it seems clear that the loci to which the term 'suppressor' was originally assigned contribute importantly to modulation of motor mechanisms as well as to other caudally and cephalically directed influences mediated by the reticular formation." Indeed, J. D. French (1958) discovered that cortico-reticular fibers originate in these areas, and go to the predominantly inhibitory portion of the brain stem reticular formation. Kaada (1960) states, largely on the basis of work in his own laboratory, that after discounting the long-latency effects as not truly inhibitory, there remain two kinds of inhibition obtained from these areas: reduction of motor after-discharge, and relaxation of existing muscular contractions. It is a matter of particular interest to us that these effects were first clearly shown by strychninization rather than by electrical stimulation. This means that the phenomena observed were disinhibitions. Since they would normally be triggered by impulses entering the area in which the strychnine was applied, it is evident that inhibitory synapses are so distributed as sometimes to permit the effective chaining of inhibitory effects.

We shall conclude our survey of inhibitions which directly influence motor mechanisms by reference again to the finding by Magoun and Rhines (1946) that the lower part of the brain stem reticular formation has a powerful inhibitory effect on spinal motor mechanisms, which is capable of stopping such movements, whether they are produced reflexly or by stimulation of the motor cortex. Magoun and Rhines look upon the reticular formation as an area in which inhibitory influences from many parts of the brain converge, to be relayed along spinal paths.

2. *Inhibition of motivational patterns:* We turn now to the second group of inhibitions: those which are primarily concerned with visceral sources of motivation. Papez (1937) advanced the theory that emotional behavior is largely dependent on a ring or circle of structures including the thalamus, cingulate gyrus, hippocampus, and hypothalamus. Recent work has tended to confirm this theory, and the term "limbic circle" is now used to refer to these structures, and to the amygdala, which seems to form a parallel link with the hippocampus in the circle. They may also be called the "visceral brain." It is of course well established that many patterns of emotional response, and many important innate forms of adaptive behavior, can be released by stimulation of portions of the hypothalamus or disturbed by its injury. As one specific example, the pattern of rage behavior appears to be integrated in the hypothalamus. Goltz (1881) described sham rage in decerebrate

dogs. Bard and Mountcastle (1947) found that in decerebrate cats, when connections of the hypothalamus were severed with all cortical structures, including the nearby amygdaloid cortex, the animals were provoked to rage very easily, but when the amygdaloid cortex remained, the animals were extremely placid, and could not be moved to rage even by extreme mistreatment. They interpreted this result to mean that the amygdala exercises a steady inhibition on the rage pattern in the hypothalamus; rage is disinhibited when the connection between these structures is broken, and presumably the normal release of rage depends upon a higher cortical disinhibition of the amygdaloid inhibition. The finding by Egger and Flynn (1962) that electrical stimulation of the amygdala suppresses rage in cats helps to confirm this interpretation.

On the other hand, Klüver and Bucy (1939), working with monkeys, obtained quite different results. Where Bard and Mountcastle found that retention of the amygdaloid in cats otherwise decerebrate made placid animals, Klüver and Bucy found that lesions of the amygdaloid made placid monkeys! Contradictions such as this point up the fallacy of supposing that a given area "excites" a given type of behavior, and indicate the need for recognizing that the same area commonly *regulates* opposing behavior patterns. It is the "balance of function" within the amygdala, or between the amygdala and some portion of the hypothalamus, which determines whether aggressive behavior shall be released or inhibited, and the relative preponderance of inhibitory and excitatory units in the structures involved in such a balance may well change from species to species. As a matter of fact, placidity is a normal aspect of cat demeanor, but a very extraordinary and unusual phase in the behavior of monkeys, who are highly excitable; it is therefore understandable that in each case, lesion of the amygdala releases what is, for the given animal, the untypical pattern of response—uncontrolled rage in the cat, placidity in the monkey. In intact animals of both species, we can be reasonably sure, inhibitory elements of the amygdala enter into control of this aspect of behavior. (The Klüver-Bucy report has led to occasional use of amygdaloid surgery in efforts to control assaultive patients; this has sometimes been successful, but not consistently so.)

Another and very different indication of the importance of the amygdala in motivational feedback comes from the work of Olds, who showed that rats will work to obtain electrical stimulation of some parts of the amygdala, and also to avoid stimulation of other parts. In keeping with this finding, and with the conflicting results cited in the preceding paragraph, is the conclusion by Gloor (1960) that "the basic defect produced by [amygdaloid] lesions [is] a disturbance in those motivational mechanisms which normally allow the selection of behavior appropriate to a given situation."

The results of direct stimulation of the amygdala include the disinhibition of mastication, sniffing, sneezing and coughing, micturition and defecation. Hypersexuality is a prominent feature of some amygdaloid lesions, and should be interpreted as a release of positive social response, that is, the opposite of released aggressiveness. When amygdalectomy has caused a loss of aggressiveness and appearance of hypersexuality in animals, destruction of the ventromedial nucleus of the hypothalamus abolishes these effects, demonstrating that they were brought about by release of the functions of that nucleus from amygdaloid inhibition.

In the hippocampus, as in the amygdala, it is often reported that destruction of a given area produces the same symptoms as direct stimulation of that area, again indicating a balance of opposing tendencies—activating and inhibiting certain kinds of behavior—at the same points. Either destruction or stimulation seems to release abnormal fears, and to produce hyperesthesia. Penfield and Milner (1958) indicate that the hippocampus is an important reservoir of memory traces; and one may therefore speculate that it mediates learned aspects of emotional behavior, as the amygdala mediates or controls emotional responses of an unlearned nature. Patients under surgery occasionally experience subjective experiences, including "peculiar sensations" as well as specific hallucinatory experiences, when the hippocampus is electrically stimulated (Pampiglione & Falconer, 1960). However, these effects are not only variable from one patient to another, but they cannot be consistently reproduced in the same patient; and often the result of stimulation is not conscious experience, but loss of contact. These results suggest the presence of inhibitory elements in this area, although it is possible that they are due only to disruption of the ongoing process.

Both the hippocampus and the amygdala receive innervation from the cingulate gyrus of the cerebral cortex. Stimulation of this gyrus causes inhibition of respiration. In human patients, this inhibition is accompanied by a feeling of tiredness and sleepiness, and impairment of consciousness. The interaction between the hippocampus and the amygdala will be discussed in Chapter 11. Later chapters will also discuss in greater detail the part that the hippocampus plays in adaptive behavior, and also the opposition or balance of functions within the hypothalamus. Each of these structures is the site of complex inhibitory effects which play an essential part in motivational feedback.

Summarizing the material of the last few pages, we may say that the motor mechanisms which are organized into postural and locomotor patterns at the spinal level, and into patterns such as feeding, defense, and sexual activity at the level of the medulla and diencephalon, are variously inhibited and disinhibited by the midbrain and cortical influences, which are organized into a number of loops providing numerous controlling feedbacks. Although we have no desire to eliminate excitatory facilitation as an element of higher nervous control, we must emphasize that its participation in this process is more problematical, because all overt facilitatory effects can conceivably be explained as disinhibitions imposed upon an undifferentiated tonic background, whereas inhibitory effects cannot be explained as caused wholly by facilitations.

3. *Inhibition of sensory elements:* We turn now to the third class of inhibitions which we wish to discuss, namely, the inhibitions of sensory input and sensory elaboration, or perception. This inhibition is a function of efferent sensory fibers, such as those shown in Figure 3, leading from the spinal cord to the stretch receptors in the skeletal muscles. Under the classical concept of the nervous system, the phrase "efferent sensory" is contradictory, since all afferent fibers are presumed to be sensory, and all efferent fibers are presumed to have effector functions. However, a rapidly growing body of evidence indicates that *every* sensory system includes efferent fibers which make it possible for central structures, including the cerebral cortex itself, to directly influence the responsiveness of the peripheral receptor organs or otherwise to modulate the activity in sensory pathways. The muscle spindle, which plays such an essential

part in the stretch reflexes and hence in all skeletal muscular action, contains a special intrafusal contractile fiber which is capable of stretching or relaxing the spindle independently of the muscle itself. This fiber is under tonic inhibitory influence, but it can be excited, and this tends to increase responsiveness of the main afferent channel from the muscle spindle. It is interesting to point out that the effect gained is similar to a peripheral inhibition of the motor apparatus—in the crustaceans, an inhibitory fiber directly depresses activity in the stretch-sensitive muscle afferent. Granit and Kaada (1952) have shown that stimulation of the upper portion of the brain stem reticular formation, in which facilitation predominates, causes an increase of muscle spindle activity; whereas stimulation of the predominantly inhibitory lower portion of the reticular formation, or of the anterior lobe of the cerebellum, reduces the spindle activity. Reticular stimulation which produces these effects is considerably less intense than that which is required to influence the discharges of the motoneurons directly, a circumstance which lends support to the supposition that these efferent sensory fibers probably play an important part in the refinement of athletic skills.

Jarbur and Towe (1960) demonstrated that sensory units in the dorsal column of the cat, which respond to stimulation of the footpads, can, with rare exceptions, be either excited or inhibited from the motor cortex. Of units which are affected, more than twice as many are inhibited as excited. The effect of such inhibition would apparently be to reduce sensitivity to forepaw stimulation as the animal is more active in locomotion or in aggression. (Just as a man may fail to notice how he bruises his hands in the course of a fist fight. Compare the delayed pain of a smashed finger.)

Hagbarth and Kerr (1954) showed that stimulation of the brain stem reticular formation, in either its predominantly facilitatory or its predominantly inhibitory parts, exerts an inhibitory influence on ascending sensory pathways in the spinal cord. This is evidently a tonic influence, because central anesthesia has the opposite effect, actually leading to increased afferent activity at spinal levels, evidently because it interrupts the tonic inhibition. Reticular stimulation also reduces activity at various nuclear relays in the medulla, and again there is the same indication, from the effects of surgical interruption or anesthesia, that this is a tonic effect which is merely increased by the experimental stimulation. Further detail regarding these phenomena, and reference to the original sources, may be found in R. B. Livingston (1959), who reaches the conclusion that "each of the major stations which relay afferent impulses within the spinal cord, medulla and thalamus appears to be susceptible to interference by inhibitory influences, and that these influences are tonically active in the unanesthetized animal."

Although the concept of sensory inhibition is old enough to be found in Aristotle, the concept of *tonic* sensory inhibition carries important added significance. Attention was first drawn to this phenomenon by Head and Holmes (1911), who noticed that thalamic lesions caused increased sensitivity to touch and pain stimulation. They stated that "the attempt to explain this condition by a hypothetical irritation fails entirely, and we must consider whether the clue is not to be discovered in the removal of some control normally exerted by one sensory centre upon another." Since this insight has been so amply justified by recent experimental evidence, we feel that the principle that *all sensory channels are subject to tonic inhibitory influence* may suitably be designated as *Head's principle*. It represents, of course, an extension of Anstie's principle to the sensory realm.

Against this background, it is not surprising to discover that the distance receptors in the head, which are such direct outgrowths of the brain, are under its modulating influence. Rasmussen (1953) showed that efferent fibers of the auditory system enter the cochlear nucleus, where fibers from the organs of Corti have their first central synapse. Galambos (1956) subsequently demonstrated that stimulation of this bundle of efferent fibers suppresses the response of the auditory nerve to a click stimulus, that is, it brings about an inhibition of the sensory response within the cochlea itself. Galambos (1954) also points out that the distinctive pattern of response to any tonal stimulus, at the cochlear level, includes inhibition of some units as well as excitation of others, and he suggests that one effect may be as important as the other for tonal differentiation. Indeed, Ades (1959) considers that even the phenomenon of loudness cannot be explained simply as a correlate of the amount of excitation which takes place, "without the addition of a factor of selective neural inhibition by recurrent elements"; and he reaches the general conclusion that "It seems most unlikely that substantially further progress will be made toward explaining the facts of audition in neurophysiological terms without considering the intrinsic and extrinsic neural processes by which excitation aroused by sound is modulated in the central auditory system."

Kerr and Hagbarth (1955) found that stimulation of the amygdaloid and other areas of the olfactory cortex would inhibit activity in the olfactory bulb. Furthermore, the fact that severing the anterior commisure leads to an increased activity of the olfactory bulb shows that this inhibitory influence is also exercised tonically; that is, that response to olfactory stimulation, like response to tactile stimulation, is normally being held to levels below the maximum sensitivity which the receptor mechanism is capable of attaining.

In respect to the eye, Granit (1955) had demonstrated central inhibition of retinal elements as early as 1933. Granit (1959) points out that there is a need for retinal inhibition to check after-discharge of excited elements, for without this we could never have the succession of relatively independent visual images which the retina provides. This need is, of course, quite comparable to that which had been recognized long before in connection with the control of movement. Granit also found a good deal of spontaneous activity in retinal neurons, and this proved to be more intense (doubtless because subject to less central inhibition) under conditions of darkness adaptation than when the eye was exposed to light. This type of spontaneous retinal discharge represents a physiological basis for the intensity of experienced "darkness" as a psychological phenomenon different from mere absence of stimulation. Also, it is now known that many retinal elements respond to the shutting off of a light, just as others do to its appearance.

Sensory inhibition is of course at the basis of every attempt to reduce pain by distraction. It has always been known that in the excitement of a struggle a man may fail to notice that he has been wounded. Although such observations have never been fully evaluated by physiologists—nor even by psychologists—now that there is a theoretical basis for the fact, application follows at once. Gardner, Licklider, and Weisz (1960) report that the pain of dental surgery can be successfully repressed in 90 percent of dental patients, using no other analgesic than a sound the intensity of which the patient controls. Another interesting report is that by Mathews and Whiteside (1960) who, while engaged in performing an experiment on the effect of free fall on the performance of the tendon reflexes, noticed that "during the drop there was no sensation of the tap being delivered to the ankle. Even if attention was concentrated on observing this sensation, it none the less appeared to be masked."

An important avenue of sensory inhibition is provided by corticothalamic neurons, which originate in all sensory areas of the cortex. Ogden (1960) has studied the function of these neurons, observing how they influence the thalamic response to peripheral stimulation. By application of penicillin to the cortex, he was able to fire the corticothalamic neurons without causing any discharge of the thalamocortical axons with which they are anatomically associated. The thalamic response to any sensory modality was greatly reduced, if the peripheral stimulation was applied simultaneously with the evocation of the "penicillin spike" from the corresponding portion of sensory cortex. However, if a subconvulsive dose of strychnine had been administered a few minutes earlier—which would have had no influence on either the penicillin spike nor the thalamic response alone—the thalamic response would actually be enhanced, rather than reduced. Ogden reasoned that the effect of the strychnine was to block inhibitory synapses on which some of the corticothalamic neurons terminated. And, in view of the enhancement effect produced under these conditions, he concluded that some of these neurons also terminate in excitatory synapses, but that inhibitory synapses predominate.

Everyday phenomena which indicate the practical importance of sensory inhibition, some of which we shall consider again in later chapters, include: (a) Sleep consists at least in part of inhibition of sensory impulses, a sort of self-imposed sensory deprivation. (b) In the state of drowsiness, entering or leaving sleep, bodily sensations such as itches or trivial pains may seem enormously more intense than in the waking state. (c) Relatively mild tactile stimulations may also acquire overpowering impact under special conditions—e.g., the Chinese water torture, tickling, and sexual play. These are but a few of many indications that the mere development of receptor sensitivity, without adequate dampening, would lead to convulsive catastrophe for the organism. Steps must be taken to insure that the brain does not function as if it were "fully joined." On the other hand, the utilization of receptor sensitivity for adaptive adjustment to the environment requires a selective disinhibition of sensory information arising from those aspects which are of immediate importance to the organism.

4. Thus we are led into a consideration of the inhibitory phenomena which can be inferred to be taking place in the cortex itself, even when they are not directly observable. When an ascending sensory impulse reaches a sensory projection area in the cortex it produces an excitatory effect, but the magnitude and the duration of that effect, and hence also its propagation to other areas and its interaction with other cortical processes, depends upon the inhibitory influences with which it contends. There are several very clear indications that an accompanying process of inhibition is a normal aspect of the cortical response to stimulation, if, indeed, there is not also a steadily ongoing inhibitory activity which is a normal part of the background activity even before external stimulation arrives, as is true in the retina.

One of these indications is the fact that topical application of strychnine to any portion of the cortex creates an epileptogenic area or focus. Amantea (1921) found that "following strychninization there always arises a sensory and motor area of the skin which is supersensitive relative to the others," and that this supersensitivity is apparent before any clonic contractions have occurred. Clementi found that after application of strychnine to the visual cortex, very weak visual stimulation would suffice to induce convulsions (1929a), and after its application to the auditory cortex, the same effect is produced by very weak auditory stimulation (1929b). These early workers were unaware that the effect of strychnine is to blockade inhibitory synapses, but they recognized that strychninization produced a situation in which cortical activity easily goes out of bounds, so that weak stimulation can produce the kind of effect which is normally expected only from very intense stimulation. Hence, we may point out, the susceptibility of a strain of rodents to audiogenic seizure would indicate relative weakness of the cortical inhibitory process, rather than excitability, and it would be reasonable to expect that just these animals would also be more prone to experimental neurosis from frustrating experiences which tax the inhibitory power to its limits. This is consistent with Pavlov's view of experimental neurosis, to be stated in Chapter 9, and throws some light on the results obtained by Maier (1949) in his studies of frustration.

Jung and Tönnies (1950) state that "The *counteractions* by which the brain normally *prevents* synchronous discharges and convulsive excitations are of greater physiological interest than the convulsive phenomena themselves." The fact that we do not experience convulsions at such times as awakening in the morning indicates, they say, that "there must be controls effective, established by some regular physiological *limitation of excitation*." Convulsions take place only when this normal braking activity fails.

Another indication of the importance of local inhibitory processes in the cortex is found in the record of activity which is observed in isolated slabs of cortex, which have no remaining neural connection with the rest of the brain although the blood supply is maintained. Burns (1951, 1958) found that the electrical response to a single external stimulus applied to such a slab would characteristically consist of a prolonged series of "afterbursts," which might then often terminate with such suddenness that it could not be thought of as simply dying out, but only as being brought to a stop by some limiting process, the operation of which was already manifested in the regularity with which each strong burst was succeeded by a phase of quiescence.

Still another indication of the importance of inhibition in cortical activity is the fact that in most parts of the cortex, outside of the motor area, direct electrical stimulation is far more likely to produce an arrest of overt activity than to initiate either action or conscious experience. Although this effect is sometimes attributed to the nonphysiological interference with the cortical processes, it is more reasonable to look upon it as the natural consequence of generalized activation of all units in an area in which inhibitory synapses are more numerous, or at least numerous enough and so strategically placed that their general activation can check any excitatory process. Perhaps the motor area is the only portion of the cerebral cortex in which excitatory processes clearly predominate (but even here, excitation of any point gives rise to strong inhibition at the corresponding point of the opposite hemisphere), so that generalized activation is likely to produce an effect which propagates. Penfield (Penfield & Roberts, 1959) describes the procedures he follows in operating on cases of focal epilepsy. He explores the temporal lobe and areas adjacent to the speech mechanisms with an electrical stylus, while engaging the patient in conversation. When he finds a point at which stimulation produces an *arrest* of the patient's speech, a transitory aphasia, he knows that this point must be spared, because it is likely to be essential for speech. On the other hand, points which give rise to conscious experience mark areas which are dispensable, and such a point may sometimes be the very focus from which the epileptic attacks start. It is plausible to assume that the points at which arrest occurs are those where inhibitory synapses predominate, so that indifferent stimulation of all units checks any ongoing excitatory activity, and that the points at which experiential phenomena are elicited are those where there is a relative deficiency of inhibitory synapses, from which excitation readily propagates.

It is with an awareness of this underlying cortical inhibitory potential, which tends to make any excitatory process self-limiting, that we must consider the nature of cortical arousal. The phenomenon of arousal is defined objectively as a shift in the pattern of brain waves, as recorded in the electroencephalogram, in the direction of higher frequency and lower voltage, with desynchronization or loss of a strongly predominating rhythm. In the normal adult, slow high voltage waves are found only in sleep. Relaxed wakefulness is characterized by so-called alpha waves, which have a frequency of eight to twelve per second and a potential of about 40 mV. Alertness is characterized by "alpha blocking" or desynchronization, in which the waves are more rapid, less regular, and have a reduced potential. This phenomenon was mentioned by H. Berger (1929) in his initial publication on the EEG, and it has become a basic criterion applied by the neurophysiologist. The measured potential at any instant is thought to be a summation of the activity of all the neurons in a given area, but there is no clear understanding of how the fluctuating surface potentials are produced by the nervous impulses. The number of elements which are simultaneously active even in a restricted area is so great that a sum of randomized activities should be very nearly constant, and therefore the occurrence of wavelike potential changes indicates the influence of some nonrandom factor. Speculation regarding this has generally been in the direction of assuming some pacemaking or recruiting tendencies of excitatory character, which cause large populations of neurons to "beat" in unison during sleep. Presumably this effect would be less marked as more elements are activated by inflowing impulses, so that we have the paradox of decreasing net potential change as the total energy expenditure increases. However, we should like to suggest the need to explore the converse possibility: that the wave potentials are the result of temporal characteristics of the inhibitory processes which limit maximal excitation. One can readily imagine that when the overall activity is low, so that units discharge infrequently, the inhibitory synapses remain relatively inactive until a moderately high potential is built up; they then come into play in large numbers, causing a fairly widespread hyperpolarization. Summative potentials would be high, and the cycle of activity relatively long. As excitation increases, inhibitory activity is mobilized more rapidly, but the oscillatory effect remains, because each time that excitation is locally reduced, a phase of decreased inhibitory activity follows, permitting the excitation to rise again. Thus, it is the rhythmicity of inhibition which underlies the EEG, just as it underlies the rhythm of locomotion and of other motor activity. This hypothesis is in agreement with the fact that responsiveness of cortical units to sensory excitation fluctuates with the phases of the wave of the EEG, which in fact reflect the fluctuation of local inhibitory activity.[2]

Leaving this speculation aside, we return to the fact that arousal, objectively defined as desynchronization of brain waves, can be produced either by some attention-capturing external stimulation (such as the sound of a buzzer which has been used as a signal for food)

[2] This hypothesis would not be invalidated by the fact that a lesser portion of the apparent facilitation of sensory input, due to reticular stimulation, takes place at the thalamic level (Bremer and Stoupel, 1959; Dell and Dumont, 1960). It is interesting, however, to consider the implications of the paradox noted by these authors, that reticular activation does not facilitate peripheral stimulation in the same way as central electrical stimulation, and even tends to depress the former. Evidently, the nature of the effect produced by the reticular activation is changed by collateral sensory influx into the reticular formation.

or by direct stimulation of any one of many brain structures, including the brain stem reticular formation, some portions of the hypothalamus, the thalamus, the amygdala, etc. In Figure 3, the mechanism of arousal is symbolized in two ways: by a single line from the reticular formation to the cortex, which branches into terminations in several directions, and by several lines running from the thalamus to different parts of the neocortex. The one line with several branches symbolizes the general arousal system of the brain stem reticular formation, which was first described by Moruzzi and Magoun (1949), and which has been prominent in the research of the Magoun group. The several lines from the thalamus symbolize the area-specific arousal system which has been stressed by Jasper and his coworkers. The distinction should not close our eyes to the fact that there is considerable differentiation in the fine structure of the reticular formation. Indeed, Olszewski (1954) states that there are scores of nuclei in the reticular formation which can be identified by the morphological characteristics of a single cell. More recent research, some of which will be discussed in Chapter 11, tends to emphasize that even the general arousal system includes subsystems which are capable of exerting quite specific modulating influences.

We know very little about the cortical events involved in arousal. However, when a condition of arousal exists in a given sensory projection area, the organism shows greater responsiveness to stimuli belonging to the corresponding sense modality. This does not necessarily involve facilitation, if facilitation is taken to mean a booster effect for the excitation process. It seems much more reasonable to suppose that the arousal process consists in a disinhibition—that is, in inhibition of the cortical inhibitory elements which of themselves tend, as we have seen, to dampen sensitivity to all kinds of stimulation. Such a disinhibition may be either selective or generalized. From this point of view the arousal effect is only a release from the generalized tonic inhibition which is normally exercised over all afferentation. The phenomenon of habituation, on the other hand —that is, the lack of arousal to an oft-repeated stimulus without biological significance—would be due to the establishment or reestablishment of such inhibitory suppression over stimuli which had previously been exercising an arousal effect. This would represent an absence of disinhibition, and hence the continuation in force of the regular dampening inhibitions.

Summarizing the implications of the entire chapter, we may say that the scope of inhibition is so broad that it touches on all of the elements that enter into behavior. If there is any instance of action by the organism which can adequately be described as "response to a stimulus," without reference either to disinhibitory release or to inhibitory suppression of other competing reaction patterns, then it is so isolated from all the other response mechanisms of the organism that it scarcely needs to be considered as a part of "behavior."[3]

[3] Descartes, in his treatise on the passions, probably gave the first neurological theory of arousal and habituation. He names "admiration" as the first of six primary emotions, but says that it differs from the others in that it is not "accompanied by any change in the heart or the blood." "It is caused first by an impression in the brain which represents the object as unusual and therefore worthy of attentive consideration, then by the movement of the animal spirits, which are made by this impression to flow with great force to the part of the brain where it is located, in order to strengthen it and maintain it there; and it also makes them pass from there into the muscles which serve to hold the organs of the senses in the same situation, so that it will still be maintained by them, if it is by them that it has been formed." (Compare Pavlov's definition of the investigatory reflex, quoted on page 234.) And as to habituation: "It is certain also that objects of the senses which are new touch the brain in parts not accustomed to being touched, and that since these parts are more tender or less firm than those which have been hardened by frequent agitation, the effect of the movements they induce is thereby increased."

CHOICE: THE CENTRAL PROBLEM OF PSYCHOLOGY

II

THE SPECTRUM OF CHOICE 7

This chapter, like the first, is concerned with the statement of a problem; but this time it is the central problem of psychology as a science. We shall try to show, first, that psychology can be usefully defined as *the science of behavioral choice,* and second, that every instance of behavioral choice necessarily involves inhibitory functions. The discussion in the present chapter will deal largely with choice as it is expressed in overt actions, while the next chapter will deal with the sort of behavior which Sechenov had in mind when he said that "Thought is a mental reflex reduced to its first two-thirds, of which the last part, the movement, has been inhibited."

The special place of psychology among the other life sciences is not entirely a matter of historical accident and tradition. Contrary to another view expressed by Sechenov, it is desirable and probably also inevitable that there should be a specialized group of behavioral scientists who are not physiologists. History seems to support this, but provides no easy clue to the definition of psychology's task as a science, which has undergone some rather sharp metamorphoses. One may well question whether it is possible to state the difference between psychology and physiology on the basis of a principle, rather than in terms of the activities currently displayed by men who call themselves psychologists and by men who call themselves physiologists.

It is sometimes said that the physiologist studies the reactions of organs, and the psychologists studies the reactions of organisms, that is, of the whole living creature. Yet certainly it is not possible to characterize the research of Sherrington or of Cannon as encompassing less than the total organism. Even Harvey's discovery of the circulation of the blood, which is often regarded as the beginning of modern physiology, could not have been achieved by someone who did not have the whole organism as the object of his study.

It is said, somewhat more defensibly, that physiology is concerned with the relations of the organs to each other, while psychology is concerned with the relations of the organism to the environment. This distinction overlooks the fact that behavior is only one aspect of the organism's interaction with the environment. The physiologist cannot neglect the dependence of the organism on its milieu, any more than the psychologist can ignore the fact that behavior is largely organized in the service of organic needs.

Again, following Comte, it is said that physiology and psychology merely mean deal with the same problems on different levels of explanation. This distinction places the two sciences on a continuum which stretches, in the modern perspective, from nuclear physics at one end to history at the other, embracing the many ways in which men try to explain why things happen as they do. It is a reasonable distinction, but it does not go to the heart of the question. Different tasks require different methods, and we must ask if there is not a difference in the task which is undertaken, as well as in the method which is adopted.

A typical problem for a neurophysiologist is to explain the circus movements of an injured animal. A typical problem for a modern psychologist is to understand the behavior of a rat which turns right rather than left in a maze which offers food in one alley and not in the other. The turn in the first case is "forced," while in the second case it represents a "choice." The physiologist is concerned with the mechanism which enables the animal to effect a turn as part of its locomotor repertoire, and with the nature of the lesion which restricts an animal's ability to turn or compels it to turn in a certain way. The psychologist is concerned with why an animal which is equally capable of turning to the right or to the left (as it will demonstrate readily enough if it is put into a novel situation), "chooses" to turn right.

One might say that the position of the psychologist depends, like the existence of the resourceful fugitive in the play *Colonel Jakobowsky*, on the condition that "there must always be two possibilities." If there are not two possibilities of action, the fugitive has lost the chance to survive by his wits, and the psychologist has lost his professional *raison d'être*—to study how living creatures survive-by-their-wits. Therefore the psychologist intervenes, contrary to the advice of Sechenov that no one but a physiologist should meddle in such matters, whenever there is a strong hint of that lack of correspondence betweeen input and output (to translate his remark into modern jargon) which Sechenov stated to be the principle characteristic of cerebral activity. It would be presumptuous of psychology to claim to be "the science of behavior," but there is good reason to call it *the science of behavioral choice.*

Not all changes of response are examples of choice behavior. The very simplest lifelike things, the viri and the microbes, have more than one mode of existence. They cannot, like Hamlet, ponder the question of life and death in ideal terms, but when outrageous fortune raises the pH above a critical level or causes too extreme a drop in temperature, they do somehow transform themselves from an active to a passive mode, better to conserve their specific form of organization. This is not choice, because it implies no variation of response under constant environmental conditions.

Between the extremes of viral or bacterial encystment on the one hand, and Hamlet's agonizing deliberations in his choice between action and a drastic end to action on the other, there is a broad spectrum of response variability. Still outside the limits of the psychological portion of this spectrum, which we call choice, there are some kinds of quasi-choice which strongly attract the spectator-interest of the psychologist despite the fact that they take place on an organic rather than an organismic level. We are interested, for example, in the problem of the embryologist who seeks to determine why a given bit of undifferentiated tissue becomes, in a certain environment, gut instead of jaw, or eye instead of leg. We are interested in the problem of the neurologist who studies the regeneration of severed nerve fibers, when he seeks to learn why it is that the jumbled fibers of a single nerve somehow find their separate ways back to thir proper muscles. These problems are close to those of the psychologist, not merely by an affinity of subject matter, but because of the way in which they are posed by the embryologist and the neurologist: not in the form—*What causes this result?*—but in the form—*Why do we get this result rather than that?*

Psychology begins when we view the behavior of the total organism and ask the question, *Why does it behave sometimes this way and sometimes that?* Behind that *sometimes*, that stigma of inconsistency, there may be a problem of satiation, or of learning, or of instability, or of individual idiosyncracy, or of volition. What is important is that the problem for investigation is not formulated in terms of different responses to different conditions, not as a question of whether this or that change in external conditions will produce a different response, but in terms of different responses which appear under the same conditions. By this it is not intended to imply that the determinants of each response are not fully accessible to explanation or even control, but only that they include a special kind of instability which attracts the interest of psychologists. The source of response variability is being sought in the organism rather than in the environment.

To make our meaning clear, let us consider some activities which are not essentially psychological, although they are sometimes labelled as psychology. One of these is the ability of the organism to respond differentially to different physical stimuli, such as different wavelengths of light. This is sense physiology. It is an area of physiology with which psychology has especially close historical connections, but it remains physiology even when it is performed by men who call themselves psychologists. The physiological nature of such a problem is evident when one considers that the basis of such differential response can be two unrelated, noninteracting mechanisms, each with its own receptor and its own effector apparatus. However, it is a necessary basis for the psychological investigation of many problems in perception, in which it is necessary to take account of the different ways in which the same organism can respond to the same set of stimulating conditions. Furthermore, when an organism which originally gave the same response to different stimuli, comes after experience to respond differently to them, this fits the definition of choice, since it necessarily involves different responses, at different times, to the same physical stimulus. It therefore represents a psychological problem.

Another such area is the study of the limits of performance, whether in muscular fatigue, or agility, or staying awake. These are physiological problems, even though the skills needed to investigate them are more commonly acquired by psychologists. However, tests of intelligence are specifically psychological, because such tests cannot achieve their purpose, any more than tests of personality or interest, without giving the subjects a choice of responses. The study of muscular fatigue per se is physiology, but a study of fatigue which concerns itself with the effect of knowledge of results on the limits of performance is psychology, because it deals with the variable degree to which physical capability is achieved under different circumstances, and this is obviously an aspect of choice.

Far more important than these jurisdictional disputes among friendly sciences is the following objection which might be raised against the statement that psychology is concerned essentially with problems of choice: What of all the research which deals with the behavior of groups that have been subjected to different treatments—like good versus poor mothering, or massed versus distributed practice—and which aims at establishing correspondences between the treatments and the observed group behaviors, while dismissing all individual differences as the consequences of error variables? How can we reconcile all this concern with the shaping of behavior by environmental influences with a presumed exclusive interest in "choice"?

The answer is that when psychologists are not investigating different ways of responding to the *same* poor mothering, or different ways of responding to the *same* stress of massed practice, then they are investigating the different kinds of behavior that arise, in some other standard situation, *as a result of, but not in response to,* different prior treatments. The "different environments" with which we deal as psychologists must be interiorized, they must somehow find their representations within the organism and as part of the organism, before they become material for psychological investigation. We do not ordinarily investigate responses to different immediate situations unless it is to compare their motivational effects, that is, their influence on the mechanism of choice.

For an organism to exhibit choice, it must be so constituted that it can perform at least two different responses in the same situation. Therefore the existence of choice always implies the possibility of internal conflict. As animals grow more complex, the possibilities of choice become more numerous, and the choice—or the preference shown by a greater likelihood for some responses to occur rather than others, in a given situation—is very often influenced by a residue of past experience. At the highest levels, the choice between actions may be based on their imagined effects, and the possibility of invention as well as learning appears. However, all these possibilities of development are based on the mutually inhibitory relationships which exist between alternative responses to the same situation, which is the necessary common element in all choice behavior, from the simplest to the most complex.

The paramecium provides us with an example near the lower end of the spectrum of choice. When a paramecium swims against a solid object, it may attach itself to the object or recoil from it. The same environmental stimulus may evoke either response, depending presumably on the internal state of the organism. The investigation of this behavior must therefore take the form of a simultaneous investigation of two forms of response, and not merely one. That makes it a problem which attracts the psychologist, because of his interest in choice. The stated interest of the psychologists who have been studying this problem is to determine whether this is an instance of learning: e.g., whether paramecia that have had recent experience with a food-coated wire are more likely to attach themselves to a clean wire, rather than swim away. Whether this is learning or not, it remains true that the unlearned fluctuation of response is a kind of choice, and that this capacity for choice rests upon a mechanism which is able to suppress one of the alternative responses. The mechanism which probably performs this function is the so-called "neuromotor apparatus" which is present in all of the ciliata. Kudo (1954) mentions that "a striking feature common to all neuromotor systems is that there seems to be a central motorium from which radiate fibers to different ciliary structures," and which appears to coordinate their activities. More than this is required for learning, but this must come first. Learning can appear only if the original repertoire of unlearned behavior includes a capacity for the suppression or inhibition of some unlearned response.

The flatworm and the earthworm provide, as we know, much better documented instances of docility. What is more important for us, they exhibit clear evidence of spontaneous variation of response in the same situation, and it is interesting to consider the relationship between this primitive kind of choice and the rudimentary learning of which they are capable. Let us keep in mind that in the worm's world, its variability of response contributes more to its survival than does learning. Harlow (1958) points out that the worm's ability to "learn a spatial maze . . . in a faltering and ephemeral way in a few hundred trials" cannot possibly have had any survival value, and therefore we must suppose that the capacity for learning has arisen as a by-product of some other developmental trend. The answer which he suggests is based on the generally accepted fact that the development of brain is correlated in evolution with the development of receptor capacities.

> As long as increasingly complex receptor systems provide the organism with slight survival advantages, one can be assured that increasingly complex nervous systems will develop; and as long as increasingly complex nervous systems develop, the organism will be endowed with greater potentialities which lead inevitably to learning. From the behavioral point of view, the evolution from reception to learning is inevitable. Reception is progressively aided by the development of mechanisms of sensory search, fixation, and attention. To be efficient, reception involves both differentiation and generalization. . . . The development of a maximally effective receptor system leads to the formation of mechanisms and processes basic to learning or involving learning which indirectly improve the efficiency of operation of the receptor processes (Harlow, 1958, p. 275).[1]

We can accept this statement, if it is understood that the "mechanisms of sensory search, fixation, and attention," *all represent processes of inhibition.* At this stage, in the earthworm, it is only the mechanism of sensory search which is prominent, in the worm's

[1] Later in the same article Harlow describes learning as primarily a process of inhibition. His remarks on this question will be discussed in Chapter 12, but he does not relate them to his argument that receptor development provides the initial basis for learning.

penchant for stopping now and then to lift its anterior tip just a bit and wave it about, or test the feel of things on the ground to the right and the left. This behavior would not be possible without a cerebral ganglion, and doubtless the ganglion would not be there without the greater concentration of receptors in the head region. But although the earthworm's capacity to learn its way about a maze makes no direct use of the exteroceptors, which can give it no clues to the correct turn, it is assuredly related to this disposition to frequent interruption of its movement, and its employment of a kind of testing behavior in which the two lobes of the cerebral ganglion seem to exercise an alternating dominance. The capacity for fixation is still quite rudimentary, but we see its beginnings in the ability of the worm to "follow its nose," right or left, after it has laid down that probing proboscis and resumed its locomotion. For the worm cannot turn all at once, and as each successive segment is stimulated to follow its predecessor by a gentle tug, the turn also moves in a wave down the length of the organism, each segment being forced to follow in the direction which the head has chosen, as the asymmetrical tension of the longitudinal muscles of one segment gives rise to a similar asymmetry in the next. Somehow a trace of this asymmetry remains as a basis for a habit of preferential turning toward one side rather than the other. Whatever the nature of this trace, it is clear that the event of learning has been facilitated by the innate disposition to exploratory and orienting behavior, that is, by the mechanism of sensory search.

It is uncertain whether the cerebral ganglia make any contribution to the worm's docility, as tested in the restrictive paths of the T-maze. Yet surely the capacity for spontaneous alternation of response—which is more frequent than would be expected by chance in the intact worm and falls below chance levels when the anterior ganglia are removed—contributes to the possibility of adaptive choice among the possibilities offered by the little space in which the worm normally moves. As the worm extends its tip this way and that, it stretches its life-space just a little bit. This marks a bright new band in the spectrum of choice, and one which may be a more important step in the evolution of adaptive behavior than the appearance of learning. If we free ourselves from our special human point of view—and a school-bred view at that—we must recognize that animals generally make less use of learning than of the disposition to explore the reality in which they move, on one side and another, and to choose the part of it into which to venture by preference. This disposition is at the same time a preparation for learning. The spontaneous fluctuation of responses (which we call "spontaneous alternation" when, experimentally, we allow the animal no more than a choice of two responses) is characteristic of the behavior of higher animals in any problem situation.

The arthropods are notable more for the rigidity of their behavior than for flexibility, and therefore they provide an interesting test of Harlow's hypothesis that receptor development inevitably creates the capacity for learning. In them, the evolution of the sense organs has made notable advances: there are special feelers for tactile exploration of the near environment, image-forming eyes for exploration at intermediate distances, and chemoreceptors which, in the insects, attain an almost incredible sensitivity which gives even greater range to their explorations. There is also a new wealth of proprioceptors giving information about movement and position of the limbs, a static sense which permits orientation to the vertical, and organs which respond to sound vibrations.

However, there is an aspect of the development of the receptor functions of the arthropods, and especially of the insects and spiders, which too often escapes our attention and understanding because it is so unlike our own experience—i.e., the extraordinary specificity of responsiveness to certain sources of stimulation. The insect's preference for a particular food, which covers the fresh rosebud with a crowd of aphids, or brings fruit flies suddenly out of nowhere after we have cut open a ripe melon, or the ability of a male butterfly to track down a female of the same species when it has been released on the other side of a metropolis (despite the assorted olfactory onslaughts of urban civilization), testify to the fact that, contrary to Harlow's supposition, it is quite possible to develop receptor functions in a direction which does not facilitate behavioral flexibility. The insect's precise adaptations evoke wonder in us not only because we are often ourselves insensitive to the particular stimuli to which they are attuned, but also because our own experience, which has been conditioned by a very different kind of wide-range receptivity, leaves us unprepared to recognize the extraordinary specificity of receptor function which dictates response to one particular stimulus among all, as well as the sharp fluctuations of sensibility which govern the succession of reactions in a chain of behavior. For the organism which, at a given instant, is endowed with incomparably more acute sensitivity to one form of stimulation than to all others, it is just as natural that the source of this stimulation should be the focus of activity as it is for a child to suck a lollipop that is put into its mouth, or for the tongue to probe a hollow tooth. To understand the marvellously adaptive behavior of these creatures, the most important thing is to understand the modifiability of their receptor functions.

In its extreme form, the prepotent stimulus is the basis for a dramatic kind of behavior which seems to be less a form of choice than of enslavement. The organism is so completely bound to a single stimulus that response variability is virtually absent. The moth beats its wings against the lamp that will incinerate it, or the beetle engaged in copulation allows its body to be dismembered rather than interrupt this highest-priority act. In such cases one stimulus is endowed with an overwhelming valence, and by contrast all other stimulation seems ineffective. However, the element of choice appears in the fact that the same creature may respond differently at another time, and the shift from one kind of sensitization to another may occur quite suddenly. It used to be natural for us to think of all such changes as due to the temporary sensitization of specific receptors by some hormonal influence. Now that we know how widespread and how powerful the phenomenon of sensory inhibition is, we must ask ourselves whether the specificity of insect reactions is not determined in great measure by the neural inhibition of competing receptor functions. One can even imagine, for example, that there might be the same kind of reciprocal relationship between receptors determining approach to food and receptors determining approach to a sex object, as between antagonistic muscles of the same limb.

Among the vertebrates, prepotency never appears in such an extreme form as with the arthropods. But it appears in milder forms, for learning itself is very often a matter of establishing preference among stimuli which are originally equivalent. One striking example of this is the phenomenon of imprinting, as it appears in the behavior of young birds. Lorenz (1952) relates how he demonstrated this phenomenon, to the immense amusement of townsfolk staring over the fence of his yard, by getting down in the tall grass with a group of newly hatched goslings and imitating as well as he could the bodily movements and the voice of the Mother Goose who had been removed. Thus he succeeded in having the goslings imprint his image and learn to follow him in the usual sort of barnyard parade. The fact of imprinting has since been demonstrated, with fewer histrionics, in laboratory experiments which permit the general conclusion that young birds of many species tend soon after hatching to follow any object in the near environment; and if they have had the opportunity to exercise this disposition with respect to a given object during a critical period which may last for several days, they develop a strong preference for this object over others (e.g., Jaynes, 1956).

Thus, imprinting represents a process by which an initial disposition to respond positively to any object of a given class becomes quickly narrowed, so that it is available only to one member of that class. It is not simply the establishment of a preference which will be exercised when two stimuli are presented, nor the consequence of a passive decay which overtakes the disposition when there has been no opportunity to exercise it. It is the simultaneous strengthening of a disposition to respond positively to one stimulus and the active extinction, before decay otherwise would set in, of an original disposition to respond similarly to many other stimuli. Hence it must be regarded as in part the expression of an inhibitory process.

Although imprinting has been most carefully studied in birds, a similar phenomenon seems to be important in the development of affectional relationships among mammals. Critical periods for the development of social relationships, particularly those of dominance, have been described for dogs, sheep, and other species. Lorenz (1952) contends that breeds of dogs can be classified as belonging to two main types, descendants respectively of the wolf and the jackal, which show such different characteristics of the imprinting process that the members of one group (like the chow) are typically one-man dogs, who exhibit a lifelong devotion to a single master, while those of the other (like the airedale) acquire new friends and masters with ease, which makes them rather valueless as watchdogs. From this, the leap is obvious to the less-standardized phenomena of human love. Legends of magic potions which insure that the drinker will fall in love with the first face he sees on awakening testify to the fact that something very like imprinting is not foreign to human experience. The infantile fixation on the mother, the adolescent selection of an ideal, and the adult selection of a mate, all bear some resemblance to this process. The social meaning of each of these forms of attachment cannot be understood without recognizing that there is a simultaneous development of a system of inhibitions. Every positive choice in life is simultaneously the occasion for many-sided restrictions on behavior. Although these may go unnoticed at the time, it is often the case that these restrictions or inhibitions represent, in the long run, the more significant changes, tending to influence behavior in many other situations as well. Although there is a good deal of historical and sociological evidence that the choice of a mate, in particular, is not made so absolutely and exclusively by humans of either sex as by pigeons, for example, it is nevertheless indisputable that it is normally accompanied by some degree of inhibition, which is more than merely moral, of sexual interest in other potential partners.

Imprinting is only one of many kinds of preferential learning, all the forms of which lead to changed behavior not in the sense that the animal has learned to do something new, or to do anything differently, but in the sense that it has learned a cue for doing what comes naturally. G. Murphy (1947) applies the term *canalization* to the positive aspect of all such learning, and he defines canalizations as "the progressive shifts in differential response to the various means of satisfying a drive." While recognizing this usage, English and English (1958) give priority in their dictionary to the following definition: "restricting a particular behavior pattern within narrower limits: e.g., settling down to take the same path home, after a period of trying out various alternatives." Indeed, the digging of a canal is quite likely to leave levees raised on both sides, so that walls are built up at the same time that the channel is prepared. However, the illustration given by English and English is not the best that could be chosen, despite the fact that it describes a phenomenon which most of us have experienced. The essential thing about the process of behavioral canalization is that it eliminates *untried* paths, which intrinsically are quite as good as those that come to be frequented, and would originally have been quite as attractive. This appears clearly in Murphy's illustration—that we become accustomed to a national diet, and therefore reject strange foods as unpalatable. However, the element of inhibition is clear in either case. One does not simply learn to like rice or potatoes; one also acquires, though without "learning" in the usual sense since there has been no trial, a reduced readiness to consume and enjoy the untried. William James described this phenomenon as the "inhibition of instincts."

> The law of inhibition of instincts by habit is this: *When objects of a certain class elicit from an animal a certain sort of reaction, it often happens that the animal becomes partial to the first specimen of the class on which it has reacted, and will not afterward react on any other specimen.* . . . Another sort of arrest of instinct by habit is where the same class of objects awakens contrary instinctive impulses. Here the instinct first followed toward a given individual of the class is apt to keep him from ever awakening the opposite impulse in us (W. James, 1890, II, pp. 394 ff).

The general principle we have been making applies to many varieties of choice behavior, which will be subjects of discussion in future chapters. Whenever choice appears in any form—as a rivalry between appetities which cannot be simultaneously satisfied, as a perceived meaning attached to an ambiguous stimulus, as a planned decision between two courses of action, as the symbolic fulfillment of an unsuspected wish—it always involves an element of inhibition. It is obvious that in every case where one act is performed, another must be inhibited. However, the role of inhibition in these complex forms of choice behavior is much more than merely to exclude the rejected possibility. Until the moment of choice, the act-to-be-performed has equal status with its rivals, which is to say, it is being inhibited. The moment of choice is a moment of disinhibition. A psychological theory which does not recognize this fundamental fact is not likely to grasp the true dynamic quality of behavior in any sense.

Let us consider the application of this principle to the question of volition, or choice *qua* choice, the very heart of our problem. What is volition, or "will"? The question was a lively one among Morgan's contemporaries, and we recall that Morgan himself thought that inhibition was the key to the problem. We shall contrast his views with those of Ziehen (1898), an emphatically physiological psychologist who recognized no laws other than those of association as governing the processes of mind.

Ziehen's published course of lectures comes to a climactic end in his discussion of Will. "Meine Herren," he began—and it is well to include this formal introductory opening to remind us of the tense atmosphere of the lecture hall at the University of Jena, scarcely fifty miles from Leipzig where the more prestigeful Wundt proclaimed his "voluntaristic psychology," as the young men prepared to note well the final lecture in a distinguished series:

> We have seen how the countless material stimulations of the environment lead to cortical excitations, to which the sensations of the mental realm correspond. We followed those excitations through the cerebral cortex, by way of the association fibers, into the motor area; from there the physical excitations were led out again toward the periphery, where they released muscular contractions. Mentally, the associative play of ideas corresponds to the transcortical process, and the ensuing movement was designated by us, in psychological terms, as behavior. We were able to derive the latter, in a completely satisfactory manner, according to the laws of association, out of sensation and out of the memory images of former sensations, the ideas, and thus we traced the psychical process to its final constituent. However, here we come up against an hypothesis which used to be accepted by psychologists almost without exception, and one which has been reached, apparently unconsciously, by the common human understanding of all times: I mean, the assumption of a special "Will" as a cause of our actions. . . . What does it mean, when I say, "I will walk"? Or better said, what psychic content is expressed by the act of speaking the words, "I will walk"? Obviously, nothing but this: the motor image of my future walking occurs to me with great intensity, and is accompanied by a markedly positive feeling-tone, and at the same time the ideational constellation [Ziehen's name for the influences arising from other associative tendencies] is such that those ideas which facilitate the emergence of the motor image of walking, and which by their irradiation strengthen the positive feeling tone connected therewith, predominate over the inhibitory ones. . . . The expression "I will" designates the objective status quo in the brain. . . . There is no reason for assuming a special faculty of volition (Ziehen, 1898, p. 251 f.).

It is clear that Ziehen, clinging resolutely to the strict separation of mind and matter, is seriously hampered by a lack of understanding of the inhibitory process, although the relevance of inhibition to the problem of will does not entirely escape him. What he lacks; what even Sechenov lacked in a not dissimilar discussion; what the child lacks when, playing at philosopher, he tries to catch himself jumping before he wills to jump, is the principle of disinhibition: the realization that each act is not the outcome of facilitations which must overcome inhibitions, but the expression of a "release" in which neural inhibitions are the agents of the positive impulse to action. Since we no longer have any difficulty in understanding the physiological means by which an excitatory impulse brings about the inhibition of an inhibition, we are indeed well on the way to solving the problem of volition.

Lloyd Morgan (1891) based his high estimate of the importance of inhibition on an inference not unlike that of Sechenov: that without inhibition all excitation would flow directly into motor activity, but the arrest of motion creates the opportunity for mind to occupy "itself more and more completely with the central processes, perception, and emotion, and also, in human beings, conceptual thoughts and emotions." Most particularly he saw inhibition as the basis for volition:

> I believe that volition is intimately bound up and associated with inhibition. I go so far as to say that, without inhibition, volition properly so called has no existence. When the series follows the inevitable sequence:
>
> stimulus : perception : emotion : fulfilment in action
>
> —the act is involuntary. And such it must ever have remained, had not inhibition been evolved, had not an alternative been introduced, thus—
>
> stimulus : perception : emotion : $<$ fulfilment in action. / inhibition of action.
>
> At the point of divergence I would place volition. Volition is the faculty of the forked way. There are two possibilities—fulfilment in action or inhibition (Morgan, 1891, p. 459).

Where Ziehen argued against the need to recognize any element of choice in behavior, Morgan sized upon inhibition as providing a possible explanation of choice. His is surely the more insightful analysis, especially since he recognized that the amplification of his hypothesis must wait upon a better understanding of the physiological process of inhibition. The weakness in Morgan's formulation is that the "forked way" of his schema has two meanings, of which only one is legitimate. In the evolutionary sense, it is permissible to state that volition arises at the "point of divergence" where immediate fulfillment of impulses is replaced by inhibition of action, if we understand this to mean not the first occurrence of inhibition, but a relatively high stage of its development. (It is interesting to note that Freud only a few years later arrived at a similar formulation, in which he emphasized the importance of deferring consummatory acts, and the part which this plays in the development of rational thinking.) But Morgan slips over into confusing this with the "faculty of the forked way" as an attribute of individual behavior, which permits fulfillment in action as one possibility for the individual, and inhibition as another. For the individual, on the contrary, the "faculty of the forked way" can only mean that alternative acts are both subject to inhibition, and that under these circumstances "fulfillment in action" is never direct, but always involves release of inhibition.

At this point, we should like to introduce a bit of history which was omitted from Chapter 3, because it would have had relatively little meaning for the reader at that time. In 1875, Freusberg argued that inhibitory effects were to be explained, not by special centers, but by the remarkable fact that the central nervous system does not allow its different parts to be simultaneously activated by different causes. One is at first disposed to dismiss this remark as being no more than a translation into quasi-physiological language of the belief in the "unity of the soul" which had been such a basic tenet of all German philosophy since the time of Leibnitz. Brunton (1883) rejected Freusberg's statement as meaningless, because it "still leaves us in the dark regarding the way in which the central nervous system comes to possess the remarkable properties which he attributes to it." Nevertheless, if Freusberg did not contribute to an understanding of the causes of inhibition, he did put his finger on one of its most important manifestations. It is important enough to deserve a name, and we shall call it, for convenience, "Freusberg's principle," by analogy with Anstie's principle, which it supplements in an important respect. Before elaborating further upon it, we shall take another long step backward in time.

The reader will remember that John Buridan, who was rector of the University of Paris in 1327, is reputed to have said that if an ass stood exactly midway between two equally attractive bundles of hay it would be rooted motionless to the spot, unable to choose between them. Of course, no ass has ever been that much of a philosopher, nor was Buridan himself so asinine; he owes his immortality to the malicious invention of an opponent, who wished to ridicule Buridan's argument that it is impossible to resolve the ethical problem of whether the will can decide for or against a given course of action when the motives pro and con are equally balanced. (See Ueberweg's *History of Philosophy*, I, p. 466.) However, psychologists have sometimes conceptualized the problem of conflict between opposing courses of action as if the body were pushed this way and that by opposing forces, the vectorial resultant of which becomes the overt act. This would obviously be in defiance of Freusberg's principle, which would free the ass to approach one bundle of hay.

It is a fact that Buridan, like any competent philosopher, could deliberate a problem for days or years on end without reaching a conclusion, and even set a problem aside as meaningless or unsolvable. However, it is not possible for an ass, if he is physically able to approach one bundle of hay, to starve because he has been offered two. For this simple creature, where there is a way there is a will. Hobbes long ago remarked that man alone has the privilege of absurdity, "and of men, those are of all most subject to it, that profess philosophy." The cause of this affliction lies in the fact that the philosopher's inhibitory powers have been developed to the point where they are capable of divorcing his actions from reality, an outcome which Nature did not foresee when she instituted the first inhibitions that were designed to guarantee that an organism did not tear itself asunder in the quest of opposite goals, or, like the crab which Bethe had deprived of its cerebral ganglion, stuff its stomach to the point of bursting. Thus it is that when the upended starfish tries to right itself, some of the rays are able to take leadership over all the others, inhibiting their frantic efforts to grasp at something solid, the continuance of which would wreck the maneuver. Thus it is that the bullhead in Retzlaff's (1959) experiment would each time flip its tail to left or right, never permitting the simultaneous excitation of both muscles, despite the intense stimulation applied to both VIIIth nerves. Thus the hungry ass turns happily to either bundle of hay, giving no sign of traumatic conflict. These are all illustrations of Freusberg's principle. In each case, inhibitory controls utterly exclude what might have become competing excitations, and the organism retains, in Sherrington's words, that "*singleness of action from moment to moment* [*which*] *is a keystone in the construction of the individual whose unity it is the specific office of the nervous system to perfect.*" However, all of nature is not so harmonious. The philosopher does have his conflicts, and even a child may hesitate not once but twice or thrice when he chooses a candy from a box of many delights. The exclusion of competitive impulses is not a universal rule.

All of these examples of behavior, along with those we mentioned earlier in this chapter, have their place in the spectrum of choice. In which direction will the starfish flip over when it rights itself? Will the fish that is threatened from both sides dart to right or left? Which bundle of hay will the ass favor? How long will the child hesitate before he selects a candy, or the philosopher deliberate his weightier problem? Inhibition will play a multiple part in each case, releasing one response in accordance with Anstie's principle, often suppressing others in accordance with Freusberg's principle. It is indeed the physiological basis of those phenomena which have in the past often been described as the effects of "will."

INHIBITORY PROCESSES IN THINKING 8

This chapter will deal with the problem of whether inhibition plays an essential part not merely in the release, restraint, and modulation of overt action, but also in purely cognitive or what might even be termed subcognitive behavior, that is, the neural activities which determine the progress of thought. This area provides many examples of choice behavior: attention, which is an evidence of the ability of the organism to choose, in a degree, those aspects of the environment to which it shall be most responsive; selective association, which refers to the directed, problem-oriented nature of the thinking process; selective perception, which demonstrates a choice of ways of responding to the same stimulation; repression, a process whereby certain contents are excluded from consciousness because of painful affect which is associated with them. Among the theories which we shall review, possibly the most interesting because of their surprising agreement with certain aspects of contemporary neurological research are those of Wundt, who at the age of seventy revised his theory of apperception in a way which made inhibition the key to all the higher mental processes, and Freud, who in his early theorizing arrived at the conclusion that a process of inhibition is essential not only to explain the phenomena of repression, but also as a basis for memory and the reality-oriented behavior which he designated as the function of the ego.

First, let us point out that there are two quite different ways in which attention and thinking can be regarded as dependent on inhibitory capacity. On the one hand, one can suppose that the inhibition of motor impulses indirectly influences the neural events which are more directly involved in thinking. That is, the inhibition of movements favors mentation by removing a competing activity so that it releases nervous energy for thought. On the other hand, one can also look upon inhibition as an essential part of the thinking process itself. The first point of view need not presuppose the second, nor can evidence of the first kind of effect be taken to prove that inhibition does enter into thinking per se.

Immediate personal experience makes it easy for everyone to understand and accept the idea that inhibition of bodily activity favors thinking. "Stop and think!" is the standard exhortation of the exasperated adult to the impulsive child. Anyone who reaches that modest level of intellectual development at which one is aware of thinking as a process separable from action, becomes aware also of a degree of incompatibility between these two components of behavior. It is more difficult to recognize that the incompatibility is not absolute, and that complete muscular relaxation is not the optimal condition for mental work. The sculptor Rodin recognized that intense thought is usually accompanied by an increase of muscular tension above the usual resting level. Indeed, there is experimental verification of the fact that some increase of tonus is favorable to such a task as mental arithmetic, although strong muscular exertion, like squeezing a dynamometer, interferes with it. But does this prove that the work, as such, inhibits thinking? Loeb (1900) showed that squeezing two dynamometers caused less interference than squeezing one, which may mean that it is not the motor discharge as such, but the task of integrating it—which is probably more complex for the asymmetric than for the symmetric performance—which is the source of interference with thinking. Real-life thinkers often resort to simple automatic activities like pursing the lips or toying with a pencil. It is easy to experiment with mental arithmetic, but how does one experiment with creative thinking? Did Kant's daily morning walk, as regular as clockwork, help to deepen the profundity of his ideas? Is it more than an accident that the solution to Poincaré's mathematical problem suddenly occurred to him as he was stepping up into a bus? (Hadamard, 1945.) Someone (whose name escapes our recollection) has remarked that, with all the current interest in arousal functions of the reticular formation, we are in danger of forgetting that its primary function is as an integrative apparatus for motor behavior. If cortical arousal is secondary to motor activity, is it not possible that a certain amount of the latter is a prerequisite for any effective degree of arousal?

Ferrier, in *The Functions of the Brain* (1876), argued that the arrest of movement is an essential aspect of the attentive process. "During the time that we are engaged in attentive ideation we suppress actual movements, . . . [and] thereby increase the internal diffusion, and concentrate consciousness. For the degree of consciousness is inversely proportional to the amount of diffusion in action. In the deepest attention, every movement which would diminish internal diffusion is likewise inhibited. Hence, in deep thought, even automatic actions are inhibited, and a man who becomes deep in thought while walking, may be observed to stand still."

Ferrier, it may be recalled, believed in definite localization of cortical functions; he thought of inhibition as a function of the premotor area, which is exercised upon the motor area. The effect of such inhibition is only to create an opportunity for thinking, a respite from action, but it does not enter directly into the process. This is true even when, like Sechenov, he speaks of the possibilities for education of inhibitory capacity: "In proportion to the development and degree of education of the centers of inhibition do acts of volition lose their impulsive character, and acquire the aspect of deliberation. Present impulses or feelings, instead of at once exciting to action, as in the infant, stimulate the centers of inhibition simultaneously, and suspend action until, under the influence of attention, the associations engendered by past experience between actions and their pleasurable or painful consequences, near and remote, have arisen to consciousness. If the centers of inhibition, and thereby the faculty of attention, are weak, or present impulses unusually strong, volition is impulsive rather than deliberate."

Indeed, thinking for Ferrier becomes pretty much a matter of inhibiting large movements in order to permit small movements. In this he clearly anticipated the behaviorist theory of thinking as implicit speech, and certainly the theory seems more acceptable when it includes a provision for an inhibitory process—"We recall an object in idea by pronouncing the name in a suppressed manner. We think, therefore, and direct the current of thought in a great measure by means of internal speech. . . . The recall of an idea being thus apparently dependent on excitation of the motor element of its composition, the power of fixing the attention and concentrating consciousness depends, further, on inhibition of the movement."

Ribot, in his *Psychology of Attention* (1889), also spoke of the part which the inhibition of movement plays in the process of attention. However, the role which he assigned to it is much more limited than that which Ferrier imagined, since he implied only the inhibition of movements which are extraneous to the thought, rather than those which are intrinsic to it. Ribot declared that attention is characterized by the fact that a given conscious content can be retained in consciousness for an extended period of time, despite the influence of stimulating conditions which ceaselessly tend to make it disappear and to supplant it by new conscious content. He said that this capacity for arresting the succession of fleeting experiences constitutes the central problem of attention; and he discussed concretely how it is assisted by the inhibition of all movement, even at times by the partial suppression of respiration, and above all by the inhibition of eye movements. By these means we seek to prolong the influence of a selected stimulus, and to reduce the effects of distracting stimuli.

William James, writing at almost the same time as Ribot, stated explicitly that in his opinion Ferrier had greatly exaggerated the role of inhibition in attention, and that he preferred the views of G. E. Mueller, who emphasized reinforcement rather than inhibition. James believed that the inhibition of movements and of ideas constitutes a secondary and incidental aspect of attention, rather than anything essential to it (1890, I, p. 455). Nevertheless, at an earlier point, near the end of his famous chapter on "The Stream of Thought," we read the following:

> We see that the mind is at every stage a theatre of simultaneous possibilities. Consciousness consists in the comparison of these with each other, the selection of some, and the suppression of the rest by the reinforcing and inhibiting agency of attention. The highest and most elaborated mental products are filtered from the data chosen by the faculty next

> beneath, out of the mass offered by the faculty below that, which mass in turn was sifted from a still larger amount of yet simpler material, and so on. The mind, in short, works on the data it receives very much as a sculptor works on his block of stone. . . . The world *we* feel and live in will be that which our ancestors and we, by slowly cumulative strokes of choice, have extricated out of this, like sculptors, by simply rejecting certain portions of the given stuff. Other sculptors, other statues from the same stone! (W. James, 1890, I, pp. 288 ff.).

It is difficult to understand how James could reconcile this eloquent passage with the statement that the role of inhibition in attention is merely incidental. When later he turned to the discussion of perception, a role is suggested for inhibition (which, it should be remembered, he regarded as based on a kind of drainage) by his statement that "it is the halting-places of our thought which are occupied with distinct imagery" (II, p. 124). To explain this, he referred back to his chapter on imagination, where he had said that in the ordinary process of associative thinking "the cortical currents which run in [to a given cell] run right out again, awakening the next idea" (II, p. 75). On the other hand, "whenever the associative processes are reduced and impeded by the approach of unconsciousness, as in falling asleep, or growing faint, or becoming narcotized, we find a concomitant increase in the intensity of whatever partial consciousness may survive" (II, p. 124). In 1894, Sigmund Exner published his *Entwurf einer physiologischen Erklärung der psychischen Erscheinungen,* in which he stressed the dependence of the attentive process on both facilitation and inhibition. Exner was one of the important early contributors to the development of physiological psychology. In the period when the more verbal Wundt was proclaiming the birth of the new science, the young Exner was already doing important work not only on sense physiology, but also on reaction time. His studies on apparent visual movement, using electric sparks as stimuli, are an essential part of the history of Wertheimer's much later work on the phi-phenomenon. He recognized the importance of motor set for speed of reaction many years before the distinction between sensory and motor reaction times was made by L. Lange (1888), in Wundt's laboratory. Indeed, it was Exner's awareness of the fact that reaction times could be facilitated in this way which led him to the concept of *Bahnung,* or facilitation, which he then demonstrated on the rabbit (see page 50). No one, therefore, had greater right than Exner to attempt the difficult task of relating mental phenomena to their physiological correlates.

Although *Bahnung* was his own brain child, Exner showed no disposition to depreciate the importance of inhibition. He says that there are two kinds of attention, which he calls attentive facilitation and attentive inhibition. Of the latter, he wrote: "I think of attentive inhibition as a state of the centers such as exists in a reflex organ or in the center serving an instinctive movement, which has been stimulated to action by the adequate stimulus, but is prevented from acting by the will: a heightened tonus in the cells, despite which discharge is difficult."

In other words, Exner conceived of inhibition as the actual suppression of a neural discharge, and not merely as its redirection into other channels by the blocking of some outlets, as in the rob-Peter-to-pay-Paul approach which had been taken by Ferrier and by James, and was to be taken later by McDougall in his elaboration of the drainage theory of inhibition. Even Exner's definition of consciousness includes reference to essential functions of both excitation and inhibition: "When an excitatory complex in the cerebral cortex reaches a certain spread . . . and thus draws into excitation other pathways, related to frequent past experience and thus almost always facilitated . . . and takes on the already often-mentioned characteristic of inhibiting weaker excitations . . . then we say it is in consciousness."

Exner's preferred illustrations of inhibitory effects are all aspects of visual perception: he mentions the loss of the childhood illusion that objects move as we ride by, the suppression of afterimages during eye movements, and the ability of the practiced microscopist not to see the specks of dust on his microscope lens. However, he also says that just as movements inhibit one another, so also any vividly imagined idea will inhibit other ideas which are inconsistent with it—a remark which certainly points the way to an explanation of phenomena such as obsessions and what we now call autistic thinking. "Thus the play of excitations in the cortex is constantly under the simultaneous influence of inhibitions and facilitations. The momentary state of each individual fiber depends on which of the two antagonistic effects has the upper hand in respect to it."

We move back again to America. In 1895, Scripture wrote:

> The principal difference between feeling and emotion consists in . . . the alteration in the train of ideas. The presence of this alteration enables us to divide emotions into two classes, excitant and inhibitory. Instances of the former are joy and anger; of the latter, terror and fear. At the same time, all very intense emotions are inhibitory in character, and it is only when they run some part of their course that their excitant side comes to consciousness. . . . The excitant emotion quickens thought and involves heightened movement of face and limbs, increase of heart activity, and dilating of the blood vessels; the inhibitory emotion paralyzes, or at least relaxes, the muscles, slows the heart-beat, and contracts the vessels (Scripture, 1895, pp. 226 f.).

In 1899 (the same year in which Meltzer, in the *New York Medical Journal*, was complaining about the neglect of inhibition by physiologists), Breese wrote a monograph on inhibition as a psychological phenomenon. An historical survey led him to the conclusion that the concept of inhibition had been used too broadly and too vaguely. "Inhibition is a term which has been used to designate all kinds of mental conflict, hesitation and arrest," he said, but its "use in psychology should be confined to psychophysical phenomena." He listed five varieties of such phenomena, to wit:

1. inhibition of one sensation by another;
2. inhibition of bodily movements by sensation;
3. inhibition of mental states by motor activity;
4. inhibition of bodily functions by emotions;
5. inhibition of voluntary movements by will.

Leaning unmistakably on William James, but writing several years in advance of McDougall's first statement of the drainage theory of inhibition, he explained the occurrence of such psychophysical effects in the following manner: "The activity of nervous energy in certain centers and paths inhibits its use in other centers and paths, and consequently the mental state appropriate to the activity of those centers. The draining off of nerve centers inhibits the continued activity of those centers."

Breese also performed an experiment in binocular rivalry—noteworthy as perhaps the first psychological experiment which was specifically designed as an attack on the problem of inhibition. The subjects simultaneously viewed two visual fields, of different color and pattern, one with each eye. Without special instruction, they experienced spontaneous fluctuations, so that now one field, now the other, would be perceived. They were asked to try to prevent these fluctuations, so that one color would be seen in preference to the other, and it was found that they could lengthen the period of time during which the "chosen" field was dominant, but they could not influence the number of fluctuations. Breese interpreted the spontaneous fluctuations as an instance of the inhibition of one sensation by another.

In 1900, Münsterberg, who had been at Harvard since 1892, published his *Grundzüge der Psychologie*. Münsterberg's action theory of consciousness is in direct opposition to the view which had been common to Ferrier and James—that impulses which "run out" to the motor apparatus become thereby less capable of arousing conscious experience. On the contrary, he asserts, "there is no sensation which does not have a motor impulse as its basis." He justifies this position by arguing that the activity of the higher centers cannot take place without motor expression. Therefore the inhibition of motor responses tends to reduce awareness, rather than to increase it.

Münsterberg contends "that the undeniable opposition of motor functions is the true basis for all the facilitating and inhibiting . . . functions of the nervous system, and that all reinforcement and suppression, choice and rejection of psychophysical processes rests on this opposition of activities. There is no psychophysical process which as such is opposed to another psychophysical process. . . . All sensory excitations of the brain as such can exist side by side with each other; only the actions which correspond to them, can never be carried out together."

Thus it is the impossibility of performing incompatible motor acts which brings about the inhibition of motor impulses, and this in turn restricts the content of consciousness. "It is not the movement which is omitted because the sensation is inhibited, but the sensation which is omitted, because the contrary movement impulse removed the possibility for the discharge corresponding to the sensation."

The same general position is stated in a short chapter on inhibition included in *Psychology, General and Applied* (Münsterberg, 1914). Here Münsterberg seems to favor a drainage theory as the most plausible way to explain the inhibition of movements, which he assumes to underlie the inhibition of mental processes. But whatever the nature of the process, he recognized that "Some selecting principle must be at work which denies entrance to the unfitting stimulations and which suppresses the undesirable associations and which cuts off large parts of the reactions."

Münsterberg's position influenced many later American psychologists. Guthrie (1930) in particular represented the viewpoint that inhibition could have no physical basis except in the incompatibility of muscular actions.

Before Ferrier and after Münsterberg, there was always the enduring Wilhelm Wundt. His physiological theory of inhibition had been formulated early, and it appeared essentially unchanged in each edition of his *Principles of Physiological Psychology* (see Wundt, 1874), as part of the exposition of the functioning of the nervous system. However, in the earlier editions it had no particular relation to any of the distinctive features of his psychological system. Hints of its importance appear in the second volume of the fourth edition (1894) and it became indispensable in the fifth edition (1902). To understand this development, we must first look briefly at Wundt's theory of apperception, and at some of its difficulties.

In its general sense, *apperception* significes the process of active assimilation of the meanings of environmental stimulation, as opposed to a merely passive sensory response to them. Rapaport (1951) points out that this distinction lost its importance after the discovery of the laws of sensory organization by the Gestalt psychologists, since all sensory perception is now recognized as a process which involves meaningful integration. The specific meaning which different philosophers and psychologists have attached to apperception depends upon their understanding of how this integration is effected. Leibnitz (1714) had used the word to designate conscious as opposed to unconscious perception. Herbart used it to designate the process by which new ideational content is assimilated to the old, the "apperceptive mass." For Wundt, whose theory of attention was formulated largely on the basis of his experience in the laboratory with the phenomena of vision, apperception was the process by which parts of the content of consciousness are given greater clarity by being brought into the focus of attention—a direct analogy to the manner in which the eye brings a stimulus to the fovea, the point of clearest vision. Wundt believed that the anterior portion of the brain—the same area which Ferrier had regarded as specifically inhibitory—contained an "apperceptive organ" which could give this emphasis and clarity to a selected portion of conscious experience. The theory of apperception was his effort to supply a physiological basis for the elements of spontaneity and individuality in mental life. The Kirchner-Michäelis *Wörterbuch der philisophischen Grundbegriffe* (1911), which is consistently favorable to Wundt's theories, says: "Because of the important position which the concept of apperception occupies in Wundt's psychology, the whole related movement of psychology, which holds to the concept of mental *activity*, has been called *apperception psychology,* in contrast to association psychology."

As Boring (1950) points out, the doctrine of apperception assumed an increased importance in the fifth edition of Wundt's *Principles of Physiological Psychology* (which is also the edition on which the English translation is based), but it would certainly be mistaken to suppose that it did not have an important place in Wundt's theories previously. Ziehen, a thoroughgoing associationist, states in the preface to the first edition (1890) of his own *Leitfaden der physiologischen Psychologie* that his book "deviates considerably from Wundt's doctrine, which is dominant in Germany." He says further: "By introducing a special auxiliary variable [today we would say: a hypothetical construct] for the interpretation of psychical processes, the so-called apperception, Wundt indeed circumvents many difficulties of explanation; whenever some psychic process appears which is difficult to explain, it is assigned to apperception. However, this is at the same time a renunciation of every psycho-physiological explanation."

Münsterberg (1900) took a similar point of view, when he declared that "the concept of apperception easily leads us to surrender a consistent prosecution of psychophysical parallelism."

> The theory of apperception is that conception of the relationship between the physical and the mental, which indeed recognizes a thoroughgoing parallelism for elementary sensations, but on the other hand looks upon decision, relations and the [complex] forms of consciousness as purely psychological, without accompanying physiological processes. If the theory of apperception is correct, then psychophysics . . . would be in a position which is approximately like that of a science of physics which acknowledges in advance that causal relationships obtain for material substances only while they exist in solid form, but that they escape all the laws of causality as soon as they pass over into liquid or gaseous form (Münsterberg, 1900, p. 452 f.).

Wundt was not a man to be intimidated by critics, but it was only natural that these vigorous attacks should motivate him to a more careful statement of the hypothetical physiological basis for the apperceptive process. As one reads his fourth edition, having in mind the earlier absence of references to inhibition in relation to the apperceptive process, one sees the new theory come into being. In the first volume, which was published in 1893, the figure illustrating the schema of inhibition (see Figure 4) is changed somewhat from the form which it previously had, but the discussion is not changed in its essentials. The most important change is that the lines *ss′* and *hh′* were added, and three short lines *x*, *y*, and *z* were removed. These had been used to symbolize centripetal paths to the apperception center, but their origins were not shown. Thus the new figure provides a new and more direct two-way connection between the lower sensory centers and the apperception center. Midway through the second volume (1894), there is renewed discussion of this figure.

> Nothing stands in the way of interpreting the effect of the apperceptive excitation of the sensory centers as *inhibitory*. . . . But of course this inhibition . . . is not to be regarded as a reduction of certain excitations in the sensory centers, but it will consist in the fact that in consequence of the evocative action of the signal stimulus the *inflow of other signal stimuli* to the apperceptive center will be inhibited. This agrees entirely with the fact that the focus of attention becomes more narrow along with

the degree of attention, and that on the other hand it can be widened for certain presentations (Vorstellungen) by practice (Wundt, 1874, 4th ed., II, p. 276).

Two hundred pages farther on, the position taken is more emphatic.

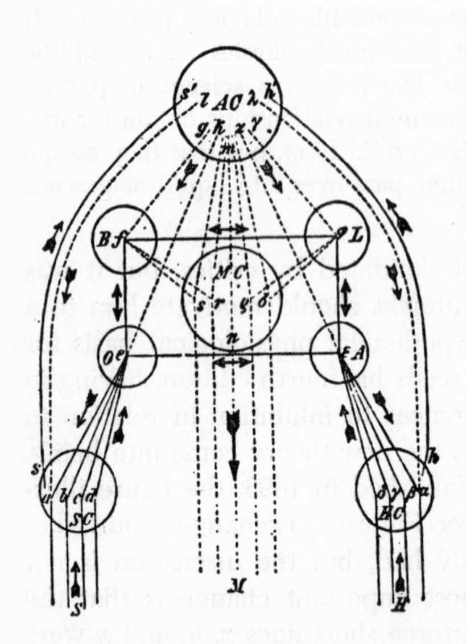

Figure 4. Wundt's "Schema of connections of the apperceptive organ." *SC*, visual center. *HC*, auditory center. *S* and *H*, central fibers of optic and auditory nerves. *A* and *L*, respectively, sensory and motor centers for speech. *O* and *B*, respectively, sensory and motor centers for writing. *MC*, motor center. *M*, central motor fibers. *AC*, apperceptive center. *ss'* and *hh'*, centripetal paths to the latter. *la*, *gf*, etc., centrifugal connections of the apperceptive center.

The figure shown is taken from the 4th ed. The corresponding figure in the 2nd ed. has no arrows, and does not have the lines *ss'* and *hh'*; it does have short straight lines labelled *x*, *y*, and *z* which enter the apperceptive organ from above (on the page) and which are designated as bringing sensory stimulation from primary sensory centers.

The basic phenomenon of all intellectual achievement is the so-called *concentration of attention.* It is understandable that in the psychological appraisal of this phenomenon we attach importance first and therefore too exclusively to its positive side, to the grasping and clarification of certain presentations. But for the physiological appraisal it is clear that it is the *negative* side, the inhibition of the inflow of all the other disturbing excitation, . . . which is more important (Wundt, 1874, 4th ed., II, p. 481).

In the fifth edition (1902), the new viewpoint is clearly stated. Whereas in earlier editions we had been led to suppose that the influence of the apperceptive organ was exercised by the facilitative reinforcement of some of the elements of conscious experience, and in the fourth edition we are asked to consider that these effects may be inhibitory, the fifth edition explains apperception as a general inhibition of all sensory data which does not occupy the focus of consciousness. In this statement (which we are fortunate to have in Titchener's translation) we see how Wundt's own searching examination of the data of consciousness helped to shape the theory:

> It might, at first thought, be supposed that the elementary process of apperception which appears in its simplest form when a sensation becomes clearer, consists, on the physiological side, merely in an increase of the nervous excitation which runs parallel to the sensation; . . . A little introspection suffices to show that a sensation, in growing stronger or weaker, alters its *own* intrinsic character; while if it grows clearer or more obscure, the change is primarily a change in its relation to *other* conscious contents. . . . These facts suggest that the substrate of the simple apperception process may be sought in *inhibitory processes* which, by the very fact that they arrest other concomitant excitations, secure an advantage for the particular excitations not inhibited. If we postulate an inhibitory process of this kind, we are able to explain how it is that apperception as such does not consist in an intensification of the sensation contents. And if we assume, further, that the inhibitory influence, in this special case, is not exerted directly upon certain excitations in progress within the sensory centers, but rather upon the conduction of the excitations to the higher centers in which the sensory contents are combined to form complex resultants, we avoid doing violence to the obverse fact that the conscious contents obscured by inhibition do not on that account lose in intensity. The arousal of the inhibition, since on the physiological side it is ordinarily dependent upon particular conscious contents, past and present, must be physiologically conceived as analogous to that of the reflex inhibitions occurring in various forms in the lower nerve centers. There is, however, a difference. The inhibitory effects are liberated, here as elsewhere, by certain excitations that are conducted to the center; but their liberation is at the same time influenced by that incalculable manifold of conditions which, for the most part, we can merely group together under the indefinite name of the current disposition of consciousness, as determined by past experience and the circumstances of the time (Wundt, 1874; trans. of 5th ed., 1904, p. 317 f.).

Thus, inhibition, which had been assigned no role of importance in the early editions of the *Physiological Psychology*, suddenly became a decisive factor touching on the very heart of Wundt's system. One cannot but be struck by the fact that Wundt, basing himself primarily on introspective data, reached a fundamentally correct understanding of part, though not all, of the process of attention: to wit, that sensory input to the cerebral cortex is subject to a cortically controlled inhibition which takes effect at lower levels. He explicitly hypothesizes, in reference to Figure 4, that "An individual impression *a* is apperceptively enhanced by inhibition of the impressions *b c d*. . . . We then have perception of *b c d* and apperception of *a*. . . . At the same time, by means of inhibitions released in [other] centers, . . . the resulting word idea and the phonetic utterance are apperceived."

Looking back at this today, one wonders how far Wundt might have gone in the experimental analysis of the inhibitory aspects of perception if he had been a younger man. When the fifth edition appeared, Wundt was seventy years old, and most of his energies were being directed elsewhere, especially into his *Völkerpsychologie*, of which the first volume had appeared in 1900 and the tenth was to appear in 1920, the year of his death. The new doctrine found no echo in the Zeitgeist of the young twentieth century, and apparently it awakened no enthusiasm even among his immediate followers. More likely than not, it contributed to the accelerating decline of Wundt's influence. However, something very like Wundt's inhibitory theory of apperception seems destined to play a part in the future psychology of thinking, and therefore we designate as *Wundt's principle* the hypothesis *that higher thought processes depend on cortically instigated inhibition of afferent excitation.*

The judgment of Wundt's younger contemporaries was expressed by Pillsbury, in his book on *Attention* (1908). After reviewing the various physiological theories of attention, he concludes: "We have been assuming throughout that there is both reinforcement and inhibition in the attention process. . . . It would be perhaps easier to explain the attention process as one of reinforcement alone, but [one almost hears the suppressed 'unfortunately'] there are certain facts which make it certain that inhibition plays a role at times. . . . But there is certainly no room for the assumption of Wundt that attention is an inhibitory process alone. . . . Exner is in this respect considerably nearer the truth than any other writers who have proposed theories."

Inhibition appeared, of course, in McDougall's books, especially in his *Physiological Psychology* (1905), but McDougall rapidly became the bête noire of American psychology, and his advocacy of a theory did little to recommend it. For American psychologists, inhibition had its last fling for a long while in Margaret Washburn's *Movement and Mental Imagery* (1916), in which she stated a motor theory of consciousness which pursued the lead given by Münsterberg but took a less extreme position. She speculated that consciousness might require the simultaneous occurrence of both excitation and inhibition; that either uninhibited reflex action, or the complete inhibitory arrest of a motor activity, would have no conscious accompaniment. Even memory images would imply some degree of implicit movement, the impulse to movement being not quite completely inhibited, and the most vivid conscious experiences would accompany some optimal ratio of the excitatory and inhibitory processes.

If one translates this into behavioral terms, one may say that for the thinking organism the problem of balance between excitatory and inhibitory processes is especially acute. As we know, the imperative need for negative feedback finds expression through many different mechanisms, including feedback loops between different levels and different nuclei; recurrent axons; diffuse local inhibition; and shorter circuits which, though they have been called reverberatory, are more likely inhibitory in function. On the motor side, any imbalance of inhibitory and excitatory processes is quickly reflected in hypokinetic or hyperkinetic pathology; in the emotional sphere, autonomic imbalance represents a similar type of malfunction. However, the limits of tolerance for imbalance between excitation and inhibition are probably even more demanding for thinking, that is, for intracerebral activities which respond sensitively to environmental stimulations but must nevertheless take place with a minimum of effector discharge, without "acting out." For this, one can well imagine, there is indeed a need not just for "more inhibition," as Ferrier or Lloyd Morgan might have thought, but for an optimal ratio of inhibition to excitation, as Washburn stated.

By the second decade of the twentieth century, the word inhibition disappeared from the vocabulary of most American psychologists. It almost seems as if all reference to inhibition was banished along with the use of introspection, as if it were a wholly mentalistic concept. In Thorndike's connectionism, excitatory bonds could be made weaker or stronger (that is, synaptic resistances could be increased or decreased), but no inhibitory process was invoked to explain the "stamping-out" which was a part of the "law of effect" until Thorndike's revision of his theory in 1932. After that, there was less need than ever for a process of inhibition. In Watson's behaviorism, only facilitatory effects were admitted. When the ideas of Freud and Pavlov demanded attention, the figurative "censor" of the one and the assumed cortical inhibition of the other were both dismissed as equally absurd. American psychology had gone extravert. It had not only achieved at last, in Lange's (1875) memorable phrase, a "psychology without a soul," but it had achieved a psychology in which there was no obvious place for thinking, and in which "inhibition," when the word had returned to the usage of psychologists, meant no more than an uncomfortable inability to act out one's impulses.

While the great Wundt still labored prodigiously in the twilight of his career, the greater Freud was publishing his first great psychoanalytic works (*The Interpretation of Dreams, Three Contributions to the Theory of Sex, Wit and its Relations to the Unconscious*), which were being received in stony silence by some, with outrage and derision by others. For our purpose, however, we must turn back a few years, to 1895, when the ideas which are basic to these works were being formulated in great travail, and parts of the process preserved for posterity in the letters written to his friend Wilhelm Fliess (Freud, 1954). As a young man, Freud had hoped some day to hold the position which Exner had gained, to be director of the Physiological Institute in the University of Vienna. He had done some research in neurology, which was good but not world shaking, and then he had left his impecunious post at the Institute in order to earn a living as a physician, specializing in neurology. He had become interested in the neuroses; and he had glimpsed the importance of repression as a psychological mechanism, not only in pathological defense, but in normal everyday living. Now he was trying to solve that riddle, for he felt confident that repression, not attention and consciousness, would be the key to unlock the secrets of mental functioning. (Cf. E. Jones, 1953.)

In May, 1895, he wrote to Wilhelm Fliess: "I am plagued with two ambitions: to see how the theory of mental functioning takes shape if quantitative considerations, a sort of economics of nerve-force, are introduced into it; and secondly, to extract from psychopathology what may be of benefit to normal psychology."

In June: "The 'Defense' has taken an important step forward, and I shall be sending you some short notes on the subject as an earnest of the fact. The construction of the 'Psychology' also looks as if it is going to come off, which would give me great cause for rejoicing."

In August: "This psychology is really an incubus. . . . All I was trying to do was to explain defense, but I found myself explaining everything from the heart of nature, I found myself wrestling with the problems of quality, sleep, memory—in short, the whole of psychology. Now I want to hear no more of it."

In September: "My rested brain is now making child's play of the accumulated difficulties, for instance, the contradictions in the fact that actions re-establish their resistance, whereas the neurones in general are subject to facilitation."

And finally, in October: "I am enclosing all sorts of things for you today, including . . . two note-books of mine."

These notebooks contain the fruit of Freud's early effort to construct a psychology which should be a natural science. Soon afterward he abandoned the effort to establish a physiological foundation for his psychological theories, and in his published works he does not discuss the problem of neurological inhibition, although he writes of the inhibition of sexuality, the inhibition of thoughts, the inhibition of affects, and tells us that the pleasure we derive from wit is due to its "economy in inhibition." All of Freud's fundamental propositions regarding inhibition, including the phenomena of defense, and the manner in which the "second process" of rational thinking overcomes the irrationality of "primary process" thinking, were developed during this early period, that is, at a time when he was still wrestling with neurological problems. We shall see that the neurological speculations which Freud soon afterward thrust aside as unprofitable helped to determine the particular form in which he expressed his psychological theories.

In the English edition of the correspondence with Fliess, the notebooks we have mentioned are given the title, "Project for a

Scientific Psychology." Freud referred to them in his letters as the $\phi\psi\omega$, a designation which is based on the fact that in his theory he distinguishes between the hypothetical functions of three kinds of neurons. Only the first two kinds need concern us. (The third, which serve for perception or *Wahrnehmung*, were represented by a *W*, which Freud replaced by the Greek letter ω.) ϕ-neurons are afferent neurons which offer virtually no resistance to the passage of nervous energy, and therefore also can never retain any of it within themselves. ψ-neurons, presumably those of the cerebral cortex, have "contact-barriers" (i.e., synapses—a word first introduced by Sherrington in 1897) which offer considerable resistance to the passage of nervous energy. Actually, the Project does not speak of nervous energy as such, but of "a quantity (Q) subject to the general laws of motion." Since this is derived from stimulations and expressed in action, it will do little violence to Freud's thought to speak of it as nervous energy, particularly in view of his reference to the "economics of nerve-force" a few months earlier. However, it need not always show itself as nervous impulse. If the amount of it in a given neuron is inadequate to overcome the resistances of the contact-barriers between this neuron and others which succeed it, it simply remains there, and the neuron is then "occupied" by this energy. (In Freud's word, *besetzt*. This translation would seem to be a simple matter, since anyone who has travelled about Europe on the railroads knows that just as a washroom is frequently *occupé* in France and *occupato* in Italy, it is *besetzt* in Germany. A more dignified rendition might be "invested," and that would seem adequate to the uses to which Freud put this word in later writings. However, his first translator, Brill, achieved an unsurpassed piece of obscurantism by coining the word *cathexis* to render Freud's *Besetzung*. In defiance of tradition, we shall use *invested* and *investment* where the published translations have *cathected* and *cathexis*, words which fail to convey Freud's simple, direct meaning.) The energy which is thus captured in some of the neurons plays an important part in the activity of the nervous system, and we are told that the ego "may be defined as the totality of the ψ-investments at any given time."

Freud, despite his personal dislike for the officious Exner, also recognized the importance of the *Bahnung* phenomenon. He assumed that it consists in a reduction in the resistance of contact-barriers which takes place with the passage of impulses. However, the ability of a given impulse to cross a contact-barrier does not depend solely on the strength of the impulse and the resistance of that barrier, because it is easier for energy to pass across a given resistance into a neuron which is already invested with energy than into one which is not so invested. Therefore the course of impulses in the nervous system is influenced not only by the distribution of resistances, that is, by the past facilitations, but also by the energy which is captured or invested in the ψ-neurons, which has not been discharged across the contact-barriers and therefore has not contributed to the facilitations.

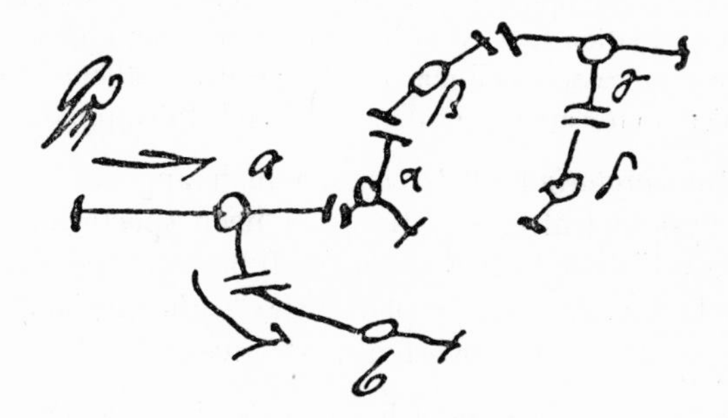

Figure 5. Freud's schema of inhibition. From Sigmund Freud, *The Origins of Psycho-Analysis*, New York, Basic Books, 1954. Reproduced by permission.

The effect of the energy invested in one neuron is frequently to inhibit the passage of nervous impulses to another neuron. Freud drew a figure which shows that the nervous energy which enters a neuron *a* from the periphery (that is, from the ϕ-neurons), can pass either to neuron *b* or to neuron α. (See Figure 5.) "If it were uninfluenced it would have proceeded to neuron *b*. But it is in fact so much influenced by the lateral investment in neuron α that it only passes on a quotient to *b*, or may not even reach *b* at all. Where, then, an ego exists, it is bound to inhibit psychical processes." In other words, wherever there is a nervous system which retains the effects of past experience and utilizes them to eliminate or reduce responses which have elicited pain, inhibition must be present.

Freud then enters into a discussion of "secondary processes"; and the importance of inhibition to his system, as envisaged in this early stage, is shown by the following sentences: "*It is the inhibition brought about by the ego that makes possible a criterion for distinguishing between a perception and a memory.*" He goes on to say:

It will be seen that the *sine qua non* of (secondary processes) is a correct exploitation of the indications of reality and that this is only possible when there is inhibition on the part of the ego. . . . Judgment is a ψ-process which is only made possible by the inhibition exercised by the ego. . . . Let us be satisfied with bearing firmly in mind that it is the original interest in establishing the situation of satisfaction that produces in the one case *reproductive reflection* and in the other case *judging* as methods of proceeding from the perceptual situation that is really presented to the situation that is wished for. It remains a *sine qua non* for this that the ψ-processes shall not run their course without inhibition, but shall be subject to the activity of the ego (Freud, 1954, pp. 389, 390, 394).

In the *Interpretation of Dreams,* which appeared in 1900, all effort at physiological explanation has been specifically excluded, but the ideas of the φψω survive in the following passage, in which, as explained above, we have replaced the "cathected" and "cathexis" of Brill's translation with "invested" and "investment."

Let us also state in plain terms how we visualize the movement of our thought. We believe that a certain quantity of excitation, which we call "invested energy," is displaced from a purposive idea along the association paths selected by this directing idea. A "neglected" train of thought has received no such investment, and the investment has been withdrawn from one that was "suppressed" or "rejected"; both have thus been left to their own excitations. The train of thought invested by some aim becomes able under certain conditions to attract the attention of consciousness, and by the mediation of consciousness it then receives "*hyper-investment*" (p. 529).

The activity of the first ψ-system aims at the *free* outflow of the quantities of excitation, and the second system, by means of the investments emanating from it, effects an inhibition of this *outflow,* a transformation into dormant investment, probably with a rise of potential. . . . After the second system has completed its work of experimental thought, it removes the inhibition and damming up of the excitations and allows them to flow off into motility (p. 534).

Let us however keep a close hold on the fact—for this is the key to the theory of repression—*that the second system can only invest an idea when it is in a position to inhibit any pain emanating from this idea.* Anything that withdrew itself from this inhibition would also remain inaccessible for the second system, i.e., would immediately be given up by virtue of the pain-principle (Freud, 1900, p. 535).

In the later development of Freud's theories, it always remained true that inhibition was recognized as a necessary condition for the development of thinking which is oriented toward reality. For example, in his essay on the "Two Principles in Mental Functioning," Freud (1911) stated that thinking was developed because the need arose for restraint of motor discharge, and "thought was endowed with qualities which made it possible for the mental apparatus to support increased tension during a delay in the process of discharge." Freud's insistence on the reality of a repressor-function, with or without an explicitly stated neurological basis, was of course one of the points which made his theories unacceptable to academic psychologists.

It would not be possible to do justice to Freud's many applications of the concept of inhibition without devoting a chapter to him alone. However, since most of these applications are related to the central concept of repression, and are no doubt well known to the reader, we shall give them no special attention. It is interesting, however, to take note that Freud also recognized the need for protective inhibition of environmental stimulation, although his discussion of this need does not include the word *inhibition,* which had acquired special meaning within his system. The following sentences are spread over several pages in *Beyond the Pleasure Principle,* the work which opened the "new phase" in Freud's thinking with the introduction of the death instinct.

Let us picture a living organism in its most simplified form. . . . The surface turned towards the external world will from its very situation be differentiated and will serve as an organ for receiving stimuli. . . . This little fragment of living substance is suspended in the middle of an external world charged with the most powerful energies; and it would be killed by the stimulation emanating from these if it were not provided with a protective shield against stimuli. . . . *Protection against* stimuli is an almost more important function for the living organism than *reception of* stimuli. . . . The main purpose of the *reception* of stimuli is to discover the direction and nature of the external stimuli; and for that it is enough to take small specimens of the external world, to sample it in small quantities. . . . We describe as "traumatic" any excitations from outside which are powerful enough to break through the protective shield. . . . The specific unpleasure of physical pain is probably the result of the protective shield having been broken through in a limited area (Freud, 1920, Sec. IV).

However, there is no indication that Freud thought of this protective function as being carried on by means of neural inhibition, which he had visualized as serving only the ego functions.

It is convenient at this point to mention that an interest in the theories of psychoanalysis led Klopfer (1924) to consider the general problem of inhibition within the context of the traditional experimental psychology of the German universities. He reached conclusions in agreement with our own, recognizing that at very primitive levels inhibition fulfills the need to limit excitation and also creates the possibility of differential response to a stimulus, and that in its higher forms it is not only essential for the phenomena of attention, but also for those of personality development, including the maintenance of personal individuality in the face of social environmental influences.

The modern theory of cognitive processes rests upon the achievements of the Würzburg school and the Gestalt psychologists. Their theories have a necessary place in our story, although inhibition plays no part in them.

The investigators of the Würzburg school (Külpe, Marbe, Watt, Ach, Bühler) demonstrated that the process of thinking includes essential phases which have no counterpart in consciousness. They found that the solutions of thought problems usually emerge suddenly from an imageless background, in which there are only vague feelings of relation rather than explicit imagery. Immediately before the solution appears in consciousness, there may be no more reportable conscious content than a strained awareness of task orientation, in which the task itself has no clear definition. Ach (1905) declared that the purposeful thinking of a wakeful person is no more consciously directed than an act which is performed in obedience to a posthypnotic suggestion, and he proposed that the source of both is an unconscious "determining tendency" which is the true basis of what has been described as the activities of the will.

Ach and the other Würzburg psychologists thought of these unconscious determinants as agents which facilitated certain associations rather than others, but anyone who reads the protocols of the Würzburg experiments—still better, who with their guidance eavesdrops on the working of his own mind—must be struck by the fact that thinking characteristically has blank moments, and that more often than not the solution to a problem emerges directly from one of these, as suddenly as a name which had been momentarily forgotten, and is then all at once recalled. Obviously, something very important is happening in those blank periods, and it is therefore natural to ask if an important inhibitory process is not taking place. Which, we may wonder, are the more important "halting-places of our thought"—the moments of vivid imagery, or the blank moments between?

Task-oriented thinking seems to proceed by a series of rejected inadequate solutions, until an accepted solution or the hint of one emerges flashlike from what seemed, an instant earlier, to be an utterly barren arrest of the thinking process. One way to conceptualize this sequence of events is to say that unconscious (facilitative) associative processes throw up suggestions, and that conscious (inhibitory) processes accept or reject them. This would be in keeping with the view that the determining tendency is entirely facilitative in its effects, and it saves for consciousness, if not the creative task of imagining solutions, at least the rational task of judging them. However, there is no logical reason why the unconscious determinants of thinking should not be inhibitory as well. Certainly there is strong indication of this in the clear phenomenal fact that the tentative solutions commonly emerge from blank periods of "no thought." This shows that the channeling of associations depends at least in part on the fact that inappropriate associations are being unconsciously excluded, or inhibited. A simple example of this is the fact that when we hunt for a six-letter word to fit into a crossword puzzle, longer and shorter words simply do not enter our thoughts. If the effect of a task orientation were merely to facilitate relevant associations, which is the assumption implicit in association theories, the man with a problem would associate more readily, not less readily, than the man without a problem. Everyday experience, as well as the therapeutic clinic, tells us that the opposite is the fact. Evidently the nature of productive thinking is such that it involves cutting off associations, as well as arousing them.

Turning to Gestalt psychology, we must recognize that its emphasis on relational interactions between the elements of experience provides an opportunity for explanation in terms of inhibitory effects. Gestalt psychology came into being as a school with the work of Max Wertheimer (1912) on illusory movement, which he called the *phi*-phenomenon. He postulated at once a correspondence between cortical and conscious events which has remained a basic tenet of Gestalt theory. At about the same time, Rubin (1911) performed experiments on visual perception, including the perception of ambiguous figures, and he formulated his results in terms of "figure and ground" relationships, a concept which has had extremely broad application to problems of thinking generally. Köhler (1920, 1929, 1940) developed Wertheimer's basic idea of correspondence between perceptual and cortical processes in his theory of *isomorphism,* which assumed electrical field processes in the cerebral cortex. That this assumption is untenable was shown experimentally by Lashley, Chow, and Semmes (1951), who showed that gold foil laid on a cat's visual cortex and gold pins thrust through it did not disturb whatever process was involved in recognition of a visual pattern used in training, and by Sperry and Miner (1955), who performed the converse test by inserting sheets of mica. The same untenable hypothesis underlies the Köhler-Wallach (1944) theory which seeks to explain figural aftereffects, and alternations in the perception of ambiguous figures, as due to local satiation of excited cortical points, which favors shift to a new pattern of excitation.

We should like to consider briefly whether the fact of cortical inhibition does not open new possibilities for the interpretation of these phenomena. First, let us consider the *phi*-phenomenon. It will be convenient to think of it in the simple form in which Wertheimer experimented upon it, that is, as an experience of movement resulting from the stimulation of the retina by two flashes of light, separated by a small interval in both time and space. For Wertheimer, in 1912, this seemed to imply just two excitatory events in the cortex, each with a tendency to irradiate. However, Forbes and Morison showed, in 1939, that the cortical response to a single flash consists of two excitations, one with short latency and one with long latency, that is, one which probably involves a single central nucleus and one which involves several thalamic nuclei, so that (in the cat) traversal of the direct path takes about 12 msec., and traversal of the indirect path takes about 75 msec. (These times are taken from Brazier, 1958.) Furthermore, the very distinctness of these two excitations reminds us of another important fact: that the first excitation (as well as the second) is followed by a local mobilization of inhibition which checks the tendency to irradiate. Now, if we label the cortical points *A* and *B*, we recognize that two flashes evoke four excitations, and under the conditions of nearly optimal timing for illusory movement, A_2 is simultaneous with B_1. Point *A*, having been in some sense alerted by its first excitation, is engaged in extinguishing the second, at the same time that point *B* is being alerted by its first stimulation. Surely, this simultaneity of similar events in different phase is a more reasonable basis for experienced movement than a hypothetical, and in fact highly improbable, movement of current from one point to the other.

Let us turn now to the problem of alternation of figure-ground relationships in unstable figures. Of course, every perceptual field is unstable in some degree, and those we label as such are only the ones that have a predictable instability which makes them suitable for experimental use. Let us suppose, following Wundt's principle, that the structuring of a given stimulus field into figure and ground depends on the inhibitions imposed on parts of the available sensory information, and that changes in the nature of this inhibition would lead to altered perception. Let us also suppose, following Heidenhain's principle, that there is a tendency for local cortical inhibition to arise whenever a process of excitation is going on. Hence, as excitations are dampened, excitation of new points would be favored, leading to altered perceptions. It is of course also possible that corticifugal inhibitions will be aroused where cortical activity is strongest. Thus the effect which has been attributed to satiation does occur, not as a consequence of some wholly hypothetical satiation, but as a result of the interplay of two experimentally demonstrated forms of neural inhibition. If the stimulus is a reversible ambiguous figure, these inhibitions will suffice to explain a succession of figure reversals. Eysenck (1955) also has argued that the figural aftereffect can be explained by cortical inhibition. He presents experimental evidence that the effect is stronger in hysterics than in dysthymics, in support of his theory that the fundamental difference between these groups is in the characteristics of the process of reactive inhibition.

However, it has not been our purpose here to undertake the very difficult task of formulating a new theory of perception, but only to introduce a discussion of certain recent research in that area. Gestalt psychology awakened a renewed interest in cognitive functions, and the growing influence of psychoanalysis, both direct and indirect, helped to encourage and direct research in the field of personality. These two influences have merged in studies of the influence of personality on perception. Out of this research has come an indication of the need to include inhibitory processes in perceptual theory, and it is that which we wish to consider in the remainder of this chapter.

In 1948, Postman, Bruner, and McGinnies wrote on "Personal values as selective factors in perception." They reached the following conclusions, based principally on their study of differential reaction times for words representing "high values" and "low values" of their individual subjects, as determined by scores on the Allport-Vernon Study of Values:

> Our results lead us to propose three complementary selective mechanisms. Value orientation acts as a sensitizer, lowering thresholds for acceptable stimulus objects. Let us call this mechanism *selective sensitization.* Value orientation may, on the other hand, raise thresholds for unacceptable stimulus objects. We shall refer to this mechanism as *perceptual defense.* Finally, the perceiver . . . favors the pre-solution hypotheses which reflect his value orientation. . . . This third mechanism we shall term *value resonance* (Postman, Bruner, & McGinnies, 1948, p. 151 f.).

With respect to the second of these hypothetical mechanisms, perceptual defense, they state:

[It] erects barriers against percepts and hypotheses incongruent with or threatening to the individual's values. We suggest that a defense mechanism similar to repression operates in perceptual behavior. . . . One may inquire at this point, "How does the subject 'know' that a word should be avoided? In order to 'repress' he must first recognize it for what it is." We have no answer to propose. What mediates the phenomena of hysterical or hypnotically induced blindness? Of only one thing we can be fairly sure: reactions do occur without conscious awareness of what one is reacting to. Psychological defense in perception is but one instance of such "unconscious" reaction (Postman, Bruner, & McGinnies, 1948, p. 152 f.).

McGinnies, in 1949, presented data on increased galvanic skin response to emotionally-toned as against neutral words, which had been exposed for periods that were too short to permit recognition. Interpreting this result, he remained loyal to the concept of perceptual defense. Still puzzled as to the mechanism, he wondered nevertheless, as one tentative hypothesis, whether the response which precedes recognition may not be due to feedback from cortical association centers. (At this time, corticifugal inhibition of sensory data at the brain-stem level was still unsuspected by physiologists.) Meanwhile, Bruner and Postman (1949), participating in a Symposium on Personal and Social Factors in Perception, thought they had developed a more parsimonious hypothesis. They state that the phenomena of so-called perceptual defense "suggest to the guileless investigator the image of the superego peering through a Judas eye, scanning incoming percepts in order to decide which shall be permitted into consciousness. . . . At first blush we seem to be facing a paradox here. In order to repress or negate a stimulus, must not the subject recognize it first for what it is?" They propose to escape this paradox by the assumption that veridical report and affective avoidance have different thresholds. Assuming a proper hierarchy of thresholds, "a Judas-eye notion of double perception is not required to account for the phenomena of 'defensive' perception. . . ."

In other words, they propose that the kind of choice displayed in these situations shall be explained as due to different levels of excitancy for different response mechanisms, rather than invoking a distinctly inhibitory apparatus. The question of conscious versus unconscious response does not enter into the problem, since in either case response takes place without awareness of the meaning of the stimulus words.

In 1957, how the situation had changed! In that year, Bruner cited the experiments of Hernández-Péon and of Galambos on inhibition of sensory input to the cortex, and said:

> Some years ago I came to the conclusion, to simplify the matter grossly, that perceptual selectivity seemed to operate like a gating process that had the characteristic of raising the identification threshold for certain classes of stimuli and lowering them for others and suggested that, rather than viewing such threshold differences as due to speed of associational processes set up by different inputs [that is, as differences in excitancy], inputs might be conceived as being differentially gated out before reaching a stage of association [that is, as subject to inhibition]. My argument was based on considerations of economy of functioning—that very likely perception had as one of its functions the task of screening out irrelevant stimuli and letting through relevant ones, an important consideration for living organisms who have a perilously narrow attention or immediate memory span (Bruner, 1957, p. 340).

And thus, after more than half a century, we are ready to give serious consideration to the position which was stated by Wundt in 1902, and to recognize the need for inhibitory elements in the thinking process which had been anticipated by many other psychologists before that time, by very few since. Having reached this point again, let us not slip into the old mistake of grudgingly admitting the existence of an inhibitory process only in those instances of behavior where it has been demonstrated beyond question. The process of inhibition has equal status with that of excitation in the nervous system. There is no reason to suppose that excitation is more fundamental, more ancient, or more widespread than inhibition. Therefore there is no reason whatever to give one of these processes preferential status over the other, in constructing hypotheses about behavior, and about that portion of behavior which we call thinking. It would be utterly false to interpret the principle of parsimony as dictating that we shall assign the greater burden of explanation to one process, excitation, and as little as possible to another process, inhibition. Inhibition must be admitted as a full partner with excitation in the business of nervous control. Specifically, we must not suppose that perceptual defense represents a special kind of choice behavior, and that the principles operating here do not operate in perception generally. On the contrary, it should help us to recognize that inhibition is part and parcel of the thinking process, in every form that thinking takes.

PAVLOV 9

Ivan Pavlov, physiologist, a man who wanted to have nothing to do with psychology or psychologists, is often enthroned with Freud in a strange duumvirate—two men of different backgrounds and different methods, who could scarcely find a common basis for discussion of any of the problems which interested them, who however had at least this in common: that either was ready to squeeze the last drop of theoretical juice out of any observation. With both, academic psychologists have been extremely selective, taking whatever fitted our needs and our fancies, usually paying for this much with generous praise, but thrusting the rest aside with almost pitying disdain as puerile fantasy, because it was so oddly at variance with some of our other convictions.

Despite the large part that the "conditioned reflex" has played in our theories of learning, by far the greater part of the work of Pavlov and his collaborators has been ignored or minimized, because learning theorists have been unwilling to go along with his emphasis on the importance of a cortical inhibitory process. On the other hand, Lenin's declared admiration for Pavlov's work and his high assessment of its social value created in the Soviet Union a climate in which Pavlov's theories have been accorded a kind of ordained preeminence, and Russian behavioral science has demonstratively enlisted "under the banner of Pavlov." However, we shall see in the next chapter that this has not kept his physiological theories immune from all adverse criticism.

In 1904, Pavlov received the Nobel award for his work on digestive secretions. In his speech of acceptance, he not only reviewed his achievements in that field but he also described the new type of research which he was then undertaking, on which his greater fame was to rest, and he explained how it arose out of the problems posed by his work on digestion. Others before him had noticed the so-called psychic secretion, that is, the secretion of digestive juices in the stomach of an experimental animal when it had only seen food at a distance, or witnessed the preparations for feeding, and had not yet taken it into his mouth. But whereas to others it had been a mere curiosity or a nuisance which upset their experimental controls, Pavlov recognized it as an opportunity to gain a deeper understanding of the operation of the nervous system.

His theoretical orientation had been greatly influenced by the "nervism" of Botkin, a clinical professor of medicine who always emphasized the part which the nervous system played in every disease syndrome. In an article which dealt with the innervation of the heart, Pavlov once wrote (as quoted by Koshtoyants, 1946): "The idea of the investigation and the execution of it were mine alone. But I was surrounded by the clinical ideas of Professor Botkin—and with hearty gratitude I acknowledge the fruitful influence, not only on this work but on my physiological views in general, of that broad and profound nervism, often outstripping the experimental facts, which represents, in my opinion, the great service of Sergei Petrovich to physiology." Pavlov added this footnote: "By nervism I understand the movement in physiology which seeks to extend the influence of the nervous system to as many of the organism's activities as possible."

In his own research, therefore, Pavlov emphasized the importance of the nervous control of gastric secretions. He carried to a new level of perfection a surgical procedure which permitted the observation of these secretions in an isolated portion of the stomach where food did not enter, but which had all of its innervation intact. He prided himself that his success in demonstrating the nervous control of these secretions was "due to the fact that we stimulated the nerves of animals that freely stood on their own feet and were not subjected to morbid irritation either during stimulation of their nerves or immediately before it."

To pursue his problem farther, it was necessary to gain an understanding of the "psychic secretions," and not to regard them as merely a nuisance or a curiosity. Pavlov indicated that considerable soul searching preceded the decision that the attempt would be made to investigate this problem by purely objective means, without constructing any hypotheses about the conscious experiences of the experimental animals. This decision, in itself, was not so revolutionary as is sometimes supposed. The credit for it must be shared with Sechenov, who had written that only the physiologist was qualified to investigate the problems of psychology; with Heidenhain, who insisted that all subjectivism must be excluded from physiological experimentation, and had specifically objected to Munk's speculative assumptions about the mental state of dogs; with Loeb and the group of like-minded young German physiologists—Beer, Bethe, and Uexküll—who had quite recently written their famous programmatic article (1899) which called for the use of a completely objective terminology in dealing with behavioral phenomena. The principle of objectivism was not new. Pavlov found a new way to apply it, by recognizing that the study of salivary secretion, which he himself described as a rather inconsequential function, provided a means for strictly objective quantitative study of problems of "higher nervous activity."

In Pavlov's laboratory, Wulfson made the first systematic study of the effects on salivary secretion of the remote presentation of both edible and nonedible objects which had been associated with feeding. Tolochinov, continuing this work, discovered the need for continued reinforcement with actual feeding if such responses were to continue. Communicating this result to a scientific meeting at Helsingfors, Finland (almost a suburb of St. Petersburg), Tolochinov spoke of the innate reflex as "unconditional," and of that to the remote stimulus as "conditional." In 1903, Pavlov brought the new line of research to the attention of physiologists generally during an international congress at Madrid, and he used these same words, stressing that "the main feature of the psychical experiment is its impermanence, its obvious capriciousness," because it is subject to inhibition of various kinds. He made the same point at Stockholm, in his acceptance of the Nobel prize, and again in England, in 1906, in delivering the Huxley lecture. But this time, by some error of translation, he used the words "conditioned" and "unconditioned," instead of conditional and unconditional. Yerkes and Morgulis (1909), in the first review of this material for American readers, remarked on the error in a footnote, but they elected to follow Pavlov's precedent. Thus a source of misunderstanding was introduced into English and American usage.

The context of Pavlov's discussion never leaves any doubt that the meaning he wished to convey is that of the words conditional and unconditional. He spoke of the conditional reflexes as "temporary connections," and he emphasized that they lack the certainty and regularity of occurrence of innate reflexes, which can by contrast be called unconditional, that is, sure to occur in response to the adequate stimulus despite other circumstances and conditions. One may, if one will, question whether any vertebrate reflex is so invariable that it deserves to be called unconditional. One cannot question Pavlov's meaning, which was that the new reflexes which were established by the procedure of paired stimulation were both temporary and variable in their manifestation. He was expressing the same thought which Sechenov had had as far back as 1856: that the response to a given stimulus is inconsistent whenever the cerebral hemispheres are involved in the reaction.

Nor did Pavlov have any doubt from the beginning, as is evident in his Madrid address of 1903, that the exploration of this inconsistency would require careful attention to the problems of neural inhibition. This aspect of Pavlov's research had no appeal to Watson and the other early behaviorists. They welcomed Pavlov's work for two reasons: first, because it provided a useful technique for the investigation of sensory discrimination in animals, and later (only after it had become clear that "frequency and recency" were inadequate as principles of learning) as a way of explaining associative learning without reference to consciousness. The *conditioned reflex*—the reflex which the experimenter produces by his arrangement of conditions—was the answer to the behaviorist's prayer for a device by which he could "predict and control" behavior, and it would have been wholly out of keeping with the Watsonian temperament to emphasize its *conditional* nature. Pavlov, the greater scientist, concentrated his attention on what he did not yet understand, on the element of inconsistency in the phenomenon he discovered, and this drew him inevitably into research on the nature of inhibition. (In order to be faithful to the spirit of Pavlov's writing, we shall replace the terms "conditioned reflex" and "conditioned stimulus," and the like, with "conditional reflex," "conditional stimulus," etc., wherever they appear in translations of Pavlov's work which will be quoted during this chapter.)

In his Madrid address, Pavlov stated that after secretion has begun in response to the sight of bread, it can be checked by the sight of meat. We are left in no doubt about his opinion that this is a phenomenon of inhibition, but it is unclear whether he thought that the inhibition arises because the dog does not characteristically salivate in response to meat, a moist food, or because of the "well-known fact that a very strong desire often inhibits certain special reflexes." The fact that the conditional reflex becomes weakened if it is repeated under conditions of nonfeeding, is described as a problem calling for investigation, but it is not yet regarded as an effect of inhibition. A number of other inhibitory phenomena are described, some specifically as inhibitions and others not, but no systematic presentation is attempted.

In 1909, Pavlov summarized the first ten years of research into conditional reflexes, and he gives us the following picture of his views on the nature and importance of inhibition, as they had developed up to that time.

> Since the center of the conditional reflexes is located in the higher part of the nervous system, where collision of numberless influences from the external world is always taking place, it is understandable that a never-ending struggle takes place between the various conditional reflexes, or a selection of them at any given moment. Hence—constant cases of inhibition of these reflexes. Three kinds of inhibition have now been established—simple, extinguishing, and conditional. Taken together they form the group of external inhibition, since they are based on the addition of a collateral external agent to the conditional stimulus. On the other hand, an already formed conditional reflex, because of its internal relations alone, is subject to constant fluctuations, even to complete disappearance for brief periods, i.e., is inhibited internally. For example, if even a very

old conditional reflex is repeated several times without being accompanied by the unconditional reflex, with whose help it was formed, it begins at once gradually but steadily to lose strength and, more or less quickly, is reduced to zero, i.e., if the conditional reflex, as a signal of the unconditional, begins to signalize incorrectly, it gradually loses its stimulating effect. This loss of effect occurs not by the destruction of the conditional reflex, but solely because of its temporary inhibition, since the conditional reflex thus extinguished is restored of itself after some time. There are still other cases of internal inhibition. Further experimentation revealed a new important side of the problem. It proved that, in addition to excitation and inhibition of excitation, inhibition of the inhibition is just as frequent, i.e., disinhibition. It is impossible to say which of these three acts is most important. It should be simply stated that all higher nervous activity, as manifested by the conditional reflexes, consists of a constant interchange, or to be more precise, equilibration of these three basic processes—excitation, inhibition and disinhibition (Pavlov, 1957, p. 213 f.).

Pavlov went on to discuss the work of the "analyzers"—a term which includes all of the neural and sensory structures by which stimuli are elaborated. This leads into the discussion of differentiation, and the statement that "differentiation develops as a result of an inhibitory process, as if through a suppression of all other parts of the analyzer except the given one. . . . If the equilibrium between the excitatory and inhibitory processes is broken down in favor of the former by the administration of stimulants such as caffeine, then the well-elaborated differentiation is immediately and sharply deranged, and in many cases disappears altogether, although temporarily."

Pavlov asked: "How is the temporary connection, the conditional reflex formed?" His answer is an approach to the theory of concentration of nerve impulses, which his critics contend should not seriously be considered as a statement of physiological facts, or even as a reasonable physiological hypothesis.

In the higher nervous system, when the process of formation of conditional reflexes occurs, the following procedure takes place: if a new, previously indifferent stimulus, upon entering the cerebral hemispheres, meets in the nervous system at that moment a focus of strong excitation, it begins to concentrate, as if working its way to this focus, and thence to the corresponding organ; thus it becomes a stimulus of that organ.

On the contrary, when there is no such focus, it disperses in the mass of cerebral hemispheres without producing any pronounced effect. Such, then, is the formulation of the fundamental law of the higher part of the nervous system (Pavlov, 1957, p. 211).

Not long afterward, Pavlov added sleep and hypnosis as forms of inhibition, because of the repeated experience of having animals fall asleep in their experimental harness, under conditions which produced strong internal inhibition. Three principal kinds of inhibition were now recognized. *Internal inhibition* is based on the relations existing among the factors directly involved in the conditional reflex and the unconditional reflex which was utilized in forming it. Its principal manifestation is the gradual extinction which takes place when the reflex is repeatedly exercised without reinforcement, and the clearest indication that an inhibitory process is involved is still the spontaneous restoration of the reflex during a period of rest following such extinction. *External inhibitions* are those which take place as a result of competition among stimuli which would normally lead to different reflexes than those directly involved in the training procedure. Stimuli which lead to orientation and defensive reflexes are especially effective. *Sleep* is regarded as a *protective inhibition* which results from fatigue of the neural elements and can be induced by repetitive stimulation of any kind. It tends to spread throughout the nervous system; but, when it is limited to certain areas, it constitutes hypnosis. In 1919, in one of his early ventures into the field of psychiatry, Pavlov defined catalepsy also as an "isolated inhibition of the motor cortex," and hence a kind of hypnosis. (Translations of all of Pavlov's papers referred to on the preceding pages may be found in Pavlov, 1957.)

In 1927, the English-reading world had its first opportunity to get a firsthand statement of Pavlov's theories, and the facts on which they were based, when Anrep translated Pavlov's revision of a series of lectures which he had delivered in 1924. The title of the Russian work was *Lectures on the Work of the Cerebral Hemispheres,* but it appeared in English with the inevitable misleading title, *Conditioned Reflexes* (Pavlov, 1927). The next year, a series of Pavlov's addresses, starting with the Madrid address in 1903 and ending with the Croonian lecture in 1928, also appeared in translation, as *Lectures on Conditioned Reflexes* (Pavlov, 1928). The translator of this volume was Horsley Gantt. Both books are "known" to all Western psychologists, but their reading in them has been extremely selective, and the fact that the experimental procedures and results as described did not seem to include all the methodological controls which psychologists usually expect made it a relatively easy matter to dismiss as unfounded hypothesis any conclusion not readily assimilated into the systematic views of the reader, whoever he might be. The doctrine of "conditioned reflexes," based on stimulus substitution, had readily become a foundation stone of behavioristic psychology, but the concept of inhibition was dismissed as unjustified. It is therefore not out of place to summarize the very extensive material on inhibition which appeared in the series of lectures translated by Anrep.

It is well to recognize at the outset what Pavlov stated near the end of the book: that he made no attempt to investigate the intimate nature of inhibition. He said: "In this research we were not concerned with the ultimate nature of excitation and inhibition as such. We took them as two fundamental properties, the two most important manifestations of activity, of the living nervous elements. . . . The primary aim of our research was the accurate determination and tabulation of different phases of the cortical activity—the absence or presence of an inhibitory or excitatory phase, the exact conditions under which the intensity of the excitatory or inhibitory process varied, and the mutual interrelation between these processes."

One might say that inhibition and excitation were, for Pavlov, *intervening variables*, in the sense defined by Tolman when he introduced that phrase. Pavlov might have avoided some confusions if this methodological clarification had been available to him, and his readers might have been less disturbed by the nonphysiological nature of his "physiological" hypotheses if they had been accustomed to think in terms of intervening variables. Pavlov might then have avoided slipping into hypotheses based on an implicit assumption that excitation and inhibition are two opposing forms of activity of the same nerve cells, and hence, for example, that inhibition is to be regarded as a result of cellular exhaustion. But there is little profit in dwelling on Pavlov's errors and confusions. We must read the record of his research, and that of his followers, for what it does contain—the evidence of simultaneously active excitatory and inhibitory processes which often seem to be contending for the control of behavior.

The first three lectures of *Conditioned Reflexes* include, in addition to much introductory material, virtually all that will be said regarding the formation of positive conditional reflexes. Even here, Pavlov found that he could not avoid mentioning certain inhibitory effects. For example, he warned that during the establishment of secondary conditional reflexes one must be careful to allow a generous interval of time between the new stimulus and the primary stimulus, if one is to avoid a totally different effect "which will be treated in the fifth lecture"—that is, conditional inhibition. The discussion of trace reflexes, where the response follows the stimulus after a considerable time interval, cannot be left without reference to the inhibition of delay, which will not be dealt with until Lecture VI.

The last part of Lecture III is given over to a discussion of external inhibition, that is, the inhibition which arises from the action of "any extra nervous excitation" which occurs. In the simplest case, "the appearance of any new stimulus immediately evokes the investigatory reflex and the animal fixes all its appropriate receptor organs upon the source of the disturbance. . . . The investigatory reflex is excited and the conditional reflex is in consequence inhibited." When the extraneous stimulus does not merely arouse the investigatory reflex, but some specialized reflex, "the resulting inhibition is extremely profound." Another source of external inhibition may be a bodily stimulus such as the need for micturition, which interferes with the performance of conditional reflexes. That is, the stimulus is external to the circumstances which usually accompany the reflex being observed, not external to the organism. Pavlov devoted only a few pages to these external inhibitors because, he said, this kind of inhibition was already well known to physiologists. However, these inhibitory phenomena are all of the kind which almost any Western psychologist would have been disposed to dismiss, at the time when the book appeared, as simple instances of conflict between two response tendencies, in which the performance of the readier response necessarily excludes the response which is incompatible with it. Outside of Russia, almost no one was ready to admit that such behavioral phenomena made it necessary to assume the existence of a process of inhibition in the brain. (It was at about this time that Sherrington defined the "central inhibitory state" as a factor in spinal reflex activity.)

It would not be misleading to say that the remaining twenty lectures deal with the problems of internal inhibition, that is, with inhibitory effects which result from relationships among the stimuli and the responses directly involved in the production of the conditional reflex. Certainly there is no chapter in which such problems do not enter, and few pages which can be read understandingly without a recognition of what Pavlov means by internal inhibition.

Lectures IV to VIII are devoted to four major manifestations of internal inhibition: extinction, conditional inhibition, delay, and differentiation. An important difference between internal and external inhibition is emphasized: "Whereas . . . external inhibition is produced on the very first application of an extra stimulus, internal inhibition on the other hand always develops progressively, quite often very slowly, and in many cases with difficulty." The experimental extinction of a conditional reflex, which takes place when the reflex is repeatedly exercised without reinforcement,[1] often progresses quite irregularly, and this is assumed to be due to the interference of minor incidental external inhibitions, which counteract the developing internal inhibition, and thus exert disinhibiting influence.

There are many evidences that extinction is an inhibitory process: (1) the spontaneous recovery of the conditional reflex after an interval of rest; (2) the fact that other conditional reflexes are weakened simultaneously, though to a lesser degree; (3) the fact that the "strength" of the reflex can be reduced below zero, by continuation of the extinction process, as shown by the slower spontaneous recovery after such extended extinction; (4) the existence of susceptibility to disinhibition—that is, the extinguished reflex will occur with full force if some sudden strong external stimulus is introduced; (5) the fact that extinction is slow in excitable dogs, and rapid in dogs of the quiet or inhibited type. All of these phenomena, and

[1] To avoid misunderstanding, let it be noted that in this chapter the term *reinforcement* is used throughout in the Pavlovian sense, as the administration of the unconditional stimulus, and not as implying the use of any "satisfier" or the occurrence of any "drive reduction."

others which we omit to mention, can be explained by the assumption that extinction is the manifestation of a special form of inhibition. It is of interest to recall that Ebbinghaus had long before demonstrated that forgetting is an active, not a passive process, and even Herbart had known, without benefit of experiment, that the strength of an "idea" can be reduced below zero.

Pavlov took up next the problem of conditional inhibition, and expressed regret that this was not more appropriately called "differential inhibition." Let us, therefore, change his sequence, and look next at the process of differentiation. When a stimulus begins to acquire the character of a positive conditional stimulus, the effect is at first generalized to similar stimuli of the same modality. But, with many repetitions of the conditional reflex, a process of differentiation takes place, so that ultimately the conditional reflex will be given only to stimuli which are very similar to the conditional stimulus which is actually in use. This process can be accelerated by what Pavlov calls the method of contrast, that is, by interspersing nonreinforced trials with differential stimuli. For example, a metronome beating 120 times a minute may be used as the positive stimulus, and a metronome beating sixty times a minute, or 240 times a minute, may be used as a differential stimulus in the early stages of training, with progressively finer discriminations being required as training progresses.

Pavlov's point is that when such differentiation takes place, either slowly and spontaneously or quickly, in accordance with a planned schedule, what happens is not that the differential or negative stimulus loses its conditional evocative power, but rather that it acquires a very definite and measurable inhibitory power. The fact that this effect may persist for a fair length of time makes it possible to demonstrate its inhibitory nature in the following manner. A given test stimulus, which under normal conditions always produces a positive response of known intensity, is applied first; the differentiated stimulus is applied next; then the test stimulus is applied again, and the reduction in salivary secretion is a measure of the persisting strength of the differential inhibition. Table 2 reproduces the data of such a demonstration, which serves at the same time to illustrate the type of evidence Pavlov offered for his generalizations, and which was rejected by many readers as possibly being

TABLE 2. Inhibition by a Differential Stimulus

Time	Stimulus Applied During 30 secs.	Salivary Secretion in Drops During 30 secs.	Remarks
12.10 P.M.	Tone	5	Reinforced
12.25 P.M.	Tone, ⅛ lower	0	Not reinforced
12.26 P.M.	Tone	0.5	Reinforced
12.56 P.M.	Tone	4	Reinforced

SOURCE: From Pavlov, *Conditioned Reflexes*, 1927, p. 125, based on an experiment by Beliakov. By permission of Clarendon Press.

based on arbitrary selections. In this instance, a dog has been trained to differentiate a difference of only one-eighth of a tone, and the application of the inhibitory stimulus causes a marked reduction in the response to the positive stimulus one minute later.

Pavlov made the extremely interesting point that the limits of differentiation for the animal are not determined by the limits of sensory discrimination (or analysis, in his terminology) but by the balance of excitatory and inhibitory processes. When an extremely fine discrimination is required, the animal may at first show himself capable of performing successfully, but after several repetitions the differentiation may break down, and with it all of the coarser differentiations which had been attained previously also disappear. "When the stage of minute differences between stimuli is reached, analysis of itself appears still feasible, but the relations existing between the excitatory and the inhibitory processes seem to present an insurmountable obstacle to its continued and permanent utilization by the animal for an appropriate responsive activity."

It is also possible to develop differentiations such that two stimuli presented together as a compound stimulus will have an inhibitory effect, although either stimulus alone will have an excitatory or positive effect; or contrariwise, that the compound stimulus shall be positive, and one or both of the stimuli given separately shall be inhibitory. But here we are obviously dealing with instances of conditional inhibition, and we can see the justice of Pavlov's statement that conditional inhibition is only a special kind of differentiation. Again, Pavlov emphasized that a conditional inhibitor is not merely a stimulus which, as a result of training, fails to evoke a reflex response, but that it is a stimulus which evokes a very definite inhibitory effect. We limit ourselves here to only one of Pavlov's arguments: When a stimulus has acquired the character of a conditional inhibitor, so that when it is paired with another positive stimulus it will tend to diminish the response to that stimulus (as a light paired with a metronome may be made an inhibitor for the secretion which otherwise occurs on presentation of the metronome beat), then the introduction of another stimulus which is not too strong, and can be expected to act as a disinhibitor, serves to negate the effect of the conditional inhibitor and thus restores the positive effect of the previously counteracted conditional stimulus. This disinhibiting effect shows that an inhibition, in the strict sense of the term, has been taking place. (Wagner's experiments with bees, cited in Chapter 4, constitute a specific example of disinhibition of this type.) The possibility of demonstrating such effects in strictly quantitative form represents one of the great advantages of working with salivary secretion as a response, rather than with the overt motor reflexes used by Bekhterev (1910).

Another manifestation of internal inhibition is the possibility of delaying the response to a conditional stimulus. For example, if during training a metronome is sounded for one minute before the reinforcement occurs, then the conditioned salivary secretion starts to flow about fifty seconds after the metronome begins to beat. Pavlov asked: Are we to suppose that the excitatory process itself begins after a long interval, or that it is present from the beginning, but is at first masked by a simultaneous inhibitory process? That the latter is the case is again demonstrated by the phenomenon of disinhibition—if an extraneous stimulus is introduced during the delay period, the inhibition of delay is at once inhibited, and the secretion commences. Furthermore, this secretion will be accompanied by the motor response which is appropriate to the stimulus being used. Pavlov emphasizes that "the extraneous stimulus acting on the positive phase of the reflex inhibits, and acting on the negative phase disinhibits, in either case, therefore, reversing the nervous process prevailing at the time." However, "the inhibitory process is more labile and more easily affected than the excitatory process, being influenced by stimuli of much weaker physiological strength." He also pointed out that it is possible to transfer inhibitory function from a primary to a secondary conditional inhibitor, by causing previously neutral stimuli to coincide with primary inhibitors.

We look next at the content of Lectures XIV to XVI, which deal with sleep and certain sleeplike states which sometimes arise in the course of experimentation. The occurrence of sleep in animals under the rather monotonous conditions of experimentation should not of itself be too surprising, for, as Pavlov pointed out to his lecture audience, "it is a common experience that man, when unused to an intensive mental life, usually falls into drowsiness and sleep when subjected to the accompanying monotonous stimuli, however unfortunate such drowsiness or sleep may be as to place and as to time." Nevertheless, the abruptness with which sleep sometimes overcame the experimental animals was surprising, and demanded explanation.

Pavlov arrived at the conclusion that sleep is merely a more generalized internal inhibition, or, to state it in other terms: "Internal inhibition during the alert state is nothing but a scattered sleep, sleep of separate groups of cellular structures; and sleep itself is nothing but internal inhibition which is widely irradiated, extending over the whole mass of the hemispheres and involving the lower centers of the brain as well. Thus internal inhibition in the alert state of the animal represents a regional distribution of sleep which is kept within bounds by the antagonistic process of excitation." Under experimental conditions, therefore, "internal inhibition invariably passes into sleep unless precautions are taken" and the appearance of sudden sleep means no more than that an inhibitory process has been evoked without a sufficiently strong excitatory process to delimit it. (The relation of this theory to other theories of sleep will be discussed in Chapter 11.)

From the theory of sleep as a form of internal inhibition it is an obvious step to the theory of hypnosis as a localized sleep—a theory already advanced more than once in the nineteenth century. Pavlov stated, furthermore, that if the inhibition embraces the entire cortex, but does not embrace the lower centers dealing with posture and equilibrium, then the animal is in a state of catalepsy. These hypotheses are less interesting, however, than certain experimentally induced transitional states first described by Razyenkov (or Rosenkov, in Anrep's transliteration). By using a positive and differential stimulus in immediate succession, Razyenkov (1959) brought about a condition which persisted for some days in which those stimuli which previously had strong positive effect became "weak," and those which previously had slight positive effects became "strong." He called this a *paradoxical phase.* It was followed by a period of shorter duration in which all the stimuli, regardless of intensity, produced equal effects, and this was called the *phase of equalization.* These experiences recalled certain observations made many years before by Shishlo, that animals in a state of drowsiness would sometimes respond positively to negative stimuli, and negatively, that is with inhibition, to positive stimuli. Fitted into the picture provided by the later experiments, this was now called the *ultraparadoxical phase.* Although the explanation of these effects is unclear, Pavlov had no doubt that they are based on the distribution of inhibition in the cortex in transitional states between alertness and sleep.

We turn back now to consider the content of Lectures IX to XIII, which are concerned with interactions between excitation and inhibition in the cortex. The theory of irradiation and concentration of cortical processes is presented. Probably no one would contest the statement that there is a tendency for the excitatory process to irradiate, but Pavlov described a series of experiments (by Krasnogorsky, Anrep, Kogan, Ivanov-Smolensky, and others) purporting to demonstrate irradiation of the inhibitory process. This was a surprising discovery, because inhibition had always been thought of as a nonpropagating phenomenon. We select Anrep's work for purposes of illustration, because the data for this experiment are more completely presented. He first established a conditional salivary reflex to tactile stimulation of any point on the skin. Then one point, between the neck and the chest, was selected for use in an inhibitory connection with a buzzer, and when it was used in this combination it was not reinforced. In each of a series of test experiments, the strength of response to one of the positive points would be tested first, then the inhibitory combination stimulus was applied, and at intervals thereafter the strength of response at the positive point was retested. Table 3 shows the strength of the inhibitory effect at various positive points and at different intervals of time

TABLE 3. Irradiation of Inhibition

Place Stimulated	Percentage of Inhibition Observed at Different Intervals of Time						
	0″	15″	30″	45″	60″	120″	180″
Forelimb	30		54		29	19	10
Fore paw	45		66		39	22	13
Between neck and chest[a]	91		75		50	37	17
Middle of chest	52	58	69	57	45	34	13
Pelvis	37		65		39	22	13
Thigh	27		57		23	17	11
Hind paw	19	26	31	22	20	10	7

[a] Place primarily inhibited.

SOURCE: From Pavlov, *Conditioned Reflexes,* 1927, p. 163, based on an experiment by Anrep (1923). By permission of Clarendon Press.

after administration of the inhibitory combination, based on averaged results under each condition. In general, the inhibitory effect declines with distance from the inhibitory point, as well as with time. Except at the point where the inhibitory combination had been applied, the inhibition does not reach its maximal strength until after an interval of about 30 seconds.

On the basis of many such experiments, Pavlov concluded that the process of inhibition irradiates, or spreads through the cortex, and then recedes again or concentrates to the point of origin, the phase of concentration being slower than the phase of irradiation. Although these results may be open to some different interpretations, it is of interest to point out that M. J. Bass and Hull (1934) did essentially the same experiment with human subjects using the galvanic skin reflex. Their procedure was to use contact on the upper back, the lower back, the thigh, or the calf as conditional stimulus reinforced by an electric shock, then to subject one point to experimental extinction and thereafter measure the responses produced by stimulation at the other points. The resulting gradients were found to be in agreement with predictions based on Pavlov's doctrine.

Lecture XI gives evidence that "induction," as described by Sherrington for spinal inhibition, also occurs in the cortex. A localized inhibitory effect evokes an excitatory process in the surrounding region, and this is called "positive induction." A localized excitatory process evokes an inhibitory process in the surrounding region, and this is called "negative induction." There is also a temporal pattern to induction—an inhibition which is aroused following an excitation will be more strongly inhibiting than it would otherwise be, and vice versa. Needless to say, the interaction of these induction effects with the irradiation and concentration of excitation and inhibition produces very complex patterns of inhibition. One consequence is a wavelike fluctuation of inhibitory effects after the cessation of an inhibitory stimulus. The biological value of the process of induction, as Pavlov saw it, is that it tends to delimit the spread of both inhibition and excitation, favoring the establishment of localized patterns which are essential to complex forms of response. In later years the Pavlov school started to study "dynamic stereotypes" consisting of organized sequences of positive and inhibitory stimuli, in which such interactional effects were quite important.

Lectures XVII and XVIII present Pavlov's theory of nervous types. Although four types are described, corresponding roughly to the so-called Hippocratic temperaments, we shall limit ourselves here to the two main types, the so-called excitable and inhibited types of nervous system, and the kinds of functional disturbance which are characteristic of these two types of dogs, under conditions of experimentally induced "neurosis." The excitable dogs are highly reactive and aggressive under ordinary conditions; but, surprisingly, they are the animals most prone to drowsiness under the monotony of experimental conditions, and they cannot be used successfully as experimental animals except by providing them with a variety of stimuli, avoiding long pauses, and simultaneously developing both excitatory and inhibitory reflexes. At the other extreme are the inhibited dogs, which are generally timid in their behavior, need uniform conditions, but tolerate these better and are therefore much more resistive to sleep under experimental conditions. Pavlov stated that the excitatory process is dominant in the first type and the inhibitory process in the second, and that it is possible to classify all dogs as tending in one direction or the other, although of course most do not belong to the extreme types.

Adaptive behavior, whether in the experimental laboratory or under the ordinary conditions of living, requires a balance of the inhibitory and excitatory processes, which each animal maintains as long as conditions are not too difficult, although the tendency to a dominance of excitation or of inhibition is apparent in the general manner of behaving. However, there are certain conditions under which the maintenance of this balance becomes impossible, and in the pathological behavior which results the animal's basic type shows itself, in a strong and excessive predominance of excitation or inhibition, as the case may be. One situation which can lead to such loss of control arises when a painful stimulus—an electric shock—is used as the conditional stimulus for alimentary salivation. Obviously, such training requires strong inhibitory control of the innate motor defensive reflexes. After successfully training an excitable animal in this manner, so that it responded with alimentary salivation even to quite strong electrical shock applied at a given spot, Erofeeva made the attempt to generalize the reflex, by applying the shock to other spots on the skin. Although this appeared to be proceeding successfully, suddenly "everything underwent an abrupt and complete change. No trace of the alimentary reaction was left; instead only a most violent defense reaction was present," even in response to very weak stimuli. The experiment was repeated on other animals, with similar results.

Another and quite different situation which leads to pathological behavior has already been mentioned in our discussion of differentiation: When very fine discrimination is demanded, the animal may lose control, and fail even to perform the coarse discriminations which it had mastered perfectly long before.

The single interpretation placed upon both sets of results is that "under certain conditions the clashing of excitation with inhibition led to a profound disturbance of the usual balance between these two processes, and led in a greater or less degree and for a longer or shorter time to pathological disturbances of the nervous system. . . . A balance of the two antagonistic processes was satisfactorily maintained until a certain critical stage was reached, when, under the stress of the delicate antagonistic relations of the stimuli, the further adjustment of the balance became impossible and finally gave way to an undisputed predominance of one of them, producing a pathological state."

When such pathology results, excitable animals become excessively excitable, losing all control because they react violently to the slightest stimulation, and inhibited dogs become excessively inhibited, so that they fail to respond at all to even very strong stimuli.

The characterization of the typical responses of these two types has been based in large part on the work of Petrova, who, it may be remarked, was exceptional among Pavlov's coworkers in that she had a previous background as a clinician. Her previous work with children doubtless prepared her for the concept that some individuals are temperamentally disposed to over-react, while others are relatively nonreactive. Selecting dogs of extreme excitable and inhibited types, she trained both in a series of long-delay reflexes, with intervals up to three minutes—a procedure involving much judicious management with the excitable dog, though relatively easy for the inhibited one. Both animals were also trained in a number of conditional inhibitory reflexes. Under stress, the inhibitory reflexes of the excitable dog, and the positive reflexes of the inhibited dog, were the first to be upset.

Pavlov mentioned that the use of bromides is an effective therapy for the pathological excitations. From the nature of the results, he deduced that "bromides should not be regarded as sedatives diminishing the excitability of the central nervous system; they simply regulate the activity of the nervous system by strengthening the intensity of internal inhibitions." This conclusion represents an insightful anticipation of the findings of recent neuropharmacology, that many sedating drugs obtain their effects by promoting inhibition, rather than by reducing excitation (see Chapter 15).

Lectures XIX to XXI deal with the effects of surgically produced lesions, and of the scars consequent upon them. The material in these chapters has probably been read in the past with an eye chiefly to its implications as regards localization of functions in the cortex. Pavlov believed strongly in the doctrine of localization—a point of view which was long out of favor among American psychologists, because of Lashley's influence. Earlier, Pavlov had described the cortex as "a mosaic of functions," in which each conditional reflex "must have definite representation in the cerebral cortex in one or another definite group of cells." Now, basing himself largely on the work of Zeliony with decorticate dogs, he takes the position that the cortex is essential for development of conditional reflexes—a needlessly sweeping conclusion which was to exercise a deterrent influence on the future development of the theory of conditioning. A variety of experiments by other investigators show how extirpation of one portion of the cortex or another restricts the range of stimuli to which the animal can respond conditionally, or the degree of differentiation that can be achieved.

Our present interest, however, is primarily in Pavlov's deductions regarding the nature of inhibition. He pointed out, for example, that when conditional reflexes get reestablished some time after the immediate effect of the surgery has worn off, "they are found not only to regain their normal strength but often to exceed it, often also becoming considerably more stable than before. The inhibitory process, on the other hand, grows weaker." Illustrations of the weakening of inhibition are: "In many dogs there is observed after the operation a very definite prolongation of the salivary secretion which follows the administration of an unconditional stimulus: the length of time required for complete extinction of the reflex also becomes in many dogs very prolonged: the development of differentiations and conditional inhibitions becomes more difficult and very often salivary secretion is observed in between the application of the stimuli—this never happening before." Also, "the inhibitory process becomes inert; and so to speak inflexible," so that it does not become concentrated in the same manner as in the normal animal. Also, the best indicator of an approaching convulsion, to which such operated animals are susceptible, is "in the disappearance of differentiations, i.e., in a disturbance in the inhibitory process."

After describing the influence of various brain lesions on the acquisition and performance of conditional reflexes, and on behavior generally, Pavlov says that these observations tend to confirm the generally accepted theories, "but what our experiments do most emphatically refute is the doctrine of special 'association' centers, or, more generally, of the existence in the hemispheres of some special area on which the higher functions of the nervous system depend." This conclusion is consistent with the picture of inhibition given by all of his work, namely, that it is a phenomenon which is as universal as excitation, and which has no special seat in the brain.

The concluding lectures deal with new problems under investigation, and with the possibility of applying what had been learned about the pathological behavior of dogs, and the techniques of their management in different types of animals, to the treatment of analogous disturbances in humans. This material was developed more extensively in later years, becoming the principal focus of Pavlov's activities after about 1930. (See Ivanov-Smolensky, 1954.)

However, a careful reader would also have found mentions that work had been begun with permanently implanted electrodes, and that the effects of various schedules of partial reinforcement were being investigated—methodological hints which would have been taken up more promptly by research workers elsewhere if they had been less skeptical about Pavlovian method in general.

Pavlov's book is a condensation of more than a quarter of a century of research, drawing on the contributions of scores of competent collaborators, whose names have for the most part been omitted in this synoptic account. It lacks the finality of Sherrington's great work, but it has a much broader scope, and serves throughout to open problems rather than to close them. It is much more than a study of conditioned reflexes, in the sense in which that phrase is usually understood by psychologists. Rather, making use of conditional reflexes as a methodological technique, it is a study of the interaction of excitatory and inhibitory reaction tendencies, in which inhibitory tendencies receive the greater share of attention. It demonstrates, over and over again, the absolute necessity of taking the inhibitory process into account whenever we wish to explain *any* response to *any* stimulus. If the conditioned-response approach to the analysis of behavior has seemed relatively sterile, the responsibility for this certainly does not rest with Pavlov and his collaborators, who adequately demonstrated the shortcomings of any account of behavior in terms of excitatory stimulus-response bonds, but with us, for whom the record of their research was spread out thirty-five years ago, and who failed to note that on its every page inhibitions are an essential part of all adaptive behavior.

RIVALS AND FOLLOWERS OF PAVLOV 10

The interest in inhibition which was initiated by Sechenov and continued by Wedensky and Pavlov has remained characteristic of all Russian physiological psychology. Regretfully, we must forego as beyond our powers the forbidding task of summarizing the truly vast literature of this subject. We shall try only to indicate some of the main lines of its development, by discussing the work of perhaps half a dozen outstanding men, some of whom may be called rivals of Pavlov, some his critics, and some his followers.

Among the rivals, Bekhterev is well known for his advocacy of an objective psychology under the label of "reflexology," and for his introduction in 1907 of a method of studying what he called motor associative reflexes, by the technique generally called instrumental conditioning in American parlance. This innovation had undoubted value, but its importance was reduced by the later development of techniques for conditioning of pupillary and galvanic skin reflexes, methods which are applicable to human subjects and which share with the salivary reflex the advantage of being free from voluntary control by the subject. History does not share Bekhterev's partisan opinion that instrumental conditioning was a more valuable scientific tool than salivary conditioning.

With respect to our central problem, inhibition, Bekhterev contributed little that was of importance. As a neurologist, he had no doubts about the reality of inhibition, but he made little use of it in his early work. The mentions of inhibition in *Objektive Psychologie* (Bekhterev, 1910) are a few sweeping generalizations, his major emphasis being on the establishment of associative bonds. Inhibition assumed a more important role in his later writings, and without a careful study of original publications it would be reckless to assign precise credits to the Pavlov and Bekhterev laboratories, which in their early years were only different departments in the same medical school. However, a reading of the *General Principles of Reflexology* (1928) gives the impression that Bekhterev has little more to offer, at least in regard to the role of inhibition in behavior, than restatement of some Pavlovian principles, with fresh demonstrations based on his own technique. In this book, the role of inhibition is almost entirely its obvious function of suppression, and although there is occasional mention of release from inhibitions, there is no systematic use of inhibition as a releasing force. Reflexology is primarily a behaviorally oriented association psychology.

Bekhterev was a dynamic organizer and a prolific writer. He exerted great influence on the improvement of hospitals for the mentally ill in Russia. He also made notable contributions to neuroanatomy; and the nucleus of Bekhterev, a part of the vestibular apparatus, preserves his name for a select posterity. But this is a small monument for a man whose near-greatness was dwarfed by his ambition. Unfortunately, there was more bombast than substance in the attempt to immortalize himself as the father of a new science of "reflexology"—perhaps in unconscious imitation of Wundt, who had been his teacher in psychology, and who attained fame a generation earlier by proclaiming the new science of physiological psychology. His books create an impression of unlimited egotism. Pavlov never mentions Bekhterev; Bekhterev mentions Pavlov infrequently, and only when he has an opportunity to point out what he regards as an error or limitation—as, for example, that although workers in Pavlov's laboratory did not succeed in demonstrating color vision in dogs, a worker in Bekhterev's laboratory did! Science and humility walk hand in hand—envy is a source of confusion.

A very different sort of challenge to Pavlov came from the adherents of the Wedensky school, which is now commonly also called the Wedensky-Ukhtomsky school. Their attitude towards Pavlov appears plainly, if only between the lines, in the following sentences which were spoken by Biryukov, in 1958, at a meeting commemorating the 100th anniversay of Sherrington's birth. After the usual proudly patriotic reference to Sechenov's priority in the study of inhibition, he said: "Subsequently, the investigations of central inhibition advanced in two directions. One of these was associated with the English school of Sherrington, which concerned itself with the interrelationship between excitatory and inhibitory processes, and the other, directed more to discovery of the nature of the excitation and inhibition processes, was the work of the Russian school of N. E. Wedensky." One cannot miss the intent behind the conspicuous failure to mention Pavlov as in the same rank with these two, as well as the ascription to Sherrington's school of pre-eminence in just that area which Pavlov had defined for himself.

Two of the outstanding students of Wedensky are Ukhtomski and Beritov. Both have made important theoretical contributions to the literature of our subject. It is Beritov who has gained the greater reputation abroad, largely because his work fits better into the traditions of the western school. Razran, in 1950, speaks of him as "probably the most critical, most informed, and most psychological of all Soviet physiologists," and he reports that Lashley, who was always severely critical of Pavlov, expressed in conversation his high regard for Beritov. His critique of Pavlov appears especially in the important monograph, *Ueber die individuell-erworbene Tätigkeit des Zentralnervensystems* (1927). As one sees in the title, Pavlov's *conditional reflexes*, Bekhterev's *association reflexes*, are for Beritov *individual reflexes*, which differ from other reflexes in their history, but not in their nature. He is extremely critical of both other men, because "according to Pavlov and Bekhterev every phenomenon of cessation of an individual reflex is determined by an inhibition." He rejects the Pavlovian concepts of irradiation and concentration, because, he says, there is absolutely no basis for supposing that one excited point can draw to itself the excitation of other points, and because it is quite absurd to suppose that an inhibition which arises from exhaustion of some neural elements—as Pavlov assumes to be the case for internal inhibition—can spread to other portions of the brain which have done no work.

Subsequently, Beritov developed a "neuropil theory" of inhibition, basing himself in part on Herrick's anatomical studies of the spinal neuropil, that is, the existence on lower levels of a reticular formation less richly developed than in the brain stem, but nevertheless important to brain function. Beritov makes this the source of a local inhibition, the only kind he will acknowledge, being true to the Wedensky principle that inhibition is a kind of nonpropagating excitation. According to Beritov, the irradiation of excitation from a neuron into the surrounding neuropil causes a reduction in the excitability of surrounding cells, and therefore it can have only a very limited spread. Since diffuse irradiation is thus limited, a directed propagation to distant parts becomes possible. Furthermore, Beritov believes that this nonspecific local inhibition suffices to explain the inhibition of antagonistic muscles, as described by Sherrington. In place of reciprocal inhibition, he proposes a law of "conjugate excitation." (One can readily see why Lashley would have welcomed this parsimonious thinking, which apparently does away with the need for a whole class of innate neural bonds.) In his *General Physiology of the Muscular and Nervous System* (1948), Beritov not only rejects the Pavlovian theory of inhibition, but he also asserts that the prevailing view among physiologists generally, that the cerebral cortex exercises an inhibitory influence on the lower centers, is based on misinterpretation of the experimental evidence. The facts of observation, he says, support the view that all cortical activity is facilitatory.

More recently, Beritov and Roitbak (1955) developed a "dendritic theory" of inhibition, which can be regarded as a further development of the neuropil theory, in that it still seeks to explain inhibition as a kind of reduced excitability produced by lesser excitations. According to this theory, the effective excitation of a neuron must take place via the synaptic terminations on the cell body and on the axon hillock, whereas impulses which reach the neuron via synaptic terminations on the dendrites set up slow potentials which are incapable of exciting the neuron to discharge, but which do succeed in reducing the excitability of the postsynaptic surfaces of the other synapses, and thus tend to block the processes which would lead to cell discharge. (There is some independent evidence, which we shall not describe here, that inhibitory synapses on motoneurons tend to be placed on the dendrites rather than the cell body (Sprague, 1958). However, the inhibitory axon collaterals described by Retzlaff (1957) seemed to synapse on the axon hillock of the antagonistic cell.) Roitbak (1955) says: "Excitation and inhibition of the nerve cell in the central nervous system are, in our view, completely different processes. . . . Inhibition of the cell is brought about, we believe, by the development in the dendrites of local potentials of excitation. It is suggested that these potentials form currents which extend electronically along the dendrites, reach the cell, and passing through it, act on the adjacent synapses and produce in them anelectrotonic lowering of their excitability and so block the transmission of the excitation through them to the cell." This theory is obviously related to the original Wedensky concept of inhibition as a reduction of lability. An extended statement of evidence for the theory is given in Roitbak (1956).

This use of slow potentials which reduce excitability is clearly related to the original Wedensky theory of parabiotic inhibition. Beritov and Roitbak also recognize that such inhibitory effects can be produced in cortical cells, by nonspecific afferents from the brain stem reticular formation (which after all is only the most conspicuous part of the spinal neuropil) terminating on the dendrites of pyramidal neurones. However, Beritov apparently still rejects the idea that inhibition can play a selective or directive role in behavior, and continues to regard it as constituting only a diffuse background for specific excitatory effects. The function of all inhibition, as Beritov sees it, is comparable to the limiting function of induction in Pavlov's system. Beritov apparently also clings to the electrical theory of synaptic transmission, and looks upon the neurotransmitters as only chemical agents which facilitate synaptic transmission, rather than being essential to it.

Ukhtomsky, though less well known outside of the Soviet Union, has considerable prestige within it, as can be inferred from the use of his name in designating the Wedensky-Ukhtomsky school of physiology. From this one can also infer that he clings more closely to the original Wedensky theories. His most important contribution is one which has direct relevance to psychological problems—the "principal of the dominant." His development of this theory was initiated by an observation, in 1904, that if the motor cortex of an experimental animal is stimulated at a point which would ordinarily bring about the flexion or extension of a given limb, but this stimulation takes place at a time when the rectum of the animal is full, so that it is physiologically close to the act of defecation, then the effect of the stimulation is not to cause a movement of the limb, but to facilitate the defecation. Another example of a dominant, which in this case is produced by hormonal influences, is the grasping reflex of the male frog during the mating season, when this reflex is readily elicited by almost any object.

To explain such effects, Ukhtomsky emphasized that the response which appears at any time is an expression of the dynamic interrelationships in the entire nervous system. The nervous system is like a complex of many funnels, each of which terminates in what Sherrington calls the "final common path." The outcome of a stimulation depends on response readiness throughout this system. There is nothing very special about the relationships between anatomical antagonists, since other responses also stand in reciprocal relationship to each other, and can be mutually inhibiting. "Only a central nervous system in complete equilibrium reacts to a given stimulus in a constant manner. If the equilibrium is disturbed by the presence of a temporary, but sufficiently persevering excitation, the same stimulus will evoke an essentially different reaction. . . . A sufficiently *persistent excitation,* which is taking place in the centers at a given moment, takes on the significance of a governing factor in the work of the other centers: it accumulates to itself the excitation of remote points, but inhibits the capacity of other centers to react to impulses *which have a direct relationship to them.*" (Ukhtomsky, 1925.)

Ukhtomsky regards as a confirmation of this theory Beritov's finding, in 1911, that if strychnine is applied to the spinal cord of an animal, reflexes at that level can be elicited by stimuli which would not otherwise have this effect. Of course, this interpretation is based on the assumption that strychnine is a directly exciting agent, which we now know not to be the case.

Inevitably, this theory was compared to McDougall's outdated drainage theory of inhibition, but Ukhtomsky (1926b) rejects this comparison. In another article (1926a) he emphasizes the distinction, which does not exist for McDougall, between excitation and excitability. "What makes a center dominant is *not the strength* of excitation in the center at the moment when some chance impulse reaches it, but the *capacity to increase* (to nourish) its excitation on the occasion of a chance impulse."

There are four ways in which a dominant may be terminated. If it is directed toward a consummatory act, such as defecation, then the performance of the act is an *endogenous* termination of the dominant. If conditions give rise to a new dominant, this represents an *exogenous* termination. (The parallel to internal and external inhibition is obvious.) Cortical inhibition of the dominant probably also takes place, but in view of the demonstrated fact that a dominant is able to inhibit voluntary motor impulses of cortical origin, it seems more likely that "the cortex fights against the dominants more successfully, not by attacking them directly, but by establishing new compensating dominants in the centers." Lastly, the action of impulses which facilitate the dominant also "prepare its inhibition and bring it to a termination." (This process is comparable to negative induction.) As the dominant fades away, the range of stimuli which can facilitate it becomes progressively narrowed, and the range of other reactions which it inhibits likewise becomes more restricted; however, once having been evoked, it is more easily reestablished. Events of the individual history tend to restrict the range of stimuli which are capable of facilitating a given dominant, and these stimuli come to evoke it more and more selectively (1925).

Ukhtomsky (1934) says that the concept of lability is central to all the work of the Wedensky-Ukhtomsky school; and elsewhere (1937) that they "do not speak of preformed coordinations of ready reflexes, but of coordinations which take place and unfold in the course of activity. Coordination is something always arising, being built again and again."

The reader may already have noticed that the phenomena of the dominant are all easily explained by the assumption that the preparation for an act involves an initial stage of partial disinhibition. This, of course, is what was achieved by Beritov's local application of strychnine to a portion of the spinal cord; this must be assumed in connection with the preparation for defecation or swallowing or any other consummatory reflex; and it has been our hypothesis, first stated at the close of Chapter 3, that the regulatory control of any act involves a pattern of disinhibitions, rather than of excitations. The "readied" act, which can be triggered by a large variety of excitant stimuli, is the partly disinhibited act. To assume a "motor set" in a reaction-time experiment represents one simple form of such preparatory disinhibition; Exner's *bahnung* is partial disinhibition; the contemplation of almost any action represents a form of preparatory disinhibition. There are acts, such as defecation, which are rarely triggered suddenly, except in abnormal cases, but which are prepared by the successive removal of several inhibitions, at different levels, before the final release. It is therefore particularly appropriate that the act of defecation should have figured in Ukhtomsky's first discovery of the "dominant." But it offers no new problem for us, and actually provides us with additional evidence of the importance of disinhibition.

Another outspoken critic of Pavlov is the Polish scientist, Jerzy Konorski. He perhaps personifies better than any other man the values of international cooperation and interdisciplinary research in the behavioral sciences. He studied with Pavlov in Leningrad, is head of the department of neurophysiology at the Nencki Institute of Experimental Biology in Warsaw, and is best known to Americans for his collaborative article with S. Miller (Konorski and Miller, 1937)—one of his many publications in the English language—which made the distinction between type I (classical) and type II (instrumental) conditioning. His comprehensive discussion of conditioning theory, *Conditioned Reflexes and Neuron Organization* (Konorski, 1948), is dedicated jointly to Pavlov and Sherrington. Basing himself on the more fundamental neurological researches of the English scientist, who devoted his studies primarily to the spinal reflexes of decerebrate animals, Konorski virtually rejects as fiction the entire quasineurological theory enunciated by Pavlov, which went so far beyond its empirical foundations. Yet he recognizes also the brilliance of Pavlov's approach to the more plastic characteristics of the higher nervous structures, and undertakes to overhaul conditioning theory in order to bring it into agreement with the facts of neuron theory. This position is in general similar to that of Beritov, but Konorski's critique of Pavlov appears to us to have been more constructive, and in any case his researches have a more direct interest for psychologists than do those of Beritov.

Pavlov had assumed that excitation and inhibition occur in a given "center" as a result of metabolic activities correlated with the state of the organism, its past experience with particular stimuli, and the like. Both processes are said to irradiate to other cortical centers or even, as in the case of sleep, to subcortical ganglia. The establishment of conditional reflexes was assumed to rest on such irradiation from one center (representing the conditional stimulus) to another center (representing the unconditional stimulus). Konorski rejects this hypothesis as not in accord with either the facts of conditioning or the known principles of neural activity. One of his objections is that this theory forces us to assume that both excitation and inhibition occur simultaneously in the same cells, in even the simplest conditioning phenomena. (While Pavlov's conception of the nature of inhibition was false, it did agree in a formal sense with much that has since been learned, and it is interesting to observe that our present knowledge of the process indicates that it does exist simultaneously with excitation, in the same cells.)

For Konorski, the important changes which occur during acquisition or extinction of conditional reflexes take place *between* the centers, not *in* them. One center becomes coupled with another because there is an increase in the number of functional synaptic connections on the multiple pathways which potentially connect them, which increases the "transmissibility" of those pathways. In the case of an excitatory conditional reflex, the coupling occurs because both centers are simultaneously excited. In the formation of an inhibitory conditional reflex, a stable excitation in the conditional center is accompanied by a decreasing excitation in the unconditional center. In either case, there is an increase in the number of functional synaptic connections between the two centers, although in one case these are of an excitatory nature, and in the other case of an inhibitory nature. Since the potential number of such functional connections is finite, their increase must be an inverse function of those already operative. Their number approaches an asymptote, a level at which the relationship between the centers is said to have reached saturation. Certain "inborn reflexes" are invariable because the "interneuronic connections have reached the saturation point." This schema obviously provides a basis for a stochastic model of conditioning, but Konorski is concerned with understanding the process itself, rather than with predictions of behavior on the basis of a formal schema.

Even early in the formation of a conditional reflex, the response may be maximal to strong stimulation. Further training does not merely increase the number of connections, but consolidates those which are already established by making them impervious to external inhibitors. However, when the conditional stimulus is not reinforced, connections are formed through inhibitory synapses and the conditional reflex may not be evoked. Thus it is possible to form both excitatory and inhibitory connections between the same centers, and these give rise to a kind of conflict—which shows itself, for instance, in the latency of the response—when the conditional stimulus is presented. The outcome depends in the last analysis on whether the excitatory synapses contribute more to the transmission than do those involved in inhibition.

What happens when a conditional reflex is reestablished after extinction? One might suppose that if the excitatory connections had reached their saturation point, and inhibitory connections were established subsequently during the period of extinction, then the existence of these would make it impossible to reestablish the reflex in its former strength. However, Konorski believes that the effect of establishing functional inhibitory synapses may be to increase the receptor capacities of the cell, so that it becomes possible to establish new excitatory synaptic connections, that is, to reach a higher saturation point. Thus the role of inhibition is not limited to acting as an interference or antagonist to excitation, but may even indirectly foster excitatory processes. If this hypothesis were confirmed, it might help to explain such puzzling phenomena as the effects of intermittent reinforcement schedules.

Konorski's extensive theoretical contributions, which have only been hinted at in these paragraphs, deserve the most serious consideration; and fortunately they are available in numerous English-language publications.

We turn now to those who regard themselves as loyal continuators of the Pavlov tradition, and who present their own work as extensions of Pavlov's teachings and not as amendments. However, the distinction is one of form rather than substance, for it is inevitable that any vigorous school of empirical investigation will uncover errors as well as new facts.

Of the many important developments which have taken place within the Pavlov school, we shall mention only some which have emphasized the importance of subcortical processes in the control of behavior. Pavlov himself asserted as a fact that the establishment of conditional reflexes always involves the participation of the cerebral cortex, and apparently he never abandoned the view that they always depend on establishment of new "temporary connections" between cortical points. Furthermore, he seems also to have implied that subcortical tissue does not possess similar plasticity, and does not participate in the establishment of new "connections." His followers have nevertheless provided abundant experimental demonstration of the influence of brain stem processes on the performance of conditional as well as unconditional reflexes. But the interpretation of these results has often been confused by reluctance to venture upon any statement which could be construed as a correction rather than an extension of Pavlov's own ideas.

In 1921, Kunstman and Orbeli observed that if the afferent fibers from the hind limb of a dog are severed, not only is there no motor paralysis, but on the contrary the limb becomes more active. It will tend to move in the rhythm of respiration, and when the dog eats, it carries out an endless succession of flexions and extensions, abductions and adductions, as a kind of somatic reflection of the process of eating. They reasoned that evidently an important function of the afferent innervation had been to inhibit the effect of excitations arising elsewhere in the central nervous system and spreading indiscriminately to all motor outlets, except as it is limited and channelled by inhibitions. Orbeli reasoned further that all afferent stimulation must play a similar role, and that the development of reflex specificity in the course of ontogenetic development probably depends in large part on the appearance of new kinds of afferentation, stage by stage.

Orbeli (1945) mentions some high points in the work that had been done up to that time on the influence of extracortical factors on higher nervous processes. Asratyan studied the effect of destruction of the cervical sympathetic ganglia, and found (quoted by Orbeli, 1945) that this led to "a reduction in the strength of the excitatory process in the central nervous system, in the cerebral cortex, and along with this, and apparently as a consequence thereof, a certain predominance of the inhibitory processes, disturbing the equilibrium between the inhibitory and excitatory processes in favor of inhibition." This effect was long lasting. Deryabin found that a destruction of subthalamic tissue, with no injury to the cortex, nevertheless resulted in the loss of all conditional alimentary reflexes, which could not be reestablished for many months (from Orbeli, 1945). Nevertheless, defensive reflexes could be established, and the alimentary reflexes functioned, though in weakened form, after administration of caffeine, which tends to strengthen the excitatory process. Orbeli also reports that Petrova found that administration of sympathomimetic substances, such as ephedrine, produced results opposite to those which had resulted from Asratyan's destruction of the cervical sympathetic ganglia, tending to strengthen the capacity for differentiation. After this survey, Orbeli ends with the almost apologetic conclusion that "although these results cannot be considered as basic for the investigation of higher nervous processes, they are nevertheless essential"—that is, that research on the subcortical processes should not be frowned upon, because it will help in the interpretation of facts obtained from the more direct study of the all-important cerebral hemispheres.

Anokhin is a prominent member of the Pavlovian school who has developed a theory of inhibition which departs in many respects from that of Pavlov, and which makes a serious effort to integrate Ukhtomsky's concept of the dominant, the work of Orbeli and others on the importance of visceral processes, and recent research relating to the functions of the reticular formation. Pavlov, it will be recalled, expressed confidence that, ultimately, internal and external inhibitions would be explained as manifestations of a single underlying process. He apparently believed that this process expresses itself more directly in the various forms of internal inhibition, and above all in sleep, than in external inhibition. Although Anokhin's recent book is titled *Internal Inhibition as a Problem of Psychology* (1958), his work may be said to take the opposite direction—i.e., to explain all inhibitory phenomena as manifestations of external inhibition. Indeed, it may be regarded as a detailed elaboration of the theoretical position taken by Münsterberg long ago, namely, that the sole source of inhibition is the incompatibility of actions.

Anokhin (1958) asks: "Why does the non-reinforcement of a conditional stimulus transform the process of conditional excitation into a process of conditional inhibition?" His method of dealing with this problem is psychological rather than physiological, since he dismisses the study of the synaptic nature of inhibition as irrelevant, and develops his answer largely in behavioral terms. He points out that although Pavlov spoke of the conflict of inhibitory and excitatory processes, whenever he chose an example to illustrate this conflict, it also involved an actual conflict of behavioral tendencies. When we "suppress" an action, some reaction tendency is being suppressed, and the conflict is not merely between excitation and inhibition, but between two systems of excitation. Very often the inhibiting system is the "orientation reflex" or the "investigatory reflex," which Pavlov himself mentioned as participating in the external inhibition of conditional reflexes. Anokhin tries to show that all inhibition has this same character. By thus accepting the idea that inhibition always arises from a conflct of excitations, he is accepting the basic postulate of the Wedensky school.

Anokhin says that the behavioral repertoire of the animal includes certain important "total patterns of response," of which the orientation-investigation response is only one. Others which are important for the inhibitory influence which they exercise are the positive-acceptant response, and the negative-rejectant response. These total response patterns or attitudes have important visceral components, and just as the salivary secretion can be used as an indicator of the alimentary response, so the pneumogram, or record of respiration, provides a convenient indicator of the positive, negative, and orientation responses, because each has a characteristic respiratory pattern.

It is these total response patterns which actually cause the inhibition of other responses. It is the positive acceptant response which is ordinarly coupled with the alimentary reflex which must be satisfied by the food reinforcement. If the reinforcement does not occur, or if it is changed in character, this is replaced by a negative or rejectant response, and the feedback from the somatic components of this response provide the inhibiting excitation.

Thus Anokhin departs also from the orthodox Pavlovian position that the effects of reinforcement depend only on the coincidence of events, and takes the position that the "effect" influences the outcome. He makes repeated reference to an experiment by Anokhin and Strezh, in which a dog that had acquired an alimentary reflex to a conditional stimulus, with dry bread being used as the unconditional stimulus in the usual manner, was given meat instead of bread on one occasion. This evoked a very strong orientation response, which persisted in the situation and totally inhibited the conditional alimentary reflex, to the point that the dog refused to eat the bread which was presented as reinforcement in future trials.

When working with alimentary reflexes, the absence of reinforcement in the extinction procedure may lead either to the orientation response or to the negative response. When working with defense reflexes, absence of reinforcement leads to the positive response, or attitude. The difference between the positive and the negative attitudes is clearly discernible in the pneumogram, not only under these conditions, but also in the response to differential stimuli during training for discrimination. The common element in all these situations is that there are always two competing total response patterns. However, the transition from a negative to a positive state does not require active inhibition, as in the reverse situation.

Stages in the development of the conditional reflex can be traced in the respiratory responses. The pneumogram shows the participation of the orientation attitude in the early appearances of the conditional stimulus, and how it disappears when the conditional reflex is established. In the event of nonreinforcement it returns, and on the next trial this orientation attitude appears immediately with the conditional stimulus, and thus becomes the source for conditional inhibition. Thus, as stated above, the internal inhibition of excitation is regarded as no more than a manifestation of external inhibition. The extinction does not take place gradually, but proceeds in two distinct phases, with a clear qualitative difference when the signs of conflict disappear. If the conditional response reappears during the later stages of the extinction process, it is accompanied by irregular breathing. Thus we see that complete inhibition is more economical, less conflictful, than partial inhibition. During the first phase of extinction, when conflict is present, the inhibition acts on the efferent organization of the conditional reflex; during the second phase, in which the conflict is absent, it acts on the afferent organization in some manner which involves the afferent collaterals into the brain stem reticular formation.

Anokhin (1958) feels that Ukhtomsky's formulation of the principle of the dominant is unsatisfactory, although the basic observations are extremely important. He gives the following illustration to show that a dominant may be a system or center which is under inhibition, rather than one which is partially excited, as Ukhtomsky assumes. If a cat is cautiously creeping forward on a window ledge, peering down over the edge, a sudden rap by the observer will cause the cat to move *backwards* immediately. Anokhin suggests that whenever there is a rivalry between two actions, such as moving forward and moving backward, or vomiting and defecation, the decisive factor is which of the two can take effect more quickly as a response organization.

In an experimental situation, the conditional stimulus only raises above threshold value an excitation which is already present, because of other elements in the situation. Hence the actual response evoked is already present as a dominant. (We would of course prefer to say that the action had already been partly disinhibited by the incidental stimuli, and the conditional stimulus only completes the disinhibition.) The same stimulus can be used to evoke different conditional reflexes, in the same room, at different times of the day. He concludes that dominance is a readiness for action which can strengthen itself, in the manner described by Ukhtomsky, by attracting excitation, and which is closely related to the subcortical emotional afferentation, since the brain stem reticular formation plays a part in all these aspects of the dominant.

Anokhin says that just as the phenomenon of inhibition depends on the simultaneity of two total response patterns, such as the alimentary and orientation responses, so the occurrence of disinhibition depends on the simultaneity of three total response patterns, such as the alimentary response, the negative response, and the investigatory response. If the alimentary response had been inhibited by the negative response, the addition of the investigatory response may strengthen the former, and permit it to appear despite the inhibition; it may also strengthen the negative response, leading to deeper inhibition; or it may indirectly inhibit the negative response, and thus free the alimentary response.

Pavlov had said that neurotic behavior arose from a conflict of excitation and inhibition; for Anokhin, inhibition is itself a conflict of excitations. For the best mental health, an effort should be made not to train inhibitions, but to develop strong positive motivations, which can then be relied upon to inhibit unwanted activities.

We shall close this chapter with a discussion of the work of Konstantin Bykov. Bykov's opus magnum, *The Cerebral Cortex and the Internal Organs,* has been available in English translation since 1957, but his work is not nearly so well known to American readers as that of many of Pavlov's lesser students. Gantt, his translator, states that Bykov has had over one hundred collaborators, and the importance of his position is perhaps best summed up in this statement by Biryukov (1958): "The finding of a basis for the problem of corticovisceral physiology is rightly attributed to Academician K. M. Bykov." The word *corticovisceral* is a better index to the nature of his work than the phrase *interoceptive conditioning,* for the essential thing is not that Bykov demonstrates the possibility of conditioning visceral processes to external stimuli or using the visceral organs as sources of stimulation for conditional reflexes of other organs, but that he shows us the importance of these phenomena in the general processes of behavioral control. In a review of the recent work in this area, all of which may justly be regarded as the outgrowth of Bykov's own work, Razran (1961) says: "These 300 recent Russian experiments contribute greatly toward making the Unconscious observable instead of inferable and the Conscious inferable whether or not it is observable." We are reminded of Freud's classic statement that the task of therapy is to make conscious that which was previously unconscious. Bykov's investigations, no less than Freud's, have brought to view relationships between hidden elements in behavior and overt acts.

Before entering on the complexities of fistulas and glandular secretions, we should like to suggest a context within which to view these experiments. We have already stated that wherever there is choice, there must also be inhibition. With increasingly complex organization of the nervous system, the interrelations among its parts become such as to defy our efforts to structure all the possibilities of interaction from any one point of view. There may be some gain in clarity if we attempt to state one point of view from which this work may be considered, even though, regretfully, we must leave aside many other possibilities.

There is one avenue of approach in the life sciences which has so many crossroads that virtually every investigator has wandered about its byways on numerous occasions: the problem of energy transfer in its many forms—direct organismic energy exchange, mediate energy utilization, and transmission of energy to new generations. We need not enter into the incredibly complex questions opened up by this pattern of transactions to see its application to our problem. The metabolic rates and storage capacities of organisms have a direct bearing on their capacity for choice. The spectrum is narrow indeed in the case of organisms which must engage in incessant search for sources of biological fuel, which is immediately consumed in the further search for more fuel. The shrew's perpetual appetite need rouse no envy in the most gluttonous human, for though the latter cannot eat so endlessly, he more than compensates for this by the satisfaction of an occasional bit of gourmandizing.

The potential for control depends not only on increased encephalization and other nervous development, but also on the correlated increase in capacity to store nutrients and air. The ability to store foodstuffs, which was so essential to the civilization of Egypt, is still one essential for a nation's ability to choose between the paths of war and peace. In the same way, the development and mastery of our individual storage facilities is an essential basis for control of behavior. The novice under water, his highly developed cortex notwithstanding, has much less capacity for choice than a fish. The impelling signalization from the respiratory centers, as the CO_2 content of the blood rises above accustomed levels, quickly leads to panic and maladaptive behavior long before the available oxygen in the lungs has been exhausted. Yet the swimmer soon learns to remain submerged for longer periods, without intense discomfort. True, he will never be able to duplicate the feats of his aquatic mammalian cousin, the dolphin, but the exercise of inhibitory controls can enable him to utilize his available storage capacity more effectively. This example shows three things: first, that internal signals which usually escape our detection may become prominent in an altered ecological setting; second, that it is possible to gain control over originally "autonomic" adjustment mechanisms organized at subcortical levels; third, that the limits of such inhibitory control are fixed by certain irreversible physiological processes of chemical exchanges with the environment.

It is no qualitative leap to compare the behavior of the infant with that of the novice at underwater swimming. We are aware that on the one hand the neonate is transacting with limited capacities for inhibition, and on the other, as all parents know, he is a very delicate input-output system. During the first weeks after birth, the vegetative apparatus is uppermost in the scheme of living. A relatively mild visceral deprivation or skin affection is likely to result in a dissonant crescendo of activity. This is the crossroad from which Freud starts his journey. Also, Ribble (1944) has emphasized the problems in breathing; L. K. Frank (1938) has developed the configurations involved in tactile stimulation; Dollard and Miller (1950) have underlined the lack of control which results from the fact that these internal signals are not controlled by verbal mechanisms. More recently, the factor of sensory deprivation has entered the picture. It is evident that the importance of the internal organs for behavior is not limited to the services which they directly perform, but depends also on the stimulation which they provide for other organs. What occurs in this early period determines to a great extent the possibilities of choice open to the individual at a later time. The gradual inhibition of impulses from the internal organs is a necessity in any culture; but cultures will differ with respect to the method of imposing such inhibitions, and the kind of release from them which is sanctioned; and these differences will have far-reaching implications for the possibilities of individual choice.

Against this background, let us consider some of the experimental results of Bykov and his collaborators, which show how the "wisdom of the body" may be enhanced, to permit new possibilities of choice, or may be so limited that ungated feedback may trap the individual, like the shrew, in an unending series of episodes involving the vegetative aspects of living.

The first phase of Bykov's experimental program was the demonstration that methods used to bring about salivary secretion by previously neutral stimuli could be extended to other internal organs and physiological processes. For example, Bykov and Alexeev-

Berkman demonstrated conditional renal secretion against a background of constant conditions of food and liquid intake and temperature. The ureters of the dogs were externalized, and the bladders removed, to prevent the muscular act of micturition. Each day a constant amount of water was administered by enema, and the amount of urinary secretion was measured. Soon it was found that the physical arrangements of the experiment began to bring about diuresis as soon as the animal was placed in the experimental apparatus. Continuing the enemas served to increase this effect. Evidently, the environment was mediating diuresis in the absence of hydremia. As a control, a syphon enema was used which ejected the water immediately, but this procedure—analogous to the sham-feeding situation in which Pavlov had first studied gastric secretions —"produced diuresis of the same or even greater intensity than the introduction of water into the intestine and its entrance into the blood." Subsequently the animal was placed on the stand without any administration of liquid, and diuresis was reduced over a number of trials. However, Bykov states that extinction of renal conditioning proceeds more slowly than that of salivary conditioning.

By using two experimental rooms—an "active" room in which water was administered and a "differentiating" room in which this was never done—differential conditioning was demonstrated, that is, elevated diuresis occurred only in the active room. Bykov comments that "when the positive complex stimulus is in action, we have to deal with cortical excitation in intensified diuresis, and, in the other, when a negative (differential) stimulus is in action we observe cortical inhibition."

Similar procedures have been used by Bykov and many collaborators to develop conditional responses in other organs, including the excretory organs, the liver, the cardiovascular system, the mucosa of the digestive tract, the respiratory system, the processes of thermoregulation, etc. (Similar results have been reported by Gantt (1953), in this country.) In discussion of these results, the occurrence of conditioning is always accepted as a *criterion* of cortical representation. It is assumed that if the arrest or activation of an internal process can be triggered by a stimulus to which it was originally indifferent, the articulation must have been achieved in the cerebral cortex. That is, there is an apparent unquestioning acceptance of Pavlov's theory of the cortical representation of all conditional reflexes, even when the stimuli do not involve exteroceptors.

In a number of experiments, Bykov has shown that interoceptors can be the source of conditional stimulation. Bykov and Ivanova, making use of the fact that saline injection into the stomach will bring about increased diuresis, established a conditional diuresis to the injection of liquid. They then extinguished the effects of the experimental environment, but sham irrigation continued to be an effective stimulus. In another experiment, Ivanov collected the bile through a fistula of the gall bladder. It was found that injection of a 5 percent solution of hydrochloric acid into the stomach, through a gastric fistula, was followed by secretion of 14.5 ml. of bile during the next three hours. After fifteen such administrations, water was substituted for bile, and the conditional secretion obtained amounted to 18.2 ml. Commenting on this increase, Bykov again implicates the cerebral cortex: "In studying the conditional reflex of the viscera, we not infrequently observe this phenomenon—a reaction produced by a conditional stimulus, i.e., through the cerebral cortex, is often very intense and lasts longer than one caused by the action of an unconditional stimulus." After six sham injections, the secretion was down to 5.8 ml., and ultimately it was extinguished completely.

Bykov cites the work of Ayrapet'yants, who, working with dogs with both gastric and salivary fistulas, effected salivary conditional reflexes by combining irrigation of the stomach with warm water (36° C) and oral feeding. Apparently the arrangement was such that the water did not remain in the stomach, but served only as a source of thermal stimulation. Subsequently, irrigation with water at one temperature was accompanied by feeding, while irrigations at another temperature were not, and discrimination between the two temperatures took place. In an experiment in which irrigation at 26° C had been differentiated from the positive stimulus, which was 36° C, the sound of a whistle was once presented along with the differential stimulus, and complete disinhibition of the conditional reflex was demonstrated.

Ayrapet'yants (1952) reports another demonstration of interoceptive differentiation. A loop of the intestine is drawn out in such a way that the experimenter can stimulate at will either side of the ileocecal valve, which guards the passage between the small and the large intestine. Mechanical stimulation of the small-intestine side is reinforced with food, but stimulation of the large-intestine side is not reinforced. A conditional salivary reflex is formed, and differentiation established. The same differentiation can be established when stimulation of one of the points is paired with electric shock to the dog's paw, so that the paw "regularly jerks back only on signals connected with the small intestine side of the ileocecal apparatus" although the distance between the two points of stimulation is not more than one or two centimeters.

The studies described have been selected for their simplicity, and are not entirely typical of the more elaborate work being done at present. Razran (1961) gives an account of the mutistimulational techniques which are now in use. However, the above experiments suffice to show that Bykov's *empirical* suppositions have been amply confirmed: the activity of internal organs can be attached to external stimuli, and the responses of peripheral effectors can be placed under the control of internal stimuli. As stated above, the term "interoceptive conditioning" does not quite capture the significance of interoception in Bykov's narrative. It is not the fact of "switching" of afferent-efferent connections which involve the internal organs and internal sources of stimulation which is most important, but the fact that every part of the entire system of afferentation, both external and internal, must be considered with respect to its influence on cortical activities.

In discussing the periodicity of physiological functions, Bykov (1957) states that bulbar and mesencephalic stimulation from exteroceptors causes an increase in excitability of vegetative centers in the region of the hypothalamus, and "because of this, diurnal periodicity may be formed independently of the activity of the cerebral cortex." He then mentions that the projections of all cortical receptors are influenced by the afferent stimulation of the diencephalic and mesencephalic structures. Thus, the reciprocal relationship of the two systems is evident. Changes in afferent impulses change the tonic state of the cortex, and, through the action of temporary connections, the higher nervous centers bring about controllable alterations in the activities of the internal organs. Language, Pavlov's "second system of signals," participates in such control, and in this connection Bykov mentions the work of Luria, as well as experiments by Geyer and others who have influenced secretion and other bodily processes by suggestion. The relevance to hypnosis is also mentioned.

Another important aspect of Bykov's work is his demonstration that these interactions do not depend on the existence of intact neural connections, but can be mediated by hormonal mechanisms alone. With Alexeev-Berkman, he demonstrated conditional diuresis even when the kidneys were deprived of their innervation. Bykov and Borodavkina showed that administration of pituitrin could lead to "either a positive or an inhibitory response, depending upon the state of the humoral milieu.' In short, conditioning takes place when either the hormonal or the nervous connections with the organ are intact. Bykov claims that two routes are possible in the formation of conditional reflexes: one nervous, the other neuro-humoral. However, the locus of closure for the conditioning is said to be cortical in either case.

With this expanded concept of conditioning in mind, let us turn to the more general aspects of Bykov's thought. In his work, as in that of Sherrington, the idea of integration is ubiquitous. If one considers only the classic analytical experiments which each performed, it is possible to regard both men as advocates of a shallow input-output theory of behavior; but this would be as false in the case of Bykov as in that of Sherrington. In his hands, the concept of integration finds its expression as "corticovisceral physiology." The use of this unhyphenated word conveys an integral relationship, not a mere interaction of largely independent systems. Bykov's holistic approach is partially expressed in this statement: "There is no reason for distinction between the processes brought forth by the stimulation of receptors which respond to impulses from the *milieu intérieur* and receptors which respond to impulses from the *milieu extérieur*" (p. 245).

Conditional reflexes involve stimulation from both interoceptive and exteroceptive fields, and these must be studied jointly. The exteroceptor and its cortical apparatus, Pavlov's "analyzer," has played a more important role in our constructions because the information which it signals is usually localized and reportable in terms of "definite individual sensation." The stimulation of the exteroceptive field leads to our knowledge of the external world, and hence, says Bykov (following Pavlov), "for ages these receptors were called sense organs." Bykov feels that this epistemic function is at least partially responsible for the distinction between "vegetative" and "animal" divisions of the nervous system.

Mentioning the "ingenious intuition" of Descartes and of Charles Bell in their descriptions of the proprioceptive control of muscular activity, it is nevertheless to Sechenov that Bykov grants credit for realization of the subtleties involved in interpreting the "obscure sensations" from the internal organs. However, the study of the interoceptor system was still held back by lack of an adequate method. Information from interoceptors "either fails to be subjectively noted or it is not followed by any definitely localized and distinct sensation." They are "screened from our consciousness." However, the method of Pavlov opened a way for study of their functional relations, and revealed their psychological import, which Bykov summarizes thus:

> Many of these subsensory impulses arising from the interoceptors may summate to stimulate the cerebral cortex. Thus, the isolated forms of interoceptive impulses may be considered as belonging to those kinds of stimuli which give rise to subconscious processes: the stimulating events conveyed from the milieu intérieur of an organism may finally become so insistent and obsessive that the nerve centers can no longer ignore them. The functional interoceptive fields formed in the cortex sometimes become powerful factors in determining behavior. In this case, stimulations conveyed from the environment become active helpers in the developing complex reaction (Bykov, 1957, p. 392).

By the concept of a "functional connection" with the cortex, Bykov escapes the restriction of Pavlov's assertion that all temporary connections are formed in the cortex. He mentions the work of Culler and Mettler (1934) on subcortical conditioning, and claims that the formation of a *typical* conditional reflex is not likely to occur in the decerebrate organism. He adds, however, that theoretically "it is possible to assume that there may be intermediate forms between a typical unconditional and a typical conditional reflex and that the possibility of the lower parts of the central nervous system being to a certain extent capable of forming new reflex arcs should not be entirely denied" (Bykov, 1957, p. 30). He states that *direct* morphological connections between subcortical structures and the cortex are not necessary for the formation of temporary connections. Afferents which terminate in subcortical nuclei, and which lack specific projection to cortical fields, may nevertheless be involved in conditioning and differentiation. In Bykov's corticovisceral physiology *all* temporary connections (in the intact organism) involve the effects of afferent stimulation from both systems of receptors. "Any conditional reflex is not the phenomenon we observe on a decerebrated animal but it is the result of a number of afferent systems of both extero- and interoceptive fields, being brought into an active state" (1957, p. 385).

Thus the evaluation of empirical evidence leads to an altered conception of the role of the cerebral cortex in the process of conditioning. Rather than simply performing the part of a flexible coupling device which forms new connections between structures which must be represented for this purpose in specific cortical projections, the cortex becomes an integral part of a complex system of regulation and modulation for the entire organism. "The conditional reflex is more than the concept of action by association; it is much more extensive, including not only complex nervous factors but humoral factors as well." And elsewhere: "It is impossible to believe that the interaction of the two essential processes of excitation and inhibition is limited to the cells of the cerebral cortex. There is reason to think that the most complex play of these two antagonistic processes develops when the conditional reflex is in progress in the *subcortical centers*" (Bykov, 1957, p. 385).

Thus Bykov's work on interoceptive conditioning fits well with the modern conception of the nervous system as a neurohumoral apparatus, as well as with recent experimentation which emphasizes the part which the brain stem reticular formation plays in all learning.

INTRACEREBRAL EVENTS AND BEHAVIORAL PLASTICITY 11

Chapter 6, which dealt with the "range of inhibition," gave very scant treatment to those inhibitory relationships which take place among the various cerebral structures, and which are involved in the interaction of the brain stem and all higher nervous structures. This chapter will make good that defect to a degree, by consideration of data which have been provided by interdisciplinary research in which the nervous correlates of behavioral events have been studied. Our interest, however, is not to multiply instances of inhibition, nor to offer a necessarily inadequate account of the relevant electrophysiological data, but to illuminate the functional relationships among the components of behavior. In particular, we shall understand better the importance of the orienting reaction to extinction and habituation, as stressed in the work of Anokhin, and the participation of visceral events in conditioning phenomena generally, as stressed in the work of Bykov, when we see that inhibitory phenomena within the so-called limbic system or visceral brain, and inhibitory influences exercised by this system, regularly accompany certain phases of the conditioning process.

In the studies described below, the records of nervous activity are of two sorts. On the one hand there are records of surface potentials, obtained by means of electrodes placed on the cortex, or more commonly on the skull. Characteristics present in such records (fast or slow waves, alpha-blocking or desynchronization, etc.) differ from one part of the brain to another, and when a change in one area regularly precedes some change in another, or when the wave pattern undergoes similar or opposite changes in different areas simultaneously, it may be possible to draw inferences about functional relationships. However, although the correlation between surface records and various stages of "activation" (Lindsley, 1951) may have general validity, it is at best a very gross index to the complex interplay of excitation and inhibition among the individual units. As Grundfest (1961) states, "the vast proportion of the neuronal activity, in the form of synaptic events and of cell discharges, is hidden from sight, even more than is the ice hidden below the surface of an iceberg. Indeed the electrocortical potentials that do appear may result from quite different types of activity so that their similar appearance need not indicate physiological or pharmacological relationships." The surface potentials therefore tell us very little about the changes in unit activities, which are the basic phenomena. However, contemporary electrophysiology (as represented, for example, in the recent volume edited by Sheer, 1961) is able also to record the discharges of single neuronal units, studied under different conditions by means of permanently implanted electrodes. Records of this sort, which show increased and decreased discharge rates for the same units under different conditions, provide fairly direct evidence of inhibitory and excitatory effects. From them we shall see that in every stage of the conditioning process, inhibition of unit activities, somewhere in the brain, is an essential part of the total pattern.

Both types of data combine to deepen our understanding of the manner in which neural structures and units interact, facilitating and inhibiting one another, during different stages of the conditioning process. They demonstrate the involvement of the overlapping centrencephalic and limbic systems in types of behavior which were formerly regarded as expressions almost exclusively of neocortical activity. As Russell (1961) states, these systems "subserve viscerosomatic and emotional mechanisms on the one hand and conscious and attentive mechanisms on the other. Clearly it is difficult to separate, even arbitrarily, these two systems by physiological criteria." Unfortunately, the complexity of the interrelationships is further confused by the lack of a uniform terminology. We shall limit ourselves, for the most part, to mentioning only such major structures as the amygdala or the hippocampus, without reference to their differentiated parts. We must anticipate, however, that each further progress in this field will necessitate closer attention to such detail. The interested reader will find an overview of the anatomical relationships in Russell (1961); other discussions of the limbic system are given by Adey (1959), Gloor (1960), Green (1960), MacLean (1959), and Pribham (1961b). Herrick (1956) has an interesting discussion of the phylogenetic significance of the brain stem, and of the old and new cortices, as well as many other related topics of interest to psychologists.

Pavlov's insistence that the cortex of the cerebral hemispheres is the seat of all the higher nervous processes, and the site of the presumptive "temporary connections" involved in all adaptive modification of behavior, was only one expression of a conviction widely held by physiologists and psychologists alike, that neocortical tissue is more capable of plastic change, as a result of experience, than paleocortical or subcortical tissue. (However, Yakovlev (1959) points out, on evolutionary grounds, that "when one deals with the hemisphere of a cat or dog, one really deals with the rhinic and the limbic lobes only," and the failure to recognize this fact has been a source of error.) Until quite recently, the problem of the extent of participation of brain stem and paleocortical structures in the modification of behavior was considered only from the standpoint of assessing the degree of this assumed functional difference, and determining whether these older structures were capable at all of mediating plastic changes similar to those which were assumed to occur almost exclusively in the neocortex. The discovery of the active part which the brain stem reticular formation plays in regulating cortical activity, and also the demonstration of the degree to which visceral processes were susceptible to conditioning effects, gave the problem a new aspect—i.e., whether these older structures might not actually play an essential part in all instances of plasticity. The suggestion has even been put forward (Gastaut, 1958) that the primary site of "closure" in conditioning may be subcortical. However, we shall find it more useful to think not in terms of locating the site of closure in one structure or another, but of following the vertical interplay of influences among structures on different levels. As Herrick (1956) states, it is possible to analyze the nervous system into levels of functioning, but interpenetration and dependency among the levels is required for integration: "Each higher level is derived from the lower and can work only with the instrumentation provided by the lower levels." Konorski (1960) also emphasizes that even unconditional reflexes are mediated by systems which extend through various levels of the neuraxis including the neocortex, with afferent and efferent parts of the reflex mechanisms represented at each level. The insight derived from the work of Moruzzi and Magoun (1949), who discovered the wakening influence of the brain stem reticular formation on the cortex, receives its full significance only with the recognition that multiple inhibitory effects, exerted both upwards and downwards, are essential to all behavior. Although debate goes on concerning the participation of cortical versus subcortical sites of closure in conditioning, it is becoming clear that this distinction does not provide a sound basis for discussion of the relevant problems. There are many avenues of convergence in the nervous system (Brazier, 1961; Magoun, 1961), and the issues are not clarified by efforts to select one area or one system as more important than others.

Many workers have tried to plot the sequence of neocortical, paleocortical, and subcortical events which are involved in the different phases of a typical conditioning procedure. These studies have achieved, if nothing more, a restatement of the problem, by their forceful demonstration of the interrelated functioning of all parts of the brain. The idea that neocortical tissue is necessary for intelligent behavior was based on the relatively crude techniques of ablation. More refined surgical procedures were needed to observe the behavior of animals with intact neocortex, suffering from lesions more deeply placed, but now we know that these are even more disabling, not solely with respect to the unconditional reflexes which have always been assumed to be dependent on these deeper structures, but also with respect to the possibilities of adaptive response. The still more delicate electrophysiological explorations, with simultaneous recording of single unit activities from various parts of the essentially intact brain, now give a much fuller picture of the activity of different structures during the acquisition and later performance of conditional acts. The results confirm some of Pavlov's conclusions about relationships between simultaneous excitatory and inhibitory processes, while rejecting his hypothetical physiology. They are full of reminders that the integrated functioning of the nervous system depends on inhibitory influences which are exercised among structures on many levels, and that it is impossible to think of behavioral plasticity as dependent solely on the special characteristics of neocortical tissue.

In the Pavlovian schema, the higher cortical centers of the cerebral hemispheres, which were the presumed seat of all conditional connections, exercised control over the nonplastic lower centers, which executed the unconditional reflexes and innate reactions. Pavlov was influenced partly by evolutionary concepts, but also by the importance which the cortical "analysers" assumed in his experimental designs. Bykov's demonstrations of interoceptive conditioning (see pages 216 ff.) cast doubt on Pavlov's sweeping generalizations. As a result, Bykov (1957) maintained that the subcortical nuclei were also the seat of the most complex interplay of excitation and inhibition, and he stressed the role of diencephalic, and especially hypothalamic, mechanisms in conditioning. He even ventured to state that certain "untypical" conditional phenomena might occur without the participation of neocortical structures. Despite these insights, he sought to retain the basic Pavlovian viewpoint, merely introducing his findings as added complications into a schema which emphasized the horizontal (that is, cortico-cortical) control systems, rather than replacing them by vertical concepts which would place primary emphasis on the interplay of structures belonging to different levels.

It has been established that the basic phenomena of conditioning can be observed in animals deprived of neocortex. Gastaut (1958) cites such a study by Sager (1960, p. 202) in which the pairing of an auditory stimulus with an electric shock to the leg eventually elicited a behavioral response to the auditory stimulus alone. It is important to note that the conditional reaction which occurs under these conditions is not a simple leg withdrawal, but a "vegetative-affective" reaction which includes general agitation, piloerection, disturbed breathing, growling, and barking. Nor was it possible to establish differentiation. Whatever the locus of such conditioning, the massive release of behavior and the lack of differentiation point to the failure of certain adaptive changes which would involve inhibition of components of the response. Beritov (Beritashvilli, 1960) comments on similar conditioning in the absence of neocortex, in both dogs and cats.

Hernández-Peón and Brust-Carmóna (1961) implicate portions of the reticular formation in such conditioning. They report that cats deprived of neocortex acquired a conditional salivary reaction after the pairing of a light with the smell of fish, and that in another experiment such animals acquired a conditional response to an auditory stimulus paired with an electric shock delivered to the foreleg. After establishing these alimentary and defensive conditional reactions, they placed lesions in the posterior parts of the mesencephalic reticular formation, with the result that the effects of the previous conditioning were obliterated, and conditioning could not be reestablished during the time span of their investigation. These lesions also altered gross segments of the animals' behavior, with obvious impairment of vision and response to pain. These results are not surprising, since the lesions were strategically placed at the crossroads of many afferent-efferent systems. To summarize, cortical ablation seems to bring losses in discrimination and recognition, while the mesencephalic lesions seem to eliminate some of the possibilities of functional sensory-holding mechanisms which are required for integration.

From the results of all such ablational studies, we can learn only the limits of performance of the surviving tissue, but not whether the lost functions were largely performed by the destroyed tissue, or depended on combined activity of parts that have been removed and some that have been retained. This is a source of ambiguity which is happily absent from investigations in which these interactional effects are traced by electrophysiological recordings in the intact brain, especially when such recordings are accompanied by simultaneous observations of behavior. The classical work of Durop and Fessard (1935) demonstrated that events of behavioral conditioning are reflected in the EEG. Thus, an "unconditional stimulus" such as a brief flash of light changes the occipital alpha pattern into the desynchronized pattern characterized by low amplitudes and high frequencies. A tone, which was initially neutral with respect to the occipital alpha pattern, is then introduced into the situation. After the tone and the light flash have been paired a number of times (with the tone leading, but overlapping the flash), the tone alone elicits the desynchronized pattern. This paradigm has been employed on many occasions, since the report by Jasper and Shagass (1941). The many recent studies which seek to elucidate further the relationship between electrical patterns in the central nervous system and behavioral conditioning are all essentially elaborations of this procedure.

One of the most illuminating of these studies, which will repay extended attention, is that of Jasper, Ricci, and Doane (1960). They obtained simultaneous records of behavioral response (hand withdrawal), the surface cortigram, and single unit discharges from monkeys placed in a restraining chair. An electric shock to the hand was the unconditional stimulus, while the conditional stimulus was a series of light pulses, occurring five times per second, which illuminated the entire field. Before conditioning, this photic stimulation was neutral with respect to the hand withdrawal which was to be conditioned, but records were made of its effects on unit responses in frontal, motor, sensory, and parietal sectors of the cortex. Simultaneously, macroelectrodes recorded the surface cortigram. Prior to the flash, many units would be firing at rates varying from one to thirty times a second, reflecting both endogenous activity and the background effects of the situation. With the photic stimulation, there was the expected desynchronization of the surface record, but individual units might show either increased or decreased rates of discharge. As these habituation trials proceeded, it was eventually found that almost two-thirds of the units in the motor area did not change their rate of firing in response to the light; of the remaining units, approximately one-half increased their rate, and the other half decreased their rate. The sensory cortex gave a similar picture. In the frontal area, 80 percent of the units were unaffected by the light after habituation, while 5 or 6 percent increased and 10 to 15 percent decreased their rate. In the parietal area, about 80 percent of the units were habituated, and most of the others decreased in rate. Summarizing these effects, Jasper, Ricci, and Doane state that "inhibitory processes are built up in frontal and parietal areas by mere repetition of the conditioning stimulus, while excitatory and inhibitory processes are about equally in evidence in the sensory-motor areas after repeated stimulation."

After several hundred pairings under the conditioning procedure, this picture had changed considerably. The units sampled in the motor cortex generally showed an increase in rate of firing (over the characteristic rates previously established) on those trials in which a motor response was elicited, but little change was observed on trials when the animal did not respond. Surprisingly, the response of units in the sensory cortex seemed not to be related to the stimulus as such, but rather to the evocation of the response, suggesting an efferent-afferent feedback. In both cases the effects were mixed, but with the predominance of rate increases accompanying behavioral response. In the frontal sector (Area 8), on the other hand, two-thirds of the units showed no change of rate, but of the remaining units most showed a decrease or inhibition of unit discharge. In the parietal area, likewise, most units did not change their rates, but those which did had a tendency to become linked to the photic stimulation. There were some units which tended to fire at the rate of the conditional stimulus, but this photic-following might represent either an increase or a decrease in rate. However, when discrimination was established between different frequencies of photic stimulation, the rate of activity in the parietal and frontal units would generally be inhibited by the differential stimulus, and this effect was especially pronounced on trials in which the motor response did not occur. In both the frontal and the parietal units, then, the picture that predominates in the responding units is one of inhibition.

Turning to still another feature of this investigation, it was found that the relationship between desynchronization and unit activity varied in different parts of the cortex. In the sensory and motor areas, alpha blocking was associated with a general increase in the unit firing; but in the parietal and frontal areas, in this avoidance situation, desynchronization was associated with a general inhibition of unit response. However, in all areas sampled, at all times, excitatory and inhibitory effects existed together. The appearance of slow wave activity, likewise, was not always associated with inhibition of unit responses.

In an attempt to gain a clearer specification of the cortical processes involved in conditioning, Kogan (1960) used as unconditional stimulus direct stimulation of the motor cortex of the dog, at a point which elicited lifting of the paw. When this was paired with an external conditional stimulus, it was found that there was a general increase in excitability as conditioning proceeded. This was fairly widespread during the early trials, but "when the reflex became well established this zone had radically shrunk to the reinforcement point while every presentation of the conditional stimulus began evoking in the surrounding analyzers an increase in the thresholds." Despite these changes in threshold, desynchronization appeared over broad areas of the cortex, including those in which the threshold had been raised. Kogan, like Jasper, also emphasizes that desynchrony may represent either inhibition or excitation.

Jasper (1961) studied cortical potentials which accompanied conditional defensive movements. During an initial habituation period auditory clicks were presented at a frequency of five per second, until the amplitude of the evoked potentials in the auditory cortex had dropped to less than one half of the original value. In the subsequent conditioning procedure, shock was paired with the clicks, after a three-second delay. The evoked potentials at first regained some of their original amplitude, but they did not exceed the prehabituation values. As the animals began to avoid shock by paw withdrawal, the evoked potentials began to decline; when performance reached a level of 90 to 95 percent consistency, "the evoked potentials declined further and reached a very low value, even below that obtained in the habituation series." During subsequent extinction of the conditioning, the amplitudes remained low at first, then rapidly rose to 60 to 70 percent of the prehabituation level, and then declined again to the very low values observed when conditioning was in effect. Upon reconditioning, the average amplitude increased and again decreased as responses reached the 90 percent level of consistency. Jasper comments that "it would seem that the level of these types of response was more related to an alerting reaction, not necessarily to conditioning as such." (Another phase of this important investigation, reported by Majkowski, is described on page 352.)

Brazier (1960a) makes the same point in a similar context, and warns that although electrocortical potentials and EEG patterns change during conditioning, these effects are more likely mediational rather than end points of pattern storage. In some studies, stability may occur on the electrophysiological level before behavioral conditioning has taken place, and in others components of the behavioral pattern may appear or become extinguished while electrophysiological events continue relatively unchanged. (However, these conclusions refer to EEG phenomena, not to unit responses.) Also, behavioral consistencies, such as conditional responses, may survive massive cortical alterations, including shock and ablation. Many workers have found that cortical areas which are responsive to stimulation during conditioning may be extirpated without preventing similar conditioning at a later time. In the study just cited, by Jasper, large bilateral extirpations of auditory cortex did not prevent the establishment of the conditional response to the click stimulus. These paradoxes point to the need for analysis of the conditioning process into several phases, rather than regarding it as a mere accumulation of similar effects. Many workers are now engaged in programs directed to this problem.

One such program has been summarized by Voronin and Sokolov (1960), and again more fully by Sokolov (1960). Before describing it, some introductory remarks are in order. It will be recalled that Pavlov (1927) introduced the term *investigatory reflex* to designate "the immediate response in man and animals to the slightest changes in the world around them, so that they immediately orientate their appropriate receptor organ in accordance with the perceptible quality bringing about the change." The investigatory or orienting reflex is also the powerful source of inhibition of conditional reflexes, and one of the best means for testing the stability of reflexes (Frolov, 1937). It has been suggested that this mechanism is the physiological basis for "attention," as well as for the preparatory acts of the organism. Frolov recalls the observation of Roger Bacon that "a miller sleeping amid the noise of his mill and the creaking of the water wheel, will inevitably wake up as soon as there is any interruption in the work of the mill," and he goes on to cite Birman's work, in which dogs were conditioned to respond to one of twenty tones on a harmonium. The dog would remain unaroused or asleep during the playing of these tones, except for one near the middle of the scale, which had been selected for use as a positive conditional stimulus. This would immediately elicit arousal and response appropriate to feeding. Pavlov termed this complex reaction the phenomenon of the "watchman," and likened it to a "local cortical effect" which remained active while the remaining cortex was in a state of sleep inhibition. Although Pavlov could not adequately account for such an effect, he nevertheless maintained that such a response would have to be supported by unconditional centers in subcortical structures. Thus, this local excitation in the presence of sleep inhibition of the cortex is one of the stated exceptions to Pavlov's theory of horizontal control mechanisms. This activation of a conditional response during sleep requires that vertical controls be operative. His theory of the cortical mosaic would seem to require that there be an acquired directionality from the subcortical center, even though the response activated is a conditional response.

Voronin and Sokolov (1960) have attempted to place the phenomenon of the watchman and orienting into the context of contemporary neurophysiology. The pattern of the orienting reflex, which is basically an unconditional reflex, includes alpha blocking, as well as changes in GSR, respiration, muscle tone, and varied adjustments of receptor organs. However, this reflex is subject to modification or "specialization," and individualized orientation reactions evidently include conditional mechanisms. Furthermore, the components of the orienting reaction can be extinguished and inhibited in different patterns, according to the quality of the stimulation, and this suggests to Voronin and Sokolov that selective mechanisms of inhibition are acting through specific cortico-recticular pathways, and taking effect on the sensory collaterals which enter the reticular formation. Since inhibition affects some afferent pathways, while other afferents continue to evoke components of orienting, they argue that there must be cortical control of collateral influx into the nonspecific activating system of the reticular formation. Evidence that the extinction of components of the orienting reaction is active inhibition, rather than a lowering of the general level of arousal or a simple increase in excitation thresholds, is found in the observation that when a tone has been repeated at a given intensity until it has ceased to evoke alpha blocking, the change to a lower intensity of the same tone will evoke it again. Such facts indicate that the orienting reaction involves some comparator mechanism which is able to relate the characteristics of the present stimulation —its duration, intensity, quality, etc.—to a trace of past inputs which are already subject to inhibition.

To account for these effects, Sokolov (1960) proposes that a kind of "neuronal model" of experience is somehow constructed and retained in the cortex, while the reticular formation acts as a kind of booster or amplifier. Afferent impulses are received at the cortical points of the analyzer, but they also proceed into the amplifying system, unless they are checked by inhibition at the level of the collaterals into the reticular formation. This inhibition will take place whenever concordance exists between the input and the neuronal model in the cortical system. When stimuli differ from those so modelled in the past, afferent impulses will reach the reticular amplifying system via the collateral pathways. The arousal system then discharges into the cortical centers, thus increasing the capacity for discrimination, until a new neuronal model is formed which is concordant with this information, and inhibition again exercises its specific effect upon the stimuli evoking orienting behavior. (The amplifying effect might, of course, be disinhibitory, as we have assumed in an earlier chapter.)

This theory, with its recognition of interaction between cortical and brain stem mechanisms, is a considerable advance over classical Pavlovian theory. The emphasis on multi-afferent-and-efferent patterns requires a concept of inhibition which is specific and directed, and not simply irradiating. This concept of cortico-reticular control seems also to be an improvement over the simpler theory of a diffusely activating or drive system, because it accounts better for the differential effects of various stimuli, as shown especially in habituation of the orientation reaction. Although Sokolov describes his amplifying system as discharging into vegetative and somatic centers, and as increasing sensitivity at peripheral levels, the theory still holds to the classical Pavlovian tradition in that these lower centers can only intensify (or interfere with) the action of cortical mechanisms which retain executive control.

It was pointed out in Chapter 10 that Anokhin also looks to the orientation reaction as the source for the inhibitions involved in the process of extinction. Anokhin (1961a) states that Pavlov believed that subcortical activity "represented a kind of 'blind force' that ensured a high energy level for the functional interactions among the cortical elements." Anokhin himself contends that the influence of reticular and other subcortical nuclei on the cerebral cortex is always "of a functionally specific character . . . and this is what determines the selective character of cortical connections that are mobilized adequately to the animals' given behavioral act." He conceives of the conditional reflex as dependent on numerous ascending subcortical influences, which are influenced by such factors as type of stimulation, background stimulation, previous conditioning, level of anesthesia, etc.

For example, Anokhin (1961b) describes antagonistic effects of alimentary and defensive conditioning on rabbits in the same situation. Both forms of conditioning evoke desynchronization, but after a considerable amount of training without shock or sudden stimulation of any kind, slow, high amplitude resting potentials may appear in the cortex. However, if even a few shocks are administered to the animal the resting potentials disappear, and a marked desynchronization again dominates the picture. Unlike alimentary conditioning, defensive reactions are associated with prolonged periods of cortical desynchronization during intervals between the administration of the shock. During painful stimulation a "stress rhythm" of four to seven cycles per second appears, following a vertical pattern: reticular formation; medial thalamus; hippocampus; and finally, after a lapse of several seconds, in the temporal cortex. Meanwhile, the sensorimotor cortex displays a desynchronized pattern. A bell that has been paired with the shock can also evoke this stress rhythm. Painful stimulation can both evoke and reinforce the total pattern. The injection of an optimal dose of chlorpromazine will cause both the desynchronization and the stress pattern to disappear after one or two minutes; and on the behavioral side the animal will then engage in searching reactions, examining and eating food if it is present. If the conditional defensive stimulus is applied under these circumstances, the animal remains indifferent. On the other hand, administration of the conditional alimentary stimulus evokes the usual activation pattern of the cortex. Thus, says Anokhin, "By means of certain pharmacological agents it is possible to block one biologically integral reaction and state of the animal and to free from the inhibiting effect of this first reaction other integral reactions of an opposite biological quality." He reasons that this selective action of chlorpromazine on the defensive reaction, but not on the alimentary reaction, points to biochemical specificity of subcortical nuclei, and hence to the possibility of multiple ascending influences on the same cortical neurons. (Such biochemical specificity will be discussed further in Chapters 15 and 16.)

Anokhin's conception of the selective action exercised by various ascending influences articulates with many other recent approaches to the problem of integrated control. For example, Jasper (1961) says: "It appears from many recent studies that the so-called extralemniscal sensory system passing up the core of the brain stem can no longer be considered an entirely non-specific system, but it must contain relatively specific components as well as relatively unspecific ones: excitatory and inhibitory mechanisms in a finely interwoven pattern of integrative organization, not adequately described as an activating or 'arousal' system." This view is supported by the report of Galambos and coworkers, that after bilateral destruction of the "classical" auditory lemniscal tracts, it was still possible to elicit recordings from the auditory cortical area in response to click stimuli (Galambos et al., 1961). Indeed, there was no difference in latency, wave shape, or duration of these effects after these lesions. The effects disappeared under barbiturate anesthesia, as expected on the basis of Brazier's (1958) report on the action of anesthetics on the reticular ascending system. (Brazier's work is described on page 346.) As Olszewski pointed out (see page 129), brain stem mechanisms are far more differentiated than most workers had previously expected. Lindsley (1961) considers that the ascending reticular system is sufficiently differentiated to serve as a monitoring and sampling system which becomes adjusted to levels of afferent-efferent traffic and may project these levels to cortical sectors. If it is sometimes an arousal system, it presumably serves at other times as a gating or inhibitory system, when too much stimulation is being received. He cites an unpublished study by S. Fox, in which monkeys were trained to press a lever in order to receive a half-second pulse of light, in an otherwise light-deprived situation. These animals might respond 1000 times in a ten-minute interval, and continue at that rate for several hours; but when light is introduced into the cage, the response rate falls.

It would seem that the cerebral cortex and the reticular formation act cooperatively in such monitoring. Jouvet (1961) found that the orienting response cannot be extinguished—that is, inhibited—after ablation of the neocortex, and it is disturbed after ablation of the frontal lobes, although a small part of the frontal and temporal cortex is sufficient to make extinction possible. He visualizes a rostral inhibitory system which acts downwards, from neocortex to the reticular level of the midbrain. Evidence for this system is found in the appearance of "spindle and slow waves first at the corticodiencephalic and later at the mesencephalic levels. This system is plastic and can be triggered by repetition of indifferent stimuli during habituation of the arousal of the orienting reflex." Thus, once again, the action of the neocortex is linked to inter-related systems of inhibition penetrating the brain stem and limbic structures. Loss of inhibition in any of these systems produces effects which are difficult to define in terms of the traditional categories of behavioral description.

In an attempt to avoid inappropriate models based on ideas of input-output or linear circuitry, as well as on the static localization theories which Lashley and others have warned against, W. K. Livingston and coworkers (1954) suggest that the reticular formation be regarded as a "trans-actional link" for all parts of the nervous system, rather than merely as an amplifier or arousal system. This conception is further developed by Worden and R. B. Livingston (1961), who point to the vast array of studies which tie the reticular system to the most varied behaviors.

The problem of the definition of function for the brain stem reticular formation is dealt with by Chow, who works in the Lashley tradition which emphasizes the possibilities of vicarious function. Chow (1961) cites the work of Adametz (1959) on the serial sectioning of the rostral reticular formation, with recovery between operative stages. Chow's account states that "practically normal behavior" was evidenced after the postoperative effects had disappeared. Using the same method, Chow himself found that even after much of the reticular formation had thus been removed, cats could "learn or retain conditioned avoidance responses and visual discriminations like normal cats. They also showed normal waking and sleeping EEG's, and normal conditioned cortical repetitive potentials." These results are a forceful warning against any theory of place "centers" in the reticular formation, but it is difficult to comprehend Chow's statement that the "behavioral significance of the reticular formation has yet to be fully determined." Indeed, we do not yet fully understand the behavioral significance of any part of the brain, but the fact that certain plastic changes can occur after neocortical, paleocortical, or brain stem lesions does not lessen the behavioral significance of these interpenetrating structures. Although the role of the reticular formation has, at times, been presented along the lines of an outmoded conception of the localization of functions, it is too late to open debate in those terms. The term "localized" remains meaningful, even if it does not signify the indispensable participation of a given structure in given behavior, but rather the participation of that structure, in an intact system, in the initiation of such behavior. And just as stimulation of certain points in the intact system, like certain nuclei of the hypothalamus, may lead to a sequence of processes which terminate in fairly well defined categories of behavior such as flight or escape, rage, and sexual function, so also localized pathologies may lead to well defined effects, as in focal epilepsies.

Regarding the problem of localization of function, John (1961) says: "The fact that an animal can learn or retain a response after a lesion does not of itself warrant the conclusion that this structure plays no role in the response. The engram, we suspect, is wily enough to elude the subcortical shot as the cortical knife. Memory seems more likely to be a set of processes, which define a state, than a 'bit' in place. That places participate in process is apparent, but we more legitimately expect the lesion of a region to alter the process than to abolish the state."

Perhaps the most interesting data relative to the localization of function comes from the experience of neurosurgeons working with the problem of focal epilepsy. Similar conditions can also be produced experimentally, by application of toxic substances to limited areas of the cortex. That the resulting seizures do not arise simply from the affected area is shown by the fact that they must be triggered by relevant afferent stimulation. (Recall the findings of Clementi and of Amantea, mentioned on page 125.) The situation is presumably similar in clinical epilepsy, although, as Gastaut and Fischer-Williams (1959) point out, "the fact that afferent stimuli precipitate a seizure is not clinically apparent because local hyper-excitability increases at the approach of an attack and is finally so marked that any volley of nervous impulses resulting from an in-significant stimulus is sufficient to fire off a paroxysm." Removal of the affected cortical area spares the organism the consequences of this pathology, but in the clinical case this method cannot be used when ablation will also eliminate functions which are vitally or even socially indispensable. Out of extensive experience with such surgery, Penfield and his colleagues (Penfield, 1938, 1954; Penfield & Jasper, 1954; Penfield & Rasmussen, 1950; Penfield & Roberts, 1959) have developed a new conception of cerebral functioning, in which major emphasis is placed on what he calls the "centren-cephalic system."

This system is conceived of as a brain stem mechanism which in-cludes "all those areas of subcortical gray matter (together with their connecting tracts) which serve the purpose of inter-hemispheral integration and intrahemispheral integration." Penfield points out that while removal of many, if not most, parts of the cortex does not necessarily entail postoperative loss of consciousness in the human being, "any lesion, such as a tumor exerting pressure or some agent that interferes with the circulation of the brain stem, is ac-companied by unconsciousness" (Penfield & Roberts, 1959).

Penfield's hypothesis of a subcortical center of integration does not minimize the importance of the cortical fields. What would seem to be minimized is the *unique* role of the cerebral cortices as a locus for integrated action and psychological function. For example, Pen-field and his colleagues have confirmed that electrostimulation of the precentral gyrus may bring about changes or movements in the peripheral musculature, chewing, swallowing, breathing, and vocal-izations. On the other hand, stimulation of the postcentral gyrus and the calcarine fissure will produce sensations such as tingling, feelings of movement, and diffuse visual effects. Since cutting around these areas does not prevent these effects, he concludes that "voluntary movement must be carried out by means of a stream of nerve impulses beneath the cortex," in the direction of the brain stem. "The precentral gyrus can do nothing by itself."

Penfield reports that stimulation of parts of the temporal, parietal, and frontal cortices may inhibit an ongoing speech pattern and produce aphasic arrest. The patient claims that "he knew what he wanted to say . . . [but] could not find the words." Speech arrest has been found in most areas which produce vocalization and, according to Zangwill (1960), stimulation of certain areas of the dominant hemisphere may produce inhibition which is a "genuine disturbance of word finding and speech control." Stimulation of the lateral surfaces of the temporal lobes may evoke flash-back reenactment of previous experience. In this case, the patient may live a kind of dual role, by being aware of the reenactment as well as of the present. He may recall speech, and the entire situation is meaningful. Penfield points out that stimulation of nearby points may produce the same recollection, and later stimulation at "what seems to be the same point may produce an entirely different memory." Similarly Baldwin (1960) points out that removal of the tissue evoking these experiences does not prevent the recall of the experience or the recall of the report of it during surgery.

Penfield sees cortical activity as one part of a continuous system for the elaboration, control, and regulation of behavior. Penfield and Roberts (1959) report many additional observations tending to support the basic theory. Observations made during stimulation of the temporal lobes point to the existence of an on-off mechanism which releases the reported experience in temporal correspondence with the original experience. The hallucinations run an ordered time pattern, and although the voluntary or selective recall of the experiences may not be possible, the automatic temporality of the recall is such that the patient is not confused. Comparing the retentive aspects of these experiences to a "strip of film," the authors comment that "A regulatory inhibitory mechanism must guard against activation of other portions of the film. As long as the electrode is held in place, the experience of a former day goes forward. There is no holding it still, no turning back, no crossing with other periods. When the electrode is withdrawn it stops as suddenly as it began." The off mechanism is illustrated by temporal lobe stimulation which produces amnesia during and after stimulation. During this period, Penfield says, the recording of experience "seems to be arrested somehow in both temporal lobes or, more likely, in the central integrating mechanism that projects the memory record to both temporal lobes." During periods of automatism, a patient may perform in a manner which suggests that he is not cut off from the effects of past experience, although he may have amnesia for the entire sequence of acts carried out during the period. Penfield feels that this is probably due to the functional failure of systems in which deep temporal lobe mechanisms are active in the scanning and the recording of experience.

Summarizing this aspect of his theory, Penfield (1958) says: "The major contribution of the temporal lobes to brain function apparently has to do with memory recording and with perception. It is evident that absence of the hippocampal gyrus and hippocampus on both sides makes any permanent recording of present experience impossible. This may mean that the ganglionic record of the stream of consciousness is located there, or it may mean that the hippocampal structures play an essential role in the laying down of the record elsewhere. Wherever it is, there must be some closely connected mechanism in the perceptional cortex capable of reactivating selected strips of the record." Work by Scoville and Milner (1957) would seem to support Penfield's concepts concerning these structures, but it is evident that the "record" is not stored in the hippocampal structures, since bilateral removal seems not to cut off the patient from the past. Penfield (1958) poses a "comparator" model in which the temporal cortex and the inner centrencephalic system and the limbic structures are mutually involved in relating present and past, in a way which suggests a perceptuo-cognitive analogue to Pavlov's "orienting reflex."

A great deal of recent experimental evidence points to the crucial role of the hippocampus in adaptive behavior generally. In the work of Grastyán and his collaborators, it has been assigned an important part in the inhibition of the orienting response. Green and Arduini (1954) had observed that stimulation of the reticular formation, which produces desynchronization of the neocortex, may also bring about the opposite phenomenon, slow theta activity, in the hippocampus. Grastyán believes that this theta activity is a correlate of the orienting reaction, and is associated with behavior during the initial periods of conditionings. Lissák and Grastyán (1960) found, however, that novel stimuli brought about this theta activity only after several trials in the conditioning situation. Grastyán, Lissák, and Kékesi (1956) found that stimulation of the hippocampus itself will elicit desynchronization in the contralateral hippocampus. On the other hand, stimulation of the reticular formation or the hypothalamus elicits the theta pattern. These authors therefore conclude that one of the functions of the hippocampus is to facilitate coordination by controlling the orienting reaction. After conditioning is consolidated, the behavioral orienting and the theta activity both drop out, and faster desynchronized activity occurs. If a differential stimulus is added to the conditioning situation, the theta activity appears again. Grastyán concludes that the desynchronized activity is associated with inhibition of orienting reactions. He cites results of Eidelberg, that lesions of the centrum medianum eliminate the evocation of the slow hippocampal potentials in rabbits, and comments that nuclei of the thalamus are crucial in control of hippocampal functions.

MacLean (1959) and his collaborators have related hippocampal activity to many other activities, as well as to orienting. MacLean stresses the functional and anatomic interrelationships among paleocortical structures, including the allocortex of the hippocampus and various subcortical structures, including the septal area, the amygdala, the hypothalamus, and other nuclei. Following Broca, he groups these phylogenetically old structures in the limbic system. The classical paper underlying modern work on this system is Papez (1937), which advanced the conception of the "visceral brain." MacLean points out that the limbic lobe structures and related subcortical nuclei participate in "a variety of behaviors involved in self-preservation and in the preservation of the species," and that this anatomically old system is a "common denominator in the brains of all mammals." He cites work by Flynn, in which the slow theta activity of the dorsal hypothalamus seemed to disappear when an exploring animal gratified itself with food or water. Flynn, MacLean, and Kim (1961) extended these studies; they observe that although limbic seizure patterns may give rise to intense electrical activity, there is no corresponding convulsive activity in the skeletal musculature. However, during such seizures the animal is unable "to respond appropriately to various stimuli." After establishing trace conditional cardiac and respiratory responses to the sound of a buzzer paired with a delayed shock to one leg of the animal, it was possible to eliminate this conditional response by propagating hippocampal seizures. Similar effects were observed in relation to delayed conditional leg withdrawal. After anticipatory leg withdrawals had been correctly performed for about 100 trials, the response was abolished by a contralateral hippocampal seizure. There was no evidence for spread of the seizure to the neocortex, and the auditory signal continued to evoke potentials in the auditory area during the seizure.

Confusional effects of hippocampal stimulation have also been reported by Olds and Olds (1961). They trained rats in a problem box with two levers, so placed that if the animal incorrectly pressed one, he had to retrace in order to press the other. Either lever might be correct on a given day, and the animal had merely to activate the correct one in order to receive food at the opposite end of the apparatus. These animals had electrodes implanted in various cortical and subcortical locations. Stimulation delivered via electrodes implanted in the neocortex, in the thalamus, and in parts of the reticular activating system had little effect. Stimulation of points throughout the hypothalamic-paleocortical systems resulted in both confusion and self-stimulation, but points which yielded only confusion were "clustered along the hippocampus proper." Olds interprets this result in the sense that "positive reinforcement" points cause confusion because stimulation in some of these hypothalamic-paleocortical areas overrides the effects of food, even in food-deprived animals. However, stimulation of the "hippocampus proper" is not in itself reinforcing, and the confusion must have a different basis. Bureš (1959), using Leão's (1944) "spreading depression," produced a reversible malfunction of the hippocampus, and he also noted confusion as a result: for example, an animal might return to an area in which it had received shock, as if "there were a complete memory loss of what had occurred immediately before."

Phibham (1960) says that interference with hippocampal processes and other limbic structures creates peculiarities in behavior which are difficult to place in the context of our conventional terminology. Human patients with limbic lesions are able to recall events prior to surgery, and immediate recall is not impaired under very simple conditions of recall; but, if distracted, such patients are unable to recall what they were supposed to do. Pribham says that such patients seem "unable to recall whatever is necessary to execute a sequence of actions." In his view, the limbic structures are involved whenever the behavior is such that it requires shifting from one activity to another. Again, the hippocampus is involved in the control of orienting reactions, although in a far more complex manner than in Grastyán's observations. Pribham states that electrical changes of the amygdaloid complex occur when "the organism is exposed to a novel event or one that has meaning in terms of reward and punishment. . . . These electrical changes subside once the organism is familiar with the event unless the hippocampal formation of the limbic system has been ablated, in which case electrical changes continue to occur when this or any other event has taken place." Similarly, Grastyán (1959) observes that although cats can still be conditioned after bilateral removal of the hippocampus, "it remains always the orientation reflex which mediates the final act." Therefore these animals could be conditioned only when the situation is so well controlled that no external inhibitors occur to complicate the situation.

Another way to state this would be that for an animal without a hippocampus, every situation is novel. Bilateral lesions of the amygdala have similar effects. Pribham (1961b) found that bilateral removal of the amygdala interferes with transposition learning in monkeys. Monkeys without such "core-brain" lesions learned to respond to the darker of two stimuli, but monkeys with lesions in these structures "act as if the test grays were 'novel': they respond on a 50:50 basis, as if they were in a totally new situation." This conforms with Olds' (1955) finding that after amygdaloid destruction animals lose capacity for performing relevant discriminations. Such gross loss of pattern discrimination may help to explain the finding of Schreiner and Kling (1953) that after amygdalectomy cats become hypersexual, responding to animals of different species including dogs and monkeys. Russell (1959) has implicated the hippocampal system, including the mammillary bodies, in the confusional states of syndromes such as Korsakoff's psychosis, involving hallucinations and disorientation with respect to time, as well as loss of memory.

Heath (1961) and Heath and Mickle (1960) have made observations on human patients over long periods of time, using depth electrodes. Some of the patients were psychotic (schizophrenic), while others were nonpsychotic, but suffering from episodic behavioral disorders such as psychomotor epilepsy. Gross correlations were obtained between acute psychotic states and spike and slow wave activity in parts of the limbic system. The electrical pattern in the septum, the rostral hippocampus, and the amygdala, is described as a "slow spike with a slow component." Similar irregularity was not found in other parts of the limbic system, and it rarely transmitted to the cortex. During periods of "psychosis in remission" the patterns obtained were nearly similar to those obtained from the nonpsychotic patients during their periods of relative normality. Heath points out that when the schizophrenic patient is severely disturbed, the marked change in pattern of the recordings from the amygdala, the septal region, and the hippocampus is not necessarily reflected in similar changes in other deep structures or in the surface cortical record.

The nonpsychotics, during episodic behavioral disorders, showed involvement of the same structures, but the pattern was more grossly evident during these shorter periods of agitation. At such times the patients reported upon were disoriented in various ways. One patient compulsively chanted Psalms in a "detached" manner and had hallucinations; another was "disoriented as to space, time, and person." Heath and Mickle state that their recordings "suggest that behavioral deviations correlate much more readily with activity of the deeper structures than with either the cortical or scalp recordings. . . . They indicate that a storm of abnormal activity can be brewing below with little or nothing showing at the cortical level."

Despite the wealth of data and theory which implicates these and other limbic structures in behavior, it must be emphasized that neither the orienting reaction nor storage of information is localized in these structures. When we recall Grastyán's report that ablation of the hippocampi did not remove the possibility of simple forms of conditioning, and the evidence from Jouvet, Hernández-Peón, and others that simple conditioning but not extinction of the orienting reaction can take place after removal of all neocortex, it is clear that these systems mediate important aspects of behavioral plasticity. Any given integrated behavioral act probably involves not one, but many comparator systems acting jointly, and performing with constant multiple feedback among them. Our neurobehavioral vocabulary is still inadequate to define the dimensions of such interaction. The brain, which changes itself in the course of its own activity, is not to be regarded simply as a spatial maze of paths and connections. We have probably come close to the limits of the understanding, in terms of behavioral analysis, which can be built upon such a conception, and we must now take account of the fact that the most important determinants of integrated behavior are to be found in coexisting and largely parallel systems which are predominantly inhibitory in nature. As neurobehavioral research focusses on the types and quantities of inhibition, revealing neural sectors of so-called "silence" as well as sectors of "activation,"—for both are of equal importance—the fundamental patterns of nervous activity will be more closely linked to the richness we recognize in behavior.

ON THEORIES OF LEARNING 12

The theories of behavior which are widely held by academic psychologists all tend to focus on the problem of learning. And, despite their differences, all alike relegate inhibition to a subordinate role, or deny that the concept has any validity whatever save in a purely descriptive sense. The facts which were adduced in the first part of this book can leave no doubt about the importance of inhibition as a physiological phenomenon which affects the outcome of behavior. On this level, it is not possible to close one's eyes to inhibition as a necessary concept for the description of empirical data. It may still be argued, however, that the question for psychology is not whether inhibition is a physiological reality, but whether an inhibition-construct is essential for the prediction of behavior, and if so, how large is the role that it must play.

The test of this pudding is in its eating. We shall not serve up a new theory of learning, spiced with inhibition, but we can sample the old ones and try to show that they all lack an essential ingredient. Specifically, we shall try to show that although each of these theories achieves a considerable success in predicting behavior in certain defined situations, none can reasonably be regarded as a "theory of learning" in the sense that it is able to fit all the kinds of plasticity which are displayed by organisms when they are not subject to the restraints imposed by experimental controls.

The point which we wish to make can be illustrated first with respect to a very old theory of learning, which Plato presents in the Dialogue of Meno. The Dialogue begins with Meno's query whether virtue can be taught or is given to man by nature or acquired in some other way. After some conversation about virtue, Socrates proposes that "all learning is but recollection," and he undertakes to demonstrate this with a slave boy who has never studied geometry. Then Socrates displays the skill which should make him the patron saint of all those who write instructional programs:

SOC. Attend now to the questions I ask him, and observe whether he learns of me or only remembers.

MEN. I will.

SOC. Tell me, boy, do you know that a figure like this is a square?

BOY. I do.

SOC. And you know that a square has these four lines equal?

BOY. Certainly.

SOC. A square may be of any size?

BOY. Certainly.

[The program continues until the boy makes an error.]

SOC. Do you see, Meno, what advances he has made in his power of recollection? He did not know at first, and he does not know now, what is the side of a figure of eight: but then he thought that he knew, and answered confidently as if he knew, and had no difficulty; but now he has a difficulty, and neither knows nor fancies that he knows.

MEN. True.

[After some further discussion, Socrates resumes the program.]

SOC. Mark now the further development. I shall only ask him, and not teach him. . . . Tell me, boy, is this a square of four feet which I have drawn?

BOY. Yes.

SOC. And now I add another square equal to the former one?

BOY. Yes.

SOC. And a third, which is equal to either of them?

BOY. Yes.

[The program continues in this fashion until the boy agrees to a statement to the effect that the square on the diagonal is just twice as great as the original square. Then the program is redirected to the astonished Meno.]

SOC. And this knowledge which he now has must he not either have acquired or always possessed?

As meekly as his slave boy, Meno answers "Yes." If he is to play the game according to its rules, he will now have no choice but to agree that the boy "recollected" what he had already known. But this conclusion depends on the tacit initial assumption that the boy was, at the start, either an empty vessel into which knowledge must be poured, or one in which this knowledge was already contained. If *this* be learning, and *this* be recollection, then there must indeed be "some other way," as suggested in Meno's original query. What would have happened, we wonder, if Meno had answered not with *yes* or *no,* but *neither?* How would the behavior of the programmer have altered to accommodate this unruly response?

Although in this chapter we shall consider a number of theories of learning, we are not ourselves disposed to accept the disjunction between learning and maturation, any more than that between heredity and environment. Nor do we wish to evade the question, as many have done recently, by answering "both." Instead, we prefer the answer "neither," because the question as put is meaningless without a particular definition of learning, and the kind of "learning" which is defined by any particular theory does not ever include all of the possibilities of choice which are open to the organism in a situation which is not controlled by a particular experimental paradigm.

All organisms exhibit what Brunswik (1952) called "stabilized achievement," that is, they adjust to changes in the environmental situation by performing actions which result in fairly systematic relationships between their internal states and their ecological surrounds. Tolman and Brunswik (1935) stated the need for behavioral plasticity in these terms: "The wholly successful organism would be one which brings, innately, normal averagely 'good' means-end hypotheses and normal averagely good 'reliable' perceptual hypotheses; but which can immediately modify these hypotheses to suit the special conditions of a special environment: which can note and include in its cue-system and in its means-end-system the presence of the further identifying features of these special environments. But further, such an organism must also, if it is to be completely successful, be equally able at once to drop out such new hypotheses when the special features as to cue or means are no longer present."

This statement includes a methodological implication which is accepted by virtually all psychologists: to study an organism, we must place it in a situation with which it is not initially prepared to cope on the basis of "innate hypotheses." It is this method of studying the plasticity of behavior with which we are concerned. Interestingly, this statement embraces both Freud's concept of development by blocking of "instinctual discharge" and the Dewey and Bentley approach which has been developed by Ittelson and Cantril (1954), who state that "hitches or obstacles, provide the occasions for increasing the scope and adequacy of our assumptions." (Ethologists, on the other hand, do not insist that an organism must be confronted by a problem in order to present behavior that is worth observing.)

Much earlier, the method had been introduced by Thorndike in his first experimental studies of *Animal Intelligence* (1898). He put newly hatched chicks into mazes, and hungry cats into puzzle-boxes. In attempting to escape from its box, the cat usually emits a relatively large number of responses, responding by "trial and error" until one "chance success" actuates the release mechanism. With successive trials, there is a decrease in time which may be plotted as a "learning curve." Guided by the concept of association, Thorndike formulated a point of view called *connectionism,* and he was able to list a series of laws relating the stimuli to the responses in such situations. (For a concise statement of Thorndike's learning theory, see Sandiford, 1942.) Although these laws have undergone many amendments since, Thorndike, like Pavlov and Ebbinghaus, set the pattern for many who were to follow him by the elegance of his method.

One may take note at this point of an interesting distinction between the method of Pavlov and that of Thorndike. Thorndike placed the animal in a problem situation, left it free to respond in many ways, and observed the gradual narrowing of the animal's actual responses in this situation during trial after trial. Pavlov observed a very specific effector response, one which could barely be described as an aspect of "behaving," and he found it methodologically useful to exclude so far as possible every opportunity for other ways of responding and every stimulus which might induce another response. In both cases, the same approximate law, a kind of "connectionism," soon emerged. But the treatment of exceptions to that law was different, and was determined to a great extent by the experimental method. For Thorndike, and for many of those who were to follow his lead, the exceptions were to be regarded as simple consequences of the impossibility of establishing complete control over the stimuli. Because absolute control of stimulation is impossible, one cannot realistically aspire to more than approximate control of behavior. This need not stop one from spinning a theoretical picture of ideal learning, based on the general trends which are observable.

For Pavlov, on the other hand, the exceptions were not to be written off as mere chance events. There has been an ideological basket to hold them, and that basket was inhibition. Now that we know the nature of synaptic inhibition, we can recognize how far wide of the mark Pavlov was in some of his speculations. However, if the nature of synaptic inhibition had gone undiscovered, the demonstration of its importance for behavior would have been no less conclusive, and the concept of inhibition, as expressed by Pavlov, was a proper semantic basket for carrying the import of this process. American psychologists, accustomed to a very different procedure, might reject his conclusions on the grounds that they were sometimes based on the observation of only one or two animals. From their point of view, any specific instance of behavior might just as well be an exception to the law as an expression of it. But Pavlov was expressing what Lewin (1935) was to call the Galilean method in science: the insistence that every individual case is fully bound by law, and every individual case is fully explicable if the laws that govern it are understood.

In Thorndike's writings, the concept of instinct survived side by side with that of connectionism, and learning theory would not have reached its dominant position in American psychology without the development of an anti-instinct environmentalist movement, under the dynamic leadership of John B. Watson. In his hands, Behaviorism grew into not only a school of psychology, but a philosophy of tremendous scope which might be understood by all who mastered the requisite habits. It offered a program not only for the investigation of what were "hitherto" called, as Watson (1924) scornfully remarks, "the mental and moral" fields, but also for the application of the knowledge thus gained to the presumed betterment of society: toward creating a generation of children raised in "behavioristic freedom," unencumbered by irrational affectional attachments to their parents.

Watson recognized the possibility for development of psychology as a molar discipline, while still retaining the firm base of known physiological facts. Although not acquainted with the work of Bykov and others in Pavlov's sphere, he stated with assurance: "No secure evidence is on hand to show that these [ductless] glands can be conditioned. . . . I for one am convinced that these can be and always are conditioned" (Watson, 1924). And although Boring (1950) calls Watson's behaviorism an expression of the *Zeitgeist* of his time, there can be no doubt that its principles still have strong appeal, and many young students of psychology implicitly translate other stimulus-response psychologies into a Watsonian version, glossing over the sophistications added by subtler thinkers. As Freud seems the master of the hidden subterranean passages, so Watson is the master of the direct and commonsense "open-air" approach, in which every form of indirection is classified as unpardonable mysticism.

Watson's thoroughgoing environmentalism dismissed the concept of instinct as unfounded, drastically reduced the number of stimulus-response connections which were acknowledged as unlearned, and thus turned the whole process of behavioral plasticity into one of "learning," or more specifically the strengthening of stimulus-response connections by exercise. With this magic formula, he undertook to "build (granting that both internal and external environment can be controlled) any infant along any specified line—into rich man, poor man, beggar man, thief."

For Watson, as for Socrates in the *Dialogue of Meno,* the question is stated in an absolute disjunction: each bit of behavior is either innate or learned. In a purely formal sense the result is similar, although now the choice inevitably falls on the opposite alternative: what the boy cannot do before his exposure to the program of stimuli, but can do after, must under the new set of assumptions clearly be classified as "learned." The maze, the puzzle-box, and the conditioning stand have been extrapolated into *all* of the environment of the organism. The generalizations which suffice to describe behavioral shifts in those situations are assumed to be principles adequate for the explanation of all changes in behavior, and he who controls the sequence of stimuli in these situations, potentially controls all the behavior of the organism. When control lapses, it is only because some stimulus has been overlooked. What else, if all behavior consists of a few "embryological responses" which can be discerned in the neonate, plus the effects of learning?

The comfortable self-assurance of this viewpoint was shaken by the emergence of Gestalt psychology. Köhler, in *The Mentality of Apes* (1925), challenged the validity of behavioral analyses based on the maze and the puzzle-box, by pointing out that the very procedures forced the animal to behave in an unintelligent, trial-and-error fashion. He proposed that the animal's perception of the situation, not its response to the situation, was crucial. How does it originally perceive the situation, and what restructuring does the situation permit? If we wish to get a true picture of the capabilities of the organism, we may block its responses, but we must not block its view of all the elements which influence the outcome. Köhler explained perceptual restructuring in terms of a redistribution of tensions in the "psychological field," making use of the hypothesis of isomorphism between cortical and psychological events which had already been suggested by Max Wertheimer (1912). Wertheimer, in turn, subsequently used this approach in his book *Productive Thinking* (1945), where he made a phenomenological analysis of problem solving on the very highest levels. (In a previous chapter, it has been suggested that the concept of inhibition offers a better approach to the problem of perceptual restructuring than the untenable hypothesis of electrophysiological cortical fields.)

This approach did not fail to exert great influence on many American psychologists, and notably on Lashley, an indefatigable investigator who never brushed real difficulties aside. However, most students of learning were unimpressed, and insisted that the so-called sudden learnings could be translated into early learnings which had taken place during the animal's uncontrolled experience. Clinging still to the sharp distinction between the "learned" and the "unlearned," they looked upon Köhler as an apologist for an extreme nativism. Adams (1931) attempted to state the problem of learning in field-theoretical terms, and in so doing he made an important distinction between learning and economy of performance. He wrote: "Economy on repetition is the most convenient and accessible and perhaps also the least unreliable sign of learning." However, it is merely an indicant of learning, and must not be mistaken to represent the substance. Adams also made another distinction which is useful to us, between learning and retentivity. Although all behavioral events result in some unknown physiological or biochemical changes in the organism, which must have some consequent effects on future behavior, these changes should not therefore be called "learning." *Retentivity* is a property of tissue on all levels of activity. Adams states that "there is no causal relationship between 'repetition' and learning. . . . Learning occurs without repetition and repetition occurs without learning." We suspect that these useful distinctions were overlooked because they were presented as part of Adams' effort to explain learning in terms of his field-theoretical position. Subsequently, some of his methodological contributions have been credited to other workers.

Ultimately, Gestalt psychology and field theory become domesticated in America. The one came to dominate the study of thinking and perception, and the other the field of social psychology. But the problem of learning continued to be the principal focus for the theoretical and experimental efforts of American psychologists, and in this field the concept of conditioning, though stated in a variety of ways, remained dominant. We shall consider particularly how two of those theories, those of Guthrie and Hull, dealt with the factor of inhibition, directly or indirectly.

Edwin Guthrie was for decades, from the heyday of Watsonian behaviorism until his recent death in 1959, the outstanding proponent of a consistent contiguity theory. A perennial target of controversy, his point of view still challenges all students of learning, and now provides the starting point for the new statistical approach by Estes (1950) and his collaborators. One of the strengths of his position is the fact that it translates readily into practical maxims for shaping behavior. On this level, few have displayed greater wisdom than he. There is no sounder advice for teachers than the simple statement: "We learn only what we do," or, more explicitly, "Whether a teacher is occupied with imparting knowledge or in correcting undesirable behavior, the problem is always to bring about by one means or another the behavior desired in the presence of the situation that should in the future be associated with that behavior" (Guthrie, 1942). The underlying theoretical principle is that "a stimulus pattern that is acting at the time of a response will, if it recurs, tend to produce that response." So much is taken from Pavlov, but Guthrie refuses to follow Pavlov into believing that any more than this is needed to explain all the plasticity of human behavior. With extraordinary resourcefulness, he applies this single principle to such varied problems as those of motivation, the acquisition of skills, and verbal habits.

Essential to Guthrie's argument is the fact that he applies this principle to *movements* and not to *acts*. Acts are the results of movements. If we describe the behavior of an organism in terms of what it is accomplishing, we may lose sight of the movements, the actual components of behavior; and then we may overlook the fact that learning is not a matter of repetition, but, according to Guthrie, always takes place in a single performance of the movement. Skills, which require that we perform different movements under different circumstances, or the same movements under different circumstances, require much learning, but each bit of learning is complete in itself.

The importance of proximal analysis is so great for Guthrie, that we must at this point break off our discussion of his theory to recall Brunswik's distinction between proximal and distal reference. Tolman and Brunswik (1935), arguing from a cognitive rather than a stimulus-response point of view, were among the first to point to the advantages of describing behavior in terms of a probability model rather than in terms of one-to-one stimulus-response relationships. In developing this argument, they distinguished between proximal and distal reference to environmental events, on both the stimulus and the response sides. On the stimulus side, a proximal description deals with receptor activities; whenever we talk about an *object* as a stimulus, we are using a distal-type description. On the response side, a proximal description is in terms of effector activities, but an act—or in their terms, an achievement—is the distal resultant of many proximal responses. The distal description lacks the detail of the proximal description, but even a very complete proximal description cannot replace the distal description completely, because no cross-sectional instantaneous "super-photograph" of the proximal stimulus pattern can provide the meaning of the *object*, which depends in part on the central organization of the organism, including the storage of past experience. As to the movements, they also become stimuli in any stimulus-response account, and their movement-character does not exhaust their stimulus-value.

There is surely an element of irreality which accompanies the extreme theoretical parsimony of any attempt to deal with behavior wholly in proximal terms. The task is clearly impossible, but this practical impasse provides at the same time an ideological escape, since it becomes possible to claim that *if* all the parts of this puzzle could be laid out in view, *then* it would be possible to assemble them into the complete picture of behavior. It is difficult, indeed, to demonstrate the theoretical inadequacy of such a system, which cannot be put to a conclusive test. However, it is not our task to show that Guthrie's system contains any fallacy, but only to show how, within this ultraparsimonious system, he accommodates the fact of behavioral inhibition.

Guthrie returns in effect to the position taken long before by Münsterberg, that inhibition can have no meaning except the incompatibility of movements. "Associative inhibition" takes place because the stimuli which had formerly called forth one response, are now associated with another. That they seem to inhibit the first response is simply the consequence of the fact that performing the second makes performing the first impossible. This inhibitory *effect* is a very important aspect of behavioral change, but no inhibitory *process* need be assumed to explain it. It is simply the negative effect of having attached a new response to the old cue, and as such it is an inevitable aspect of all learning. Pavlov (1932) specifically rebukes Guthrie for his failure to accept inhibition as a physiological datum.

At this point, Guthrie (1942) again shows his extraordinary ability to turn abstract principles into concrete guidance. To destroy an undesirable association, one may (1) present the cue along with other stimuli which will produce an incompatible response, or (2) present the cue until the response is fatigued, and beyond, or (3) present the cue at subthreshold strength, and gradually increase it, so that "the individual becomes habituated to doing something else in the presence of the stimulus." We shall see later how Wolpe incorporated these procedures into a therapeutic setting.

A weakness in Guthrie's position is the fact that, consistently applied, it must mean that very slight responses, involving only minimal movements, often have the power to prevent the occurrence of other responses which would involve the expenditure of a great deal of energy. Indeed, one may well wonder how the organism ever succeeds in getting a moment of quiet rest, if the inhibition of one response must depend always on its doing something else. It is this difficulty, perhaps, which brings Guthrie finally (1959) to emphasize the importance of attention. He writes: "It is possible that the linguistic solution is to recognize that responses of *attention* form a special category of responses. These are subject to a system of change (continuous ranging or scanning) that is relatively independent of movement routines of other systems." It is "a variegated class of response which have in common only the fact that they involve movements of orientation, changes of posture, the inhibition of movements that interfere with orientation of sense organs, and minimize distraction."

With this definition of attention, it seems as if Guthrie may have retrogressed from Münsterberg to Ribot! In doing so, he has found a new and more economical way of achieving inhibitory effects. For attention "intervenes in the causal chain between stimulus and response," even to the extent of removing the stimulus which originally called forth a given response pattern, or by disrupting a movement pattern, as in the case when "if attention is diverted from the script to the moving fingers, writing becomes difficult or impossible."

By this emphasis on attention, the possibility of an adequate proximal account of either stimulation or response becomes even more remote than before. This difficulty renders the concept of pure contiguity learning virtually immune from experimental test. That variability of response which was, for Pavlov, an important characteristic of conditional responses and an indicator of the inhibitory process, is safely ascribed to our lack of control over the minutiae of environmental stimulation. Guthrie has, with elegant parsimony, attained on paper a complete control over the responses of the organism, but it may never be possible to exercise this absolute control even in an experimental situation—not under the conditions of Pavlov's method, he writes, where "physical stimuli extended over long periods during which changes in attention were inevitable"; nor under the conditions of maze learning, where posture and movement as well as attention are uncontrolled; but only in some unknown situation in which "we take precautions to have the subject in the same posture or movement and to ensure attention at the proper moment."

Who shall say whether the effect of this drastic situational restraint, in which the senses as well as the body are held in a kind of experimental harness, is only to exclude the effects of chance, or to cut away, as it were, all the parts of the organism which might function in ways unforeseen in the system?

Because Guthrie's system makes a virtue of simplicity, one feels no need to apologize for a synoptic statement. In the case of Hull, the situation is very different, and one feels the danger that any attempt at simplification may turn into a caricature. In his posthumous work, *A Behavior System* (1952), Hull wrote: "To arrive at a genuine understanding of behavior is a personal achievement requiring a lifetime." To this achievement he devoted himself untiringly and with unusual success. The years that Guthrie spent in sparkling variations on a theme, Hull devoted to painstaking revision and amendment, until at the end he offered "a" system, in place of the *Principles of Behavior* (1943) which had been enunciated about ten years earlier. His method, a fertile combination of mathematical and empirical procedures, marks him as an original thinker of the first rank. Hull's system of behavior, which is much more than a theory of learning, has probably exerted greater influence than any other on a whole generation of psychological researchers and thinkers. It is with trepidation that one undertakes to state a few essentials of this system in brief, to provide the context for our discussion.

These essentials, the bare skeleton of only a part of the system, may be stated as follows.

1. At birth the organism possesses certain receptor-effector con-

nections which are unlearned. This class of connections is symbolized $_SU_R$. They serve the general purposes of adaptation for the species and the individual.

2. The system $_SU_R$ is activated under the joint effects of stimulation, S, and conditions leading to a need state or drive, *D*. The responses of the system $_SU_R$ are likely to result in the reduction of this drive state.

3. If, in the presence of *D* and S, a response (*R*) is emitted which reduces the need, then there is an increased tendency for S to elicit *R* on its next presentation. This reduction of need is the definition of reinforcement. (A more exact statement would refer to the neural traces of S and *R*, rather than to the events.)

4. The combined occurrence of S, *D*, and *R* leads to an increased tendency for the occurrence of *R*. This increased tendency, with other variables held constant, is measured by habit-strength. The symbol for habit-strength is $_SH_R$, but for our purposes, we may abbreviate this to *H*.

5. Habit-strength is a function of the number of reinforcements, or drive reductions, and it increases as a continuous growth process up to a physiological limit for the particular organism.

Let us stop for a moment to consider this abbreviated model of Hull's theory. There are two connecting or affector-effector systems, $_SU_R$ and $_SH_R$. Both are activated by *D*, in the presence of S. Thus, there is a starting system of needs, which puts the organism into action, and a system of stimulus-guided response tendencies, or habit-strengths, which tend to satisfy the needs. The behavioral act is a consequence of needs and habit-strengths, as well as unlearned response tendencies, interacting. This leads to the next principle, which is a guess that requires empirical validation.

6. The reaction potential (or excitatory potential) of an act is a multiplicative function of needs and habit-strength. That is, $E = f(D \times H)$.

Even in this grossly simplified account, from which many essential variables are still missing, one can see why Hull's theory is appropriately called a behavior *system*. Response is always a joint function of several variables. The system can readily grow to accommodate more variables, as in fact it has. For example, if *D* and *H* are both held constant, the reaction potential varies with the magnitude of the incentive or reward, *K*. It varies also with the stimulus-intensity dynamism, *V*, and with delay in reinforcement, *J*. All of these variables enter into a common multiplicative relationship, that is, $E = f\ (D \times H \times K \times V \times J)$. However, we are interested in three variables whose effects, as Hull sees them, will not be felt inside this parenthesis, but will detract from the magnitude of the reaction potential. These variables are: reactive inhibition, I_R, conditioned inhibition, $_SI_R$, and oscillation, $_SO_R$.

At this point, it is of some interest to note that Hull (1929) at first was greatly influenced by Pavlov's (1927) views on inhibition, and at that time he described the process of conditioning as consisting of an initial excitatory phase followed by a subsequent inhibitory phase. In the development of Hull's theory, he moved more and more away from physiological reference toward purely formal quantitative relationships. This progress toward abstraction is discernible in connection with each of the variables we are about to discuss.

The need for reactive inhibition arises from the fact that just as habit-strength increases with the number of reinforcements, it *seems* to decrease with the number of nonreinforced repetitions, in the process of extinction. But this appearance is deceptive, for the phenomenon of spontaneous recovery from extinction revealed to Hull, as it did to Pavlov, that something quite different from a decay of habit-strength is taking place, and that it is necessary to assume the operation of an active force of opposite tendency. Hull (1952) defines it in these words: "Whenever a reaction (*R*) is evoked from an organism there is left an increment of primary negative drive (I_R) which inhibits to a degree according to its magnitude the reaction potential ($_SE_R$) to that response."

It is important to note that reactive inhibition is not defined as a consequence of unreinforced repetition of a response, but as a consequence of *each* repetition. Where there is reinforcement, the reactive inhibition is masked by the stronger positive effect; in the absence of the latter, the former becomes apparent.

Another point of importance is that reactive inhibition is defined as a negative drive state, perhaps in analogy to fatigue. One consequence of this is that, like drive, reactive inhibition dissipates when the conditions producing it are no longer present. That is why a reaction potential may be reduced below the response threshold and yet return—while other factors of drive, stimulation, etc., are held constant—to above threshold value, in the phenomenon of spontaneous recovery. Long-range extinction must therefore be explained in some other manner.

This brings us to the phenomenon of conditioned inhibition. Since reactive inhibition is a drive, the event of its dissipating constitutes a drive reduction, and hence it will tend to reinforce the association between any stimuli and responses which are active during this period. The response which is reinforced, according to Hull, is the *cessation* of the very response which had given rise to the reactive inhibition. Thus, in the absence of any positive reinforcement for the act itself, a conditioned inhibition develops, by which stimuli associated with performance of the response come to inhibit it.

In Hull's 1943 system, conditioned inhibition has the status of a separate postulate, which we quote in part: "Stimuli (S) closely associated with the cessation of a response (R) (a) become conditioned to the inhibition (I_R) associated with the evocation of that response, thereby generating conditioned inhibition; (b) conditioned inhibitions summate physiologically with reactive inhibition. . . ."

Accordingly, reactive inhibition and conditioned inhibition both tend to diminish the magnitude of the reaction potential, leading to an effective reaction potential, $\overline{E}$, of reduced size. Thus, $\overline{E} = E - (I_R + {}_SI_R)$. The value of E, it will be recalled, is a multiplicative function of D, H, K, V, and J. From this product function, the inhibitory potentials are simply subtracted, to arrive at the effective reaction potential.

In 1952, conditioned inhibition is defined by Hull in a corollary to the postulate defining reactive inhibition, as one of its effects. This corollary reads: "Stimuli and stimulus traces closely associated with the cessation of a given activity, and in the presence of considerable I_R from that response, become conditioned to this particular non-activity yielding conditioned inhibition (${}_SI_R$) which will oppose ${}_SE_R$'s involving that response, the amount of ${}_SI_R$ generated being an increasing function of the amount of I_R present."

Comparing the 1943 and 1952 statements, one sees that the situational generality of reactive inhibition has been reduced, and as a result the importance of conditioned inhibition also has declined. The changes appear to be directly due to a difficulty which arose in quantification of the "inhibitory aggregate" ($I_R + {}_SI_R$). This inhibitory aggregate is made to depend both on the number of massed trials, and on the amount of work involved in "operating the manipulanda." However, the formidable difficulties which Hull meets in the reappraisals of inhibition, which lead to what Koch (1954) calls "localisms" of theory language, also express the inevitable embarrassment of any attempt to deal with inhibition as an aspect of a response-generating mechanism.

A number of authors have criticized Hull's treatment of inhibition as inconsistent. Hilgard (1956) suggests that since I_R is considered to be a drive state, it should logically subtract from D. Similarly ${}_SI_R$, since it is a kind of habit-strength, should combine with I_R multiplicatively, and not by addition. H. G. Jones (1958) offers an extensive reformulation of the status of inhibition in Hull's system, which leads to this new equation:

$$ {}_SE_R = f\,[(D - I_R) \times ({}_SH_R - {}_SI_R)]. $$

This equation includes a drive term, in which drive has been reduced by reactive inhibition, and a habit term, in which habit-strength is reduced by conditioned inhibition. Developing the mathematical implications of this formula, Jones points out that under certain rare conditions, if both the drive state and the habit-strength were negative, the effect of the inhibitions would be to produce a positive reaction potential, and he says that this "may furnish a theoretical explanation of such phenomena as the 'ultra-paradoxical' phase of inhibition observed by Pavlov."

A more fundamental reformulation of Hull's treatment of inhibition is offered by Spence (1956, 1958). In his account, different formulas are used to compute the reaction potentials under classical conditioning and under instrumental conditioning. The principal difference is that under instrumental conditioning the inhibitory potential, I_n, is a quantitative construct which not only serves as an indicant of the effects of extinction trials, but also serves to summate the effects of incompatible responses which have been acquired on the basis of contiguity. Spence (1958) explains this concept as follows: "While the basis of this inhibition is assumed to be competing, frustration-aroused responses that are established during extinction, the molar intervening variable, I_n, has been introduced to represent their quantitative effects." Spence's approach is tied very closely to particular situations, and although he loses some of the generality of Hull's account, he does so with the deepest knowledge of the strengths and limitations of Hull's position.

In a very recent review of most of the major revisions of Hull's constructs of inhibition, Jensen (1961) concludes that none of these revisions, with the possible exception of Spence's, can be considered as offering any real advantage in dealing with the empirical materials. He adds: "Advances will be made, not by the mere algebraic manipulation of Hull's intervening variables, . . . but by the postulation and quantification of new intervening variables, along with the experimental investigations of their interactions."

In Hull's system, a third contender as a source of inhibition is his concept of behavioral oscillation. In the 1943 set of postulates, a probability conception of behavior enters Hull's system in these terms: "Variability, inconsistency, and specific unpredictability of behavior have long been recognized as the chief molar distinctions between organisms and inorganic machines. Clearly a characteristic so fundamental as this must find an important place in any adequate theory of organismic behavior." This consideration leads him to the following postulate:

"Associated with every reaction potential (${}_SE_R$) there exists an inhibitory potential (${}_SO_R$) which oscillates in amount from instant to instant according to the normal 'law' of chance. . . ." This quantity also leads to a reduction of the reaction potential which, thus reduced, becomes the "momentary effective reaction potential," $\dot{\bar{E}}$. This is the strength of the tendency to perform a given act at a given time. It is the resultant of many interactive constructs, of which at least three may be considered inhibitory. Stimulus interaction, which we have not included, may also be regarded as exercising an inhibitory or reductive effect on the reaction potential.

In *A Behavior System*, Hull's posthumous work (1952), the concept of behavioral oscillation plays an important role in the development of a number of behavioral patterns. Besides serving as the principle which underlies response alternation and response generalization, it also helps to account for conflict, multidirectional maze learning, partial recovery from early extinction effects, variable path-selection in multiple-unit mazes, and valuative behavior. On this last point, Hull comments: "Behavioral inconsistency in evaluative behavior choices of both human and lower animals is believed . . . to be a function of the spontaneous oscillation of the reaction potential. . . ." Therefore we can only expect consistent behavior when reaction potentials are vastly different in value, or when we pool the data taken from many subjects. This qualification points to an important development: that in Hull's final work there is less willingness to deal with inhibition as a "lawful" element in behavioral control, and a disposition to expand the influence of chance factors which make control unattainable. This outcome is to a great extent a result of the methods of quantification of such constructs as habit-strength, reaction potential, inhibitory potential, and "chance" oscillation.

This discussion of Hull's contribution has been all too brief. Even if the grand scheme of his postulate system is to be rejected in full, his many brilliant papers and secondary formulations will continue to illuminate our work.

Skinner (1938, 1950) has avoided some of the difficulties of other students of learning by confining himself to a "descriptive behaviorism," in which he carefully refrains from the introduction of hypothetical constructs. He takes a position like that of Kantor (1947), that attempts at physiologizing have brought only difficulties to psychology, and therefore he writes a psychology which, it has sometimes been said, is "about, yet without" the organism. It is impossible to quarrel with his right to do this, but one may well question whether this refusal to consider explanations for behavioral events, and to construct theories which relate them among themselves and to the data of other sciences, does not also constitute an abdication of some of the possibilities of behavioral science. Although psychology has been led astray, more than once, by errors in neurological theory, it has also been helped by insights derived from that source, and it has had insights to give in exchange. At the present time, interdisciplinary research of neurologists and psychologists makes excellent use of the very methods which Skinner himself devised. Some of these studies will be cited in later chapters.

Errors and half-truths are inevitable hazards in the prosecution of science, and it would be foolish to suppose that psychology will never again be "misled" by neurology. Yet most psychologists will probably agree that on balance, from Gall to the present, psychology has gained more than lost, and neurology has gained more than lost, in the exchange of ideas. Perhaps the errors are those to which psychologists were predisposed by other factors. If we are to have theory construction at all—and few psychologists can exercise a full measure of Skinnerian control over this aspect of their own behavior —it is good that theories should be checked by the need to agree with the data of other sciences.

Wolpe (1958) comes to learning theory with the interests of a psychiatrist, and hence he is more intensely interested in what is often called "unlearning"—the extinction of undesirable ways of responding—than in the positive phases of learning. The therapeutic technique which he advocates, and which he calls *reciprocal inhibition,* is a direct application of Guthrie's prescription: to eliminate an undesirable association, present the cue under circumstances which evoke another response. However, he is not satisfied with Guthrie's explanation of the effectiveness of this procedure, as resulting from competition between reactions, nor with a Hullian explanation, in terms of reactive and conditional inhibitions. Indeed, he asks why, if conditioned inhibition is the consequence of a drive reduction, would it not follow that even on reinforced trials it would be the response cessation, which is closest in time to the reinforcement, that would be conditioned, rather than the response initiation?

Wolpe makes reference to neurological demonstrations of central synaptic inhibition on the spinal level, properly assumes that the same phenomenon exists on the cortical level, and looks to it for an understanding of conditioned inhibition. He says that just as "positive learning seems to depend upon certain neural chains becoming increasingly conductive," so conditioned inhibition may be assumed to result from "decreased conductivity of these neural chains." He offers a neurophysiological hypothesis to show how this may come about. It rests on the assumption that a "fatigue-associated substance" stimulates inhibitory neurons, and that inhibitory impulses produce modifying effects at synapses which have recently been active in response-evocation. This effort to relate neurophysiological inhibition to behavioral inhibition is a refreshing departure from the too common tendency to disregard inhibition or to depreciate its importance. However, the role of inhibition in behavior generally, and in the plasticity of behavior most especially, goes far beyond the part that it plays in producing response decrements, and therefore Wolpe's hypothesis must be regarded as concerned only with some of the special effects of inhibition, and not with its wider role. Even within its limited field of reference, it seems to us to rest upon too narrow a conception of inhibition, since it makes no reference to the local inhibitory potentials which appear everywhere in the nervous system as dampeners of excitation. Would not this provide a better base for a hypothetical explanation of extinction than a wholly speculative "fatigue-associated substance" released by somatic effectors?

Finally, we wish to comment briefly on the treatment of inhibition in Razran's theory of learning. From time to time, Razran has earned the gratitude of psychologists by his informative reviews of the Russian experimental literature, and he has made notable experimental contributions of his own, particularly with respect to the problem of semantic conditioning. His evolutionary theory of conditioning defines three distinctive levels, man alone being capable of all three. Most of the details of this interesting but difficult theory are not essential for our purpose. Our interest relates to two points: his theory of extinction, and his adaptation of Ukhtomsky's principle of dominance.

We consider first his concept of *dominance*. Although Razran stresses the importance of empirical foundations for theory, and he speaks a good deal of "neural events," he seems to have made no effort to relate his theoretical constructs to the data of contemporary neurophysiological research. In view of his position that "whatever extra constructs the behavioral psychology of learning may need, they must be grounded in and modelled after neural action rather than merely fashioned in the form of abstract logical relations," (Razran, 1957), it is disappointing that he should still talk in terms of a hypothetical "neural dominance," and even more specifically to hypothesize that classical conditioning can only take place when there is "minimal dominance," that is, when the US-initiated neural event is stronger than the CS-initiated neural event, that its efficiency rises with the ratio of these strengths up to a level of "optimal dominance," and that it declines thereafter, due to a relation of "overdominance." Wolman (1960), citing a more recent unpublished manuscript of Razran's which apparently deals with these matters in greater detail, says that Razran describes dominance as "a principle of sheer 'force.' "

In his theory of extinction, Razran posits a two-phase sequence: "automatic deconditioning" followed by "counter conditioning." The first phase "is a direct result of the loss of the interoceptive and proprioceptive conditional stimuli (feedback CS's) which . . . when the unconditional stimulus is withheld and the evoked reaction is reduced cease to be present." In other words, the response has lost some of its force, due to the diminution and disappearance of a positive feedback which was needed to nourish it; and this permits other neural processes, those involved in the counter conditioning, to become dominant.

Razran's emphasis on empiricism and on "neural events" places him under obligations which he does not meet. His rejection years ago of the Pavlov concept of internal inhibition, as a process which "irradiates and concentrates," was made on quite reasonable grounds, but the same sort of reasons do not apply to modern electrophysiological demonstrations of central inhibitory processes. Once one grants the existence of these "neural events," any physiologically oriented theory of behavior which does not include them is an anachronism. If, as Razran (1957) says, "anything that is neurally represented may become a conditioning datum," then he will have to make room in his theory for the hard fact of inhibition.

And that, after all, is a demand which is now placed on every theory of learning.

PLASTICITY OF BEHAVIOR 13

It is the task of this chapter to suggest some possible uses of the construct of inhibition in dealing with the plasticity of behavior. However, only a distorted picture would result from an attempt to do this without some consideration of other factors which influence plasticity, and it will therefore be necessary to discuss the relation of inhibition to three other constructs: reactivity, sensitivity, and retentivity. We assume that each of these constructs is, like inhibition, valid at the molecular level, and we shall try to show that at different times one or another of these four may play the leading role in regulating or controlling all of the others.

The most intensive studies of behavioral plasticity have made use of the paradigms of classical and operant conditioning, which provide fine-grain basic experimental prototypes for the prediction of behavior. However, it may be that a theoretical approach which is based too exclusively on these laboratory-defined situations, from which chance events must be so rigorously excluded, cannot provide the base for predictions of broader application. Brunswik (1947) has defined the need for study of behavior in its "representative" aspects, but the interests of many individual scientists have provided techniques for studying behavior in a variety of situations which do not fit the conditioning paradigms. To mention only a few: Harlow (1949) stresses the importance of intertrial influences; Frank (1938), Riesen (1961), and others point to special characteristics of plasticity during critical periods of growth; Berlyne (1960) demonstrates change in behavior due to expanding situations said to involve "novelty of stimulus situations"; Bruner (1956) and his associates have demonstrated long-range strategies or models of thinking which are employed by organisms in the development of decisions.

However, the principles developed out of any one of these situations are not likely to be generally valid in all the others. The attempt to form a unified theory based on a single approach is likely to result in a sense of parsimony of effort rather than in a parsimony of theory. Plastic changes take place in organisms with cerebral hemispheres or without them; alpha blocks are not the invariant measures of behavioral arousal; the old divisions between voluntary and involuntary, autonomic and somatic, are repeatedly being questioned; homeostasis no longer seems a universal key to behavior. These examples show us that a generalization which arises out of one paradigm rarely seems applicable, save in the view of its inventor, to all others. We wish to avoid the pitfall of a narrow specification, and speak, so far as possible, in terms which are applicable to behavior generally.

The problem of accounting for plastic changes in behavior, which result from experiences of the organism, is perhaps the most difficult which confronts any theory of behavior. We have taken the position that wherever choice exists, inhibition must be present. Furthermore, the variability out of which choice appears is not based solely upon evolutionary developments with respect to sensitivity and reactivity to external and internal stimulation. The mammal's variability is largely determined by its capacity to achieve independence from proximal sources of external stimulation, and even to replace or supplement compelling forms of internal stimulation with other kinds of internal guidance. Inhibition is an integral link in this more flexible coupling of the organism with its surround, on the one hand, and with its internal milieu, on the other. Inhibition is thus responsible for creating the very possibility of what we term "acquired" behavior, and those aspects of behavior which have been called "learning."

However, any consideration of the role of inhibition in plasticity requires that we consider it in relation to the other parameters we have mentioned. If one abstracts out of many situations those properties of organisms which lead to plastic changes, at least four indispensable constructs emerge: reactivity, sensitivity, retentivity, and inhibition. We shall consider them in order.

The most obvious manifestation of reactivity is, of course, myogenic action. Muscles demonstrate isolated proximal activity before they have neural connections. Herrick (1956) says that motility is "the cradle of the mind. . . . The body acts before it reacts." Autogenic motility, however, does not provide integrated action. Elements of sensitivity must appear to permit its more complex expressions, which include generalized intraorganismic patterns, such as the tonic cycles emphasized by Sherrington, Coghill, Freeman, and others. Against this background of tonicity, relatively rapid or phasic changes occur as in reflex adjustments or proximal activity. At a still higher level, proximal actions are organized into the intersubstitutable patterns which Brunswik called "achievements" or "distal effects." The definition of reactivity is in itself a complex problem, calling for morphological, temporal, and situational specifications.

In many cases it is possible to separate reactivity and sensitivity only in the analytic sense. Thus, Granit (1955) points out that the "simple" stretch reflex of Liddell and Sherrington (1925) includes four components, including an inhibitory influence from the Golgi tendon receptors. In Bykov's work on interoceptive conditioning, effector actions involving glandular secretions, such as pituitrin, served as the "stimuli" in conditioning procedures. Skinner (1938) has shown that response rates may be chained so as to set the occasion for other rates.[1] In short, reactivity itself is a determiner of sources of intraorganismic experience. Solley and Murphy (1960) point out that in addition to simple sensory registration, experience may result in new sensitizations and sensory differentiations. This is a problem which we cannot consider as one independent of retentivity and inhibition.

The forms of sensitivity are so far from obvious that we often require cross-situational comparisons in order to establish their effects. Thus, the differential reaction patterns of bees demonstrate that they have been receptive to information socially transmitted by other members of the colony. As another example, it has recently

[1] See Ferster and Skinner (1957) for excellent development of this concept.

been learned that moths probably possess an ultrasonic detector mechanism which allows them a somewhat better chance to escape their better-equipped predator, the visuo-sonar guided bat. The capacities of porpoises to transmit social information, and to utilize self-produced patterns of sonic feedback, are being intensively investigated. Whether, in a given instance of behavior, we focus our attention on the elements of reactivity or sensitivity which enter into its composition, depends to a great extent on the nature of the changes which we detect in the organism as a function of its developmental level or its history.

In the molar sense, the functional correlates of sensitivity are usually translated into extra- or intraorganismic dimensions specifiable as stimuli. Stimuli, however, may be defined in physical terms independently of the organsm. In the same way, reactivity may be translated into responses, such as a left turn or a bar press. Thus the molecular processes of sensitivity and reactivity provide the basis for the molar events which enter into a stimulus-response description of behavior. In such an account, both processes are viewed as wholly excitatory. The addition of drives or needs does not change the model appreciably, because a parsimonious stimulus-response psychology merely translates these states into new kinds of stimulation and into qualitatively different response patterns. In such a system, the stimulus usually leads the response, and thus we have an organism which is portrayed as possessing little flexibility or proximal independence. Behavior is described as a function of the stimulus plus the need states of the organism, and this statement implies a rather tight coupling between stimulus and response. If the organism does not possess a sufficient wealth of reaction patterns, it may not survive ecological shifts.

The organism's capacity for adaptation may be greatly enhanced by the addition of a third mechanism: retentivity. On the simplest levels, retentivity may consist in the retention or storage of a needed substance. This may lead to variability in response, for example, to the cessation of food intake. Retention of this basic kind is essential to all organisms.

However, the effects of retention may transcend the immediate situation of the organism, giving rise to forms of adaptation which are explored by theories of learning. Such theories often utilize the concept of an association between stimulus and response, which is usually thought to depend on increased ease of excitation of the neural tissues involved in the original behavior. However, there is scant evidence to support this assumption, and such formidable difficulties stand in its way that Lashley (1950) once remarked, with tongue in cheek: "I sometimes feel, in reviewing the evidence on the localization of the memory trace, that the necessary conclusion is that learning just is not possible." Actually, his doubts apply with telling force to all such concepts as reverberation, associative connections, the growth of synaptic knobs, increases in synaptic efficiency, etc. All such concepts arise out of basic assumptions about nervous circuitry which are quite misleading. They may be used to construct crude analogues to the action of the nervous system, but it no longer seems likely that the actual storage of experience consists in modifications of neural circuits or connections. More likely, the ultrastructure of storage is of a chemical nature, and although in the higher forms of life it is mediated by neural activity, it probably does not take place in the neurons themselves: Gerard (1961) suggests that it may take place at the macromolecular level, and Galambos (1961a) proposes that information storage may take place in the glial cells which surround the neurons, and which are much more numerous than the neurons themselves.

Whatever the nature of information storage within the brain, there are a number of observations which indicate that it is sometimes stored in multiple form, in different tissues—a fact which has bearing on the ability of such information to survive the destruction of neural structures which were necessary to its recording. An example of this is in the description which Penfield and Rasmussen (1950) give of the experiences which were evoked by electrical probing of specific cortical points in epileptic patients. In one girl 14 years of age, a "dreamlike" sequence of events could be aroused, in different stages depending on the site of stimulation. In this girl, the focal lesion created constant epileptic hallucinations which dominated her life. After removal of part of the right temporal lobe, the hallucinations ceased, but the possibility of recall was not eliminated. Penfield and Rasmussen comment: "She no longer had the hallucinations. But, when she was asked about the experience she could still remember it: the meadow, the man, and her fright. One may assume that she called upon an identical neurone pattern somewhere else in the brain when she voluntarily summoned this memory after operation. We may assume further that this identical pattern was located in the other temporal cortex, although this conclusion is purely hypothetical."

This hypothesis is supported by the results of recent experimental work by Morrell (1961) on "mirror foci." He applied ethyl chloride spray to a small (2 mm.) area of sensory cortex. At this time, there was no discharge on the contralateral cortex corresponding to the paroxysmal discharge of the treated area. Three days later, however, the symmetrically placed electrode did disclose a new focus. That is, a secondary discharge now appeared on the contralateral hemisphere; it is described as "a reflection of the primary discharge," and disappeared after ablation or surgical isolation of the primary lesion. However: "After a given period of time (24 hours to 7 days in the rabbit, 4 weeks to 3 months in the cat, about 8 weeks in the monkey) the secondary contralateral focus becomes independent in that it does not disappear upon ablation or coagulation of the primary region of discharge."

The development of this independent focus is prevented if the corpus callosum is sectioned within approximately twenty-four hours of primary lesion formation (in the rabbit), or if the site of the primary lesion is otherwise isolated. An isolated slab of such tissue is fairly readily excited by ephaptic (i.e., nonsynaptic) transmission from surrounding regions, and this leads Morrell to state: "We believe this to be a crucial observation because it demonstrates that the mirror focus is a region that has not only 'learned' to behave in terms of paroxysmal discharge, but which 'remembers' this behavior even after months of inactivity." He comments on the role of a possible chemical organizer substance which may regenerate molecular configurations and store patterns of information.

Summarizing to this point, we believe that a meaningful distinction may be made between sensitivity and reactivity on the one hand, as excitatory processes, and retentivity, as an information storage capacity. Changes in any one factor bring about changes in the others, and highly differentiated storage capacities, such as those observed by Penfield, produce very marked changes in sensitivity to external and internal sources of stimulation. (As we point out elsewhere, the pathologic aspect of such changes seems to depend on a marked reduction of local inhibitory potential.)

There is, of course, a tremendous range in the potential for plasticity. E. H. Hess (1956) has sought to appraise the functional plasticity of Leghorn chicks, with respect to the natively determined pecking response to visual stimuli. The chicks were hatched in complete darkness and immediately fitted with hoods containing goggles. The goggles of the experimental chicks displaced the visual field 7 degrees to one side or the other, while those of the control animals did not displace the visual field. One day was allowed for adaptation to the hood, and the chicks were then tested for pecking accuracy by exposing them to brass nails imbedded in clay. The pecks of the experimental animals fell about 3 to 4 mm. from the target, representing the 7 degree displacement over a pecking distance of 25 to 30 mm. Evidently, then, the specificity of the response is controlled by the animal's morphological structure.

To test the effects of experience, half the experimental animals and half of the controls were fed from bowls of mash, so that accuracy of pecking was of no importance. The remainder were permitted to peck at scattered grain, a condition which required accuracy for optimal food intake, and which might be expected to foster a trial and error mastery of visuomotor coordination, if the response was capable of modification. When placed again in the test situation, between 3 and 4 days of age, it was found that the control animals had improved their performance by narrowing the range of scatter about the target. The experimental animals also narrowed the error cluster, but the systematic error found in the original test remained. That is, the pecks were still dispersed around a point about 4 mm. from the target. That there was real need for learning in the target situation is shown by the fact that the experimental animals fed in this situation were in poor health, and two of them died. Hess concludes that "the chick's visual apparatus for locating objects in space is innate and not learned."

These results are in sharp contrast to those of essentially similar experiments with human subjects. G. M. Stratton (1897) covered one eye, and wore a prism which inverted the image on the other. At first the "upside-down world" was reacted to with confusion, and visual perception in the ordinary sense was difficult. By the eighth day, however, Stratton was able to smooth out the clash between body cues (tactile, kinesthetic, proprioceptive, etc.) and visual cues. He says that he was then able to react in a way which was harmonious with body sensation. However, he says that if he then compared the adjusted visual field with recall of the older visual cue system, he appeared to be observing the situation from an "inverted body."

Stratton's findings have been corroborated repeatedly. Snyder and Pronko (1952) report that Snyder adjusted the visuomotor clash sufficiently to drive a car and swim successfully. Once again, however, there was a definite clash between the visual field and recall if the factor of recall of the original visual set was introduced. Kohler (1951) reports similar experiments of much longer term, up to four months' duration, some of which involved top-to-bottom or right-to-left reversals of the visual field, while others involved angular displacement of the whole visual field or part of it. In these prolonged experiments, a dependable reorganization of the perceptual field followed after the achievement of satisfactory habits of locomotion and manipulation. Kohler points especially to the aftereffects of such experiments—to the distortions of opposite sense which appear when the prisms are no longer being worn—as evidence that the process of adjustment is central as well as peripheral. For example, aftereffects that follow a long period in the use of half-prisms distorting only the upper part of the visual field and not the lower, were not associated with any particular portion of the retina, but with a particular position of the eyes and the head, a circumstance which leads Kohler to call them "conditional sensations."

We cannot say for sure whether the nervous apparatus of the chick would be adequate to effect a similar reorganization, if the experiment could be arranged to allow the chick as much time as Kohler and his subjects had. However, it is clear that the reorganization effected by the human subjects in these experiments is not simply a matter of the establishment of new stimulus-response associations, nor can it be regarded as a change taking place wholly in the sphere of sensitivity. It is a reintegration which involves the relationship of sensitivity and retentivity to a fourth parameter of plasticity, inhibition. Kohler himself concludes that "one must think in terms of an *hypothesis of central (reciprocal) inhibitions and facilitations of aftereffects.*" Even the simpler adjustment of visuomotor habits, which precedes the perceptual reorganization, necessarily involves inhibitory elements. Instead of the lifelong habit of reaching to the right, this response was arrested and directed to the opposite side. The ability thus to change previous stimulus-guided integrations, and to form new integrations within a matter of days, points to highly developed inhibitory capacities. Such a reintegration would probably not be possible, in the face of long-practiced reactive dispositions, on the basis of merely retaining information associated with specific stimuli. The control and integration of all stimuli and response dispositions, those newly arising from moment to moment as well as those already experienced during the learning period, is effected by inhibition.

But if the "associational" account is inadequate in respect to the results with human subjects, so also is the simple statement that the chick's visuomotor coordinations are innate. There can be no quarrel with the fact that this apparatus is "given" in the morphological sense. But that statement is as true for man as for the chick, as can be readily determined by observing the visual pursuit of a well-developed human infant a few days after birth. (Since these lines were written, Michael Wertheimer (1961) has reported eye movements directed toward auditory stimuli within the first minutes of postnatal life.) The difference in functional plasticity, which permits one organism to alter what is morphologically "given" while another cannot, is a reflection of differences in inhibitory capacity. With respect to sensitivity and reactivity, the chick's visuomotor apparatus is quite adequate. With respect to retentivity, we know that the chick is capable of altering other response probabilities (for example, those involved in imprinting behavior, as well as those in a maze). The reason for the lack of plasticity in respect to the pecking pattern must be sought elsewhere.

Actually, the pecking pattern represents a very tight and effective coupling with the environmental surround, and one with high survival value under ordinary circumstances. The chick does not normally need choice in this situation, except in the sense of preference for targets of certain size and shape, which has been demonstrated elsewhere. Long ago, Lloyd Morgan (1896) observed that such preferences could be modified by experience, and his half-anecdotal, half-experimental account of the responses of chicks to cinnabar caterpillars leaves no doubt of the chick's ability to inhibit its pecking response, under certain circumstances and at a somewhat more advanced age. In a famous passage, he says that chicks "strike at first with perfect impartiality at *anything* of suitable size. . . . They soon learn, however, what is good for eating, and what is unpleasant, and rapidly associate the appearance with the taste." Morgan, who had such a clear vision of the importance of inhibition in 1891, but who had meanwhile stated his canon of parsimony in 1894, refrained from any speculation concerning inhibition in this case. However, it is clear that when and where the chick lacks plasticity, it is because he lacks capacity for inhibition. The chick simply does not have the capacity to inhibit one peck pattern in order to gain another which is displaced 4 mm. to the left or right. The fact that one of these pecks is directed at a slightly different angle from the other does not make one "learned" and the other "innate," but rather the fact that the chick lacks the freedom of choice between these pecks, being restricted to one of them, indicates his impoverishment in respect to capacity for inhibition of proximally guided, stimulus-bound behavior. It is not simply a difference in the visuomotor system that is involved, between man and chick, but the possibility of bringing to bear upon that system an inhibitory control which is extraneous to it, and which would represent an organismic contribution.

Sperry (1951, 1958) studied the limits of plasticity in respect to the use of crossed sensory nerves or antagonistic muscles involved in locomotor patterns. In one experiment, he switched the nerve connections to muscles governing the movement of the ankle joint in the hind limbs of rats. The animals were unable to adjust to this situation. "When they tried to lift the affected foot, it pulled downward; when they tried to rise on the ball of the foot, their toes swung up and they fell back on their heels." In another experiment, muscles were crossed instead of nerves, but the result was the same. But if muscles *and* nerves were crossed, successful integrated movement took place. In this case indeed, two negatives became a positive. In still another experiment, the sensory nerve trunk was crossed from the left foot to the right, and electric shock was applied to the left foot; the animal would raise its right foot for each shock, and this continued to the point that, after a sore had been developed on the left foot, the rat hopped about on three feet, keeping the unharmed right foot suspended above ground!

Anokhin (1961a) discusses results of similar experiments performed in his laboratory, on cats. These animals were able to compensate for the interchange of flexor and extensor muscles after about one year, and electromyographic analysis indicated that the new functions were being correctly performed. However, when these animals were spinalized the muscles reverted to their original functions. It is clear that the important plastic changes did not occur at the spinal level. Although Eccles (1961) has demonstrated that spinal synapses increase in efficacy as a result of use, and therefore considers it likely that such changes are basic to plasticity at least as regards motor phenomena, the findings of Sperry and of Anokhin indicate that some very different process, not at the spinal level, must be involved. Human beings do seem to be able to control the actions of transplanted muscles, but in this connection Sperry makes the following comment: "In most cases humans can learn to control transplanted muscles only in simple, slow, voluntary movements. The control of complex, rapid and reflex movements is limited at best and is subject to relapse under conditions of fatigue, shock or surprise." These, of course, are the conditions which commonly give rise to disinhibition. The transplanted muscle is held in a very delicate state of control, which does not permit the usual autonomization of function. It is fairly obvious that inhibitory controls, other than those on the spinal levels, are involved, and it is also obvious that these are unstable and extremely subject to disinhibition, which precipitates relapse or loss of control.

The effects of deprivation in visual experience constitute another area of fruitful experimental investigation of behavioral plasticity. In *The Organization of Behavior* (1949), Hebb cites the observations of Senden (1932) and the experiments of Riesen (1947) regarding the effects on perception of the limitations of such experience, and the possibilities of overcoming them. Senden observed that after removal of congenital cataracts, considerable experience is required before one can identify objects in terms of simple shapes without having the opportunity to touch them. For example, it required considerable experience to discriminate a square from a triangle. However, perception does eventually approximate normal perception. In his analysis of how such "normal" perception develops, Hebb assigns an important role to eye movements, although he points out that after long-standing experience the perception of patterns is not dependent on eye movements.

The experimental analysis of this problem was continued by Riesen (1958). Two chimpanzees, Snark and Alfalfa, were kept from birth in a room completely darkened, except for a period of approximately 45 seconds each day. In a test at the age of sixteen months they demonstrated low-order reflexes to light, but they failed to show any responses to more complex light sources. Feeding bottles and play objects were not responded to unless they touched the animals' bodies. Threatening movements did not produce a blink. They were then placed on limited schedules of light. At thirty-three months, Snark was transferred to "the normally lighted nursery and later out of doors with chimpanzees of his own age. It was expected that he would rapidly acquire normal visual behavior. He did improve slightly at first, but after his small initial improvement he actually lost ground in visual responsiveness, until even reflex activity began to die away."

Riesen has demonstrated that these results were not due to lack of visual experience per se, but to lack of patterned visual experience. Even after early normal visual experience, deprivation may lead to extreme retardation. The chimpanzee, Faik, was placed in darkness at the age of eight months, and remained there until twenty-four months. He showed profound visual disturbances which were similar to those of the animals in the early darkness experiment. His return to the normal pattern was slow and, at the time of Riesen's writing, still partial. (Accompanying morphological changes have been discussed by Riesen, 1958.)

Riesen's more recent work (1961) demonstrates another aspect of the problem, which is directly connected with inhibition. A cat, Furry, was raised for one year in a dark cage, where it appeared to be normal in most of its transactions. Subsequently it was introduced into a phased schedule of the visual environment. However, for as long as one year it exhibited hyperexcitability whenever it was placed in a strange visual field. At three and one half years it was not proficient in spatial detour problems. Similar results are reported for chimpanzees.

Another cat, White, was also raised in a dark cage, but for one hour of each day it wore a white translucent hood which admitted only differential gradients of brightness. This animal adapted readily and played with other cats in a larger pen. However: "At the age of 2 years and 11 months this well adjusted cat was suddenly introduced into a strange, sound-shielded room, 5 feet by 5 feet, and 9 feet high, and the hood was removed. There was one light bulb shining at a height of 4 feet. Almost immediately White began to run rapidly and frantically about the room, bumping into corners or up the side walls." A second exposure to the room nine days later led to a tonic-clonic seizure which lasted for three minutes and was followed by "sporadic attempts to orient towards the light." A third exposure was milder, and White was finally placed in a cage in the normally lighted laboratory. There "he lay quietly in the cage most of the time, eating poorly or not at all. At the age of 3 years, White died. No further seizures had been observed. No acute symptoms or any obvious cause of death could be determined."

Surely, White's death was precipitated by the proximal sensory overload, which could not be arrested. There seems to be little point in distinguishing here between learned and innate patterns of reaction. It makes no sense to call the adjusted pattern a learned one and the maladjusted something different. The result ensues from the peculiarity of drastic proximal-to-central coupling without the intervention of inhibition. On the basis of Riesen's earlier work, we can assume that no patterned or distal perception was possible in this case. The proximal situation was not controlled by inhibition, and the unmodulated arousal, which in the less extreme case showed itself as hyperexcitability, here produced a tonic-clonic seizure.

Riesen does not report any observations relative to eye-blink rates and eye-closing, but it is unlikely that this animal did not possess, in the morphological sense, the capacity to close its eyes. This simple act might have returned it to its well-adjusted state, in an environment devoid of visual objects. Opening and closing its eyes, it might even have developed its own program of visual events. Its failure to do this is difficult to explain under any stimulus-reduction theory of drive. But in the nonselective excitatory state into which this animal was plunged by its visual experience, even this relatively simple act of control was evidently unavailable to it. The fact that, in Riesen's earlier work with the chimpanzees, the effects of a similar program were so much less drastic, may be ascribed to the fact that the higher primates were able to disregard the unwonted stimulation, even to the point of obliterating reflex-type responses, not by closing their eyes, but by a kind of negative adaptation or habituation. For the visually-deprived chimpanzee, visual stimulation provided very poor cue-validity when compared with the kinesthetic-tactile stimulations with which it had more extensive experience. Whenever clashes between the two arose, the visual effects would be "partialled out" as noise. Thus successful adaptation might be best served by inhibition of the less reliable cues, bringing about the actual decline in reliance on vision which was noted by Riesen.

Experimental studies of habituation show another important aspect of plasticity, in which factors of retentivity and inhibition are both prominent. Instances of habituation have been reported for virtually every organism whose behavior has been studied, and it is perhaps the lowest common denominator of experientially acquired change. Thorpe (1956) defines habituation as "the relatively permanent waning of a response as a result of repeated stimulation which is not followed by any kind of reinforcement." Solley and Murphy (1960) contrast sensitization and habituation as "antipodal effects," for in the first case we gain sensory responsiveness, while in the second there seems to be a loss of the positive aspects of responding. They point out, of course, that there is nothing contradictory in considering inhibitions and excitations simultaneously. In the case of habituation, however, we must consider inhibition in relation to retention, for the decreased reactivity is associated only with specific forms of stimulation, and any change of stimulation, either quantitatively or qualitatively, may bring about dishabituation. This point will be illustrated below.

The Peckhams, in 1887, demonstrated that a spider which would at first drop out of its web in response to the vibratory stimulation of a tuning fork, would cease to do so after a number of such trials.

We have previously discussed instances of habituation in the stentor and the hydra. Thorpe's survey provides evidence for the phenomenon on all levels of phylogeny, extending from protozoa to mammals. The extinction of the "investigatory reflex," as described by Pavlov, may also be ascribed to habituation, although it is apparent that Pavlov's theory of the role of cortical elements cannot be accepted as an explanation for this phenomenon. Sharpless and Jasper (1956) studied habituation in cats in the form of reduced cortical arousal, in response to a repeated tone which originally produced a marked arousal pattern. Jasper noted some of the implications of this important study:

> Before any specific stimulus can acquire a positive significance for a given response, the animal must learn the insignificance of all irrelevant stimuli. . . . Habituation of the alerting response is not due to a general refractoriness or unresponsiveness of the reticular system, but to a selective unresponsiveness to the quality and pattern of the alerting stimulus. . . . The function of the reticular system in normal adaptative or integrative behavior may be more in the nature of a prevention of a general arousing reaction to all stimuli, with a control of selective responsiveness to significant stimuli. . . . This implies that inhibitory rather than excitatory functions may be most important, either during sleep or during wakefulness (Jasper, 1958a, pp. 320, 322).

Studies of habituation with human subjects are also numerous. Seward and Seward (1934) demonstrated response decrements in subjects exposed to mild intensities of shock administered to the feet at sixty-second intervals. Dodge (1923) found some response decrement to repeated elicitation of the patellar and eye-blink reflexes. Wendt reviews the controversy on the role of habituation in postrotation nystagmus. His comments are interesting, because they point to the participation of two forms of inhibition.

> There are two factors in habituation, two kinds, in fact, which may be present separately or together. The one shows up especially in the usual method of observing after-nystagmus with the subject's eyes open. In this case visual stimuli tend to inhibit the vestibular nystagmus, and with repetition these stimuli become increasingly dominant. Such habituation is probably not preventable. The other shows up with the eyes closed. In this case loss of nystagmus occurs when the subject fails to remain alert to his external surroundings. This habituation is

preventable by keeping the subject attentive to the external surroundings and avoiding inward-directed revery states (Wendt, 1951, p. 1214).

Hernández-Peón and his collaborators have carried out extensive electrophysiological studies of habituation on different levels. He, too, regards habituation as a kind of primary learning process which is necessary to permit establishment of more complex behavioral patterns. Hernández-Peón and Brust-Carmona (1961) cite the earlier work of Griffith (1920), who found that in one case a reduction of postrotatory nystagmus in man, as a result of repeated rotation, lasted four years. Using electromyographic recording from ocular muscles, they demonstrated inhibition of nystagmus not only in intact cats, but also in those deprived of all neocortex. Lesions in the mesencephalic reticular formation also did not prevent habituation of postrotatory nystagmus, but those in the pontile tegmentum did. Taking this result together with those in other studies by Hernández-Peón and collaborators (which demonstrated habituation in the cochlear nucleus, the retina, the olfactory bulb, and the sensory nucleus of the fifth spinal segment, as well as dishabituation by an added acoustic stimulus after habituation had caused a decrement of spinal potentials evoked by tactile stimulation), Hernández-Peón and Brust-Carmona reach the conclusion that "afferent neuronal habituation at second order sensory neurons results from centrifugal inhibitory influences proceeding from the reticular system of the lower brain stem." This interpretation is supported by the fact that section of the spinal cord at the level of the second cervical nerve resulted in augmented potentials below that level in a previously habituated animal.

This is one more line of evidence (like those arising from the work of the Magoun-Moruzzi-Lindsley school, from Penfield's work on the "centrencephalic system," from Jaspers' work on the diffuse thalamic projection system, from Bykov's work on conditioning of "autonomic" processes, etc., etc.) which points to a kind of interconnectedness which goes far beyond anything provided by the old classical conception of input-output systems based on afferent and efferent excitations, connections, or traces. Everywhere, the plastic shaping of behavior is related not only to factors of reactivity, sensitivity, and retentivity, which might conceivably be accommodated by such a system, but also to inhibitions which occur at all levels of biological experience, which influence and are influenced by the other factors named. Even at the spinal level, afferent inhibition occurs as a result of some process of retention of experience due to prior controlled exposure to the situation. The fact that this afferent inhibition is selective, and that it may be attenuated by a change in the intensity of stimulation, illustrates the interrelatedness of sensitivity, reactivity, retentivity, and inhibition in integrated behavior. Functional plasticity involves all four factors in complex relationships. What we call learning may often be the shifting emphasis among them.

We have already made repeated use of Brunswik's distinction between proximal and distal stimulations and responses. In his discussion of perceptual constancies, Brunswik (1944) calls our attention to the fact that in a shifting ecological setting, a reliance upon proximal or mediational aspects of either the stimulus or the response may lead not to behavioral achievement, but to possible behavioral chaos. He argues for an approach which involves wide-spanning functional relationships between distal events, objects and acts, and central events. That is, the organism has the task of achieving independence of particular stimuli and particular muscular patterns of performance. However, many classical learning experiments deal very largely with situations in which such independence cannot take place, or, if it does take place, it is treated as error variance. Under these circumstances, the organism *becomes* a simple stimulus-response mechanism, its responses being placed under the control of situational factors, which permit excellent predictive control by the psychologist who is master of the situation. In the preceding chapter, we considered the virtues and the limitations of some behavior theories which are based on such situational analyses. However, the factors of plasticity which we have been discussing have a much wider relevance, for they appear to have an explanatory and heuristic value in many varied circumstances—all the way from purely phenomenological description to the spinal habituation of a cervically transected cat.

Although these factors operate simultaneously, the place which they hold in the general pattern of control does undergo change. Brunswik's concept of relative independence of proximal events, can be translated into altered patterns of relationship, in which retentivity, inhibition, or both, become the major controlling influences, in place of reactivity and sensitivity. In Sperry's experiments on nerve and muscle transplants, and in Hess's experiments on pecking by the chick, the excitatory components led the other components. Such close couplings, in which fixed morphological structures determine sensitivity to certain objects, are usually highly adaptive for lower organisms in most ecological settings. To some extent, plastic changes in behavior take place on the basis of changes in sensitivity and reactivity. But the more important plastic events in which these processes are involved are those which are mediated by the factors of retentivity and inhibition acting upon them. Phenomena of attention, and different states or levels of consciousness, reflect such influences. The influence of retentivity on sensitivity appears clearly in the Stratton-type experiments, as for example in Kohler's experience of the "bend" in the visual field after he removed the prisms which introduced the opposite bend, for which he had been compensating.

For such plasticity to appear, there must first be the possibility of experiencing differently. In the pecking of the chicks, morphology controls the specifics of behavior to such a degree that inhibition and the retention of experience can occur only within narrow limits. Higher order behavior seems to require the functional plasticity which is made possible by a delicate interaction between retention and inhibition. Either factor may remove the organism from the control of specific proximal events. We shall return to this aspect of our problem after discussing another viewpoint on the role of inhibition in plasticity.

Harlow (1958) has stated a point of view which coincides in part with that which is presented here. His theory, if confirmed, would be more parsimonious than the present account. Harlow believes that "All learning and all thinking may be regarded as resulting from a single fundamental operation, the inhibition of inappropriate responses or response tendencies." And again: "Inhibition is the single process accounting for all learning. It is presumed that this unitary inhibitory process acts to suppress the inappropriate responses and response tendencies operating to produce error." This analysis arises fairly directly out of Harlow's work with the establishment of "learning sets" (1949), that is, his demonstration that animals, particularly primates, which have had practice in solving discrimination problems, display an intertrial transfer which enables them to solve new problems more efficiently. In the learning of more than 300 discrimination tasks in the Wisconsin General Test Apparatus (Harlow, 1949), monkeys showed a steady increase in the proportion of correct choices. Harlow's "oddity" problem (1958) requires that in each group of three objects presented, the response must be directed to the object which is different from the other two, which are similar. It is only this set for oddity which can be carried over from trial to trial, or problem to problem, the animal being required on each trial to choose perhaps an item which was wrong on the previous trial, perhaps among fresh items. This problem may be further complicated by combining oddity and non-oddity problems. For example, the odd object is to be chosen if the objects are presented on a green tray, the non-odd objects if on an orange tray. This type of problem "can be mastered by monkeys and apes without undue difficulty," but we are told that no subprimate has approached its solution.

The ability to acquire "learning sets" is related to maturation. Harlow (1959a) states that "For the neonatal and infant rhesus monkey each learning task is specific unto itself, and the animal's intellectual repertoire is composed of multiple, separate and isolated experiences. With increasing age, problem isolation changes to problem generalization, and thus fundamental reorganization of the monkey's intellectual world apparently begins in its second year of life. From here on, we can no longer specify the monkey's learning ability for any problem merely in terms of maturation age and individual differences. The variable of kind and amount of prior experience must now be given proper value."

Harlow's empirical work is of the greatest value, and his approach represents one of the most important advances which have been made toward widening the range of situations in which behavior is being studied. However, we feel that on the one hand he ascribes too much to inhibition, and that on the other his concept of inhibition is too narrow, since he thinks of it only as the learned suppression of response, rather than as the interactional process by which organismic integration is achieved. He says, for example, that "all learning which has been adequately described and measured, appears to be the learned inhibition of responses and response tendencies which block the animal or fail to lead it to some terminal response, such as eating or escape from noxious stimulation. . . . The law of parsimony requires at the very least, that we seek as simple a fundamental explanation of vertebrate learning, including human learning, as is consonant with fact" (Harlow, 1958). We feel that this very limited interpretation of the role of inhibition in behavioral plasticity is an example of misapplication of the law of parsimony, which threatens again to oversimplify essential relationships.

Returning now to the question of proximal independence, we wish to emphasize again that at different times, in the same organism, each of the four factors of plasticity—reactivity, sensitivity, retentivity, and inhibition—may lead in exercising control over the others. All four factors are present on all phylogenetic levels, and even within part structures of intact organisms. In general, however, sensitivity and reactivity are the controlling factors in lower organisms, and as we ascend the phylogenetic scale, retentivity and inhibition become more prominent factors in adaptation. It is only by a formalism, or the neatness of a paradigm, that we are able to throw together into a single classification, as learning, behaviors which are so widely disparate as the peripherally guided fluctuant gel-sol cycles of amoeba, the mastery of a maze by the proximally guided ant, the maze-solving behaviors of the rat, and the insightful solution of problems by primates. Schneirla (1939, 1959) calls attention to relationships which exist between stimulus intensity and biphasic adjustment processes, leading either to approach or to withdrawal, as trans-situational mechanisms of adaptation to the changing stimulus flux of the physical surround. He points out that in the early ontogenetic development of all organisms, "*low intensities of stimulation tend to evoke approach reactions, high intensities withdrawal reactions with reference to the source,*" and he states the principle that "*Intensity of stimulation basically determines the direction of reaction with respect to the source, and thereby exerts a selective effect on what conditions generally affect the organism.*" We would add that the capacity for plastic change could not arise, even with a million-fold decrease in various sensory thresholds, if there were not also a corresponding increase in the capacity to inhibit afferent input selectively. We have seen that the mammal, particularly, possesses many inhibitory mechanisms which enable it to modulate its own afferent input. While it is true, as Leuba (1955) suggests, that all organisms seek certain optimal levels of stimulation, they do not do this merely by approach and withdrawal, but also by inhibition of afferent and efferent systems at several levels of the neuraxis. Excitatory mechanisms by themselves cannot yield the types and quantities of proximal independence demonstrated in the behavior we observe.

Thorpe (1961) calls attention to the fact that young birds are faster than adult birds in solving some tasks which depend upon the level of activity, but that older birds perform more efficiently on tasks which require the ability to "refrain from" doing something. Utilizing a concept of internal inhibition which is similar to that of Pavlov, Thorpe suggests that "internal inhibition is unstable in young birds and . . . the process of development from the unstable type of inhibition found in younger birds to the more stable type found in older birds, depends not only upon age but also on experience." Thus, an essential difference between young and adult organisms, just as between lower and higher animals, lies in the fact that retention and inhibition come more and more to exercise this regulating and controlling influence rather than acting only as subsidiary mechanisms. In Sperry's studies of transplanted nerves and muscles, and in Hess's work with the pecking response of chicks, we are dealing with organisms which have tremendous capacity for inhibition of part processes, relative to the lower organisms, and yet we see that the arrangement of the peripheral apparatus is not such as to permit independence of proximal stimulation under the conditions tested. However, there are other situations in which the rat or the chick does have a choice of patterns, where central inhibitory components may control the situation and where, as a result, a different integration becomes possible.

After much experience in a given situation, retentivity may play the leading role, rather than inhibition. Thus, a rat that has overlearned a multiple maze may race through the alleys with incredible speed. The change from slow to swift performance can scarcely be said to represent new learning, although retentivity now plays a greater part in the performance. But if the overzealous rat crashes into a barrier which is not opened quickly enough, the entire performance may change its character on the next trial, and other aspects of the stimulus situation may become more prominent. An experience of this type is subject to retention, and it may thus contribute to conflict in future trials. Thus a few failures may even upset the long-practiced integrations of a professional athlete. Such highly skilled performances depend on a sequence of disinhibitions which must be timed to very tiny fractions of a second, so that a displaced excitation or added inhibition may easily upset them. Lashley (1951) has discussed this problem of the central integration of serial responses, emphasizing its importance in all kinds of behavior, and not merely in motor skills. It is in such skills, however, that the serial chaining of part responses is most obvious, and the reader, most especially if he is a golfer, has doubtless had personal opportunity to observe how the smooth timing of a practiced act can be upset by the unwelcome intervention of an intellectualization. The factors of inhibition and retention interact on all levels, and the same organism which may be able to adjust to major shifts in the proximal stimulus pattern can have its performance upset by minor changes in either inhibition or retention.

Something may be added here to what was said in Chapter 8 about the participation of inhibition in conceptualization and thinking. The attainment of concepts, even at a fairly low level, epitomizes the organism's relative independence of proximal events. The concept may be defined as a consistent response which is given to "identities" in diverse situations. In the initial experiences of these diverse situations, before the concept has been developed, sensitivity and reactivity control the responses given to objects under their various transformations. The factors of retention and inhibition must both come into play in order to attain the degree of proximal independence which is represented by a concept. After its attainment, stimulus attributes or their signs are related to the class defined by the concept, and, if they possess the necessary criteria, the object is symbolized by or subsumed under the concept. It is clear that retention must provide the criteria which are essential for this purpose, and inhibition must govern the act of comparison and decision.

On the higher levels of conceptualization, the attainment of each new concept represents a novel pattern of relationships between inhibition and retention. New functional sensitivities develop, giving increased independence from proximal stimulation. When these are successfully symbolized and communicated, they become—like such concepts as number, zero, and infinity—part of the common thought models available to men in society. Such concepts as non-durative time, and the anomalies of quantum mechanics, may become everyday symbolic forms of thinking for another generation. Society is thus able to assist the individual in attaining the prescribed pattern of retentions and inhibitions, and thus to extend the range of his sensitivity and to further increase his capacity for plastic changes in thinking behavior. Morphologically, man is likely to undergo relatively little change, barring the catastrophe of an undamped cataclysmic mutation. What will change will be the physical and symbolic aspects of the surround in which future human beings will behave. G. Murphy (1958) has drawn an inspiring picture of *Human Potentialities* under these conditions.

We shall close this chapter with several illustrations of the interaction between retention and inhibition which takes place in the performance of complex behaviors. As a first example, let us consider the act of riding a bicycle. This is a motor skill which is not difficult in itself, since it requires only very minor modification of a natural locomotor pattern—to "walk sitting down," as it is described in an item of the Stanford-Binet, Form L. However, learning to ride a bicycle involves one difficulty: under these circumstances, the natural righting reflexes, which are so effective when we have our feet on the ground, only help to upset the equilibrium. As the beginner struggles to inhibit his reflexes, an excess of voluntary inhibition comes to hamper all his movements. With practice, the inhibition becomes specific rather than generalized, and the need for balance is served by a slight body sway. Riding becomes automatic, which means that the inhibitory elements are of the same kind as, and no more prominent than, those involved in walking. Skill develops, reflecting changes which have taken place in the reaction mechanisms. The act is governed by a kind of motor memory.

Our second illustration deals with the more complex skill of typewriting. This partakes somewhat of the nature of language, because the patterns of movement are associated with meanings. Some years ago, the resourceful Knight Dunlap was plagued with the tendency to type *hte* instead of *the*. He cured himself of the habitual error by negative practice: he deliberately typed *hte* a great many times, thinking all the time that it was an error, and reported that thereafter the error did not recur (Dunlap, 1928). This result obviously did not fit the then prevailing theories of learning, but subsequently it has sometimes been regarded as an evidence of reactive inhibition. However, it seems unlikely that the same effect would have been gained by speedily typing *hte-hte-hte* . . . without thought that this was an error. In that case, the rut would probably have been deepened, yet the reactive inhibition should have been even greater from the fast typing than from the slow. To understand the effect of the negative practice, one must first understand the nature of the error. Typing *the* requires more than a sequence of three movements. A correct performance, as part of an integrated typing act, depends on preliminary readying of the three movements, and their timely release or disinhibition. If an inhibition which is awaiting release is not strong enough, it may be prematurely released, and presumably it is thus that the finger of the right hand gets to strike the *h* before the finger of the left hand strikes *t*. The negative practice served to raise the general inhibitory tone attached to the intent to type *the*, and thus to improve the control of its parts. The act had become too automatic, and row on row of *the* could not provide the corrective. Exercising *hte*, consciously as a wrong response, reinstated the inhibitory control.

A third and final illustration of the interaction of retention and inhibition is provided by certain studies of decision making in a situation with uncertain outcomes. On each trial, the subject is required to guess or predict which of two events will occur. Unknown to him, the probabilities of these events have been predetermined, but the fact that one is more frequent than the other becomes fairly obvious as the trials proceed. It is possible to maximize the number of correct predictions by always predicting the more frequent event. However, this strategy does not seem to occur to most subjects. Brunswik (1939) using rats, Humphreys (1939) using human adults, and Messick and Solley (1957) using children, have found that guesses are distributed between the two events approximately in proportion to their probabilities. This has been confirmed in additional work by Grant, Hake, and Hornseth (1951), Jarvik (1951), Hake and Hyman (1953), Estes and Straughan (1954), and many others. These findings provide a part of the basis for Estes' statistical theory of learning. They indicate, he reasons, that human subjects tend "to behave in accordance with the principles of associative learning and not, in general, in the most rational manner as 'rational' is usually defined" (Estes, 1954). In the terms which we have been using, this means that probability-matching behavior is guided chiefly by the factors of sensitivity and retention, and it is proximally determined to a considerable degree.

However, exceptions occur. Balvin (1956) gave monetary rewards for correct predictions, and assigned a higher reward to prediction of the less frequent event. Under this condition, there was a significant shift in the distribution of predictions. This still might be regarded as proximally determined behavior, in which the weight of each event depends on the amount of reward. However, the subjects under subsequent questioning were still able to give highly accurate estimates of the relative frequencies, showing that retention of the proportions was not influenced by the differential reward or the change in response rates. Most subjects, then, are excellent estimators, but poor maximizers of the expectancies. The reason for this is that something more than retention and sensitivity is needed to bring about optimal choice behavior in this situation. Maximizing behavior was clearly shown by only three, or perhaps four, of ninety-six adult subjects. The answers which these maximizers gave in the subsequent inquiry showed that for them the stimulus situation had a simpler aspect than for the probability-matchers. One of them stated that once he knew no tricks were involved, and that the situation was like coin tossing, he needed only to decide which event occurred more frequently and bet on that one on every trial. Thus, this subject became independent of the trial-by-trial results, and maximized his predictions over the future events. This trans-situational strategy only required a judgment of "greater than," rather than an exact estimation. The exact proportions became an irrelevancy which was treated as "noise." This independence of trial-by-trial events involves inhibition, as does also the complete suppression of one of the two responses possible in the situation. It brings with it, as another gain, an absence of conflict in the situation, for now it is no longer necessary to choose between two possibilities which vie with each other on every trial. On the other hand, complete insensitivity to proximal changes would expose the subject to the danger of fixated behavior, which might become maladaptive if the probabilities were to change. In short, each of the four factors of plasticity in behavior must be ever ready to play its part, in changing interrelationships, as old patterns of behavior yield to new.

INHIBITORY DEFICIT AND MENTAL HANDICAP 14

We have shown that wherever choice exists, inhibition must be present. Conversely, where the capacity for choice is defective, inhibitory deficit should be suspected. In the mentally handicapped, where the ability to make successful choice is so grossly inadequate, we can expect to find a defect or deficit in inhibitory controls, and it should be possible to relate many of their characteristic personality patterns to inhibitory deficit. It is this thought which will guide our examination of some of the more common conditions associated with mental retardation.

The study of the behavior of brain-injured and mentally retarded children provides unparalleled opportunities for the investigation of problems in child development. Brain injuries, low levels of mental functioning, and anomalies in development which result from environmental and genetic factors are substitutes for experimental interventions in the life process which the scientist would neither wish nor dare to make. The associated forms of mental handicap, such as cerebral palsy, epilepsy, aphasia, autism, Down's syndrome (mongolism), and cultural-familial retardation all help in different ways, to make evident the importance of the smooth functioning of inhibitory processes.

The use of the inhibition construct is not new in child psychology. McGraw (1946) used it as a neurological construct in her studies of longitudinal development. She paid particular attention to the action of the cerebral cortex as a governing influence at each stage of development, and she points out that "the cerebral cortex is twofold in function. It not only exercises an activating influence upon neuromotor behavior, but also exerts an inhibitory influence upon behavior controlled at infracortical levels." It is essential to Gesell's principles of development, such as spiral reincorporation and reciprocal interweaving. Gesell (1945) states that the embryogenesis of mind must be sought in the beginnings of postural behavior, and that "fixation of posture is sustained inhibition of a potential or a completed action." The inhibition construct is used implicitly by Lewin (1935) in his formulation of the field theory of the life space, where the barriers act as essential controls to shape behavior in an inhibitory sense. It is used explicitly, though not in directly physiological terms, in the theoretical framework of Freud and the psychoanalytic school, where not only does the ego act to inhibit id behavior, but the parents are interpreted as regulators of internal tension systems. Thus, Margaret Mahler (Mahler, Furer, & Settlage, 1959) calls the mother "an external executive ego."

In considering whether the construct of inhibition has value for the understanding of child development, we have had three questions in mind. Does it help in understanding the pattern of the child's progress in time? In understanding his relationship to space? Finally—since one of the most debated areas in clinical psychology is the effect of maternal deprivation—does it have value for understanding the social role of the mother in the development of the child? We turn first to considering these three questions, and then will review several of the major syndromes.

The Pattern of Development. In the title of an article, Shirley (1931) asked the rhetorical question, "Is development saltatory as well as continuous?" Whenever behavior or growth is observed longitudinally, it becomes apparent that it does not proceed in a smooth curve but through a succession of relatively discrete stages. Even Lewin, despite his essentially ahistorical approach, recognized the critical nature of physiological stages of growth, for he wrote that "developments frequently show a rhythm like, for example, the biological development of the egg: they occur in steps which are within themselves highly autonomous. The concepts of maturation and of crisis become essential" (Lewin, 1935). Although McGraw disagreed with Gesell with respect to the relative importance of maturation and practice, and neither was comfortable with Freud, all three recognized that development proceeds by relatively discrete stages, rather than gradually. And as will be set forth more fully below, stages of development are determined by the action of inhibition and disinhibition.

In order to determine the etiology of pathological development, and manage the effects of defective development, it is necessary to reckon with the stages of growth and with the nature of the inhibitory controls which are available at each stage. By the same token, the emergence of normal patterns of behavior and the planning for normal development are likewise dependent upon the stages of inhibitory controls. Some psychologists are still committing what Lange (1873) called the *error of potentiality*. They expect that whatever capacities appear in later development must already be detectable in earlier stages. Efforts are still being made to devise infant intelligence scales which will measure capacity for conceptual thinking, without considering whether the development of the necessary brain processes has taken place; and conversely, the assumption is still being made that if a child with no obvious pathology appears intellectually bright at an early age, he would necessarily be bright at a later age, and if not, that only socioeconomic factors or maternal deprivation can be responsible. (Cf. Sarason, 1949; Clarke & Clarke, 1958.) Carmichael (1946b) says: "The error of potentiality may be avoided quite simply. It is necessary only to remember that the scientist who is dealing with development must study a series of temporally separated stages of growth. These are his facts."

It is the general rule in ontogenesis that structures are prepared prior to the time when they will be required to function, and that behavior patterns are established prior to their need within the organism's economy. Thus, the fetus can blink its eyes months before the lids are separated (Hooker, 1943); the lungs are able to function months before birth (Barcroft, 1938); an anencephalic two-month-old infant may be able to sit upright before the control over the antigravity muscles has matured (see discussion of Gamper, below). Even such complex behavioral patterns as "courtship, mating, and care of the young are fully organized and ready to function relatively early in life, well in advance of the time when they will normally be activated" (Beach, 1948).

Freud (1905) recognized this pattern in the psychosexual development of the child, and he comments on the priority of organic factors in the inhibition of sexual behavior developed during the latency period. He says: "It is during this period of total or at least partial latency that the psychic forces develop which later act as inhibitions on the sexual life, and narrow its direction like dams. . . . We may gain the impression that the erection of these dams in the civilized child is the work of education; and surely education contributes much to it. In reality, however, this development is organically determined and can occasionally be produced without the help of education. Indeed, education remains properly within its assigned domain if it strictly follows the path laid out by the organic, and only imprints it somewhat cleaner and deeper."

Since each stage must prepare for the next, and often for still later stages to follow, it is inevitable that each transition shall consist of the disinhibition of some function or group of functions which were readied but inoperative. These functions are first present as potentials, but are normally under inhibitory control, and their first appearance is the result of an inhibition of an inhibition, which takes place at a preordained time. This is well illustrated by Barcroft's (1938) description of the mechanism by which the lungs begin to be integrated with the activities of the heart. The root of the lung artery is joined by a short channel to the main artery. Attached to this channel is a small muscle, also prepared in advance for a function which it will perform just once, and which then will atrophy. It is ready, but in a state of inhibition. At the period of birth, this muscle is disinhibited, closing the channel, and then the lungs begin to receive the rich supply of blood directly from the heart. This is but one of many acts of disinhibition which transform the fetus into a neonate.

If the hidden function has not been readied for its release or if the release itself fails to take place at the right time, there is a disorder in development which cannot be reversed, though it may be compensated at least in part, by later corrective developments.

Causes for the disorder may be due either to an organic defect or to a failure of the environment to provide the necessary supplies. When an environmental influence is necessary for the orderly development of the organism, as for example sensory stimulation during the early periods of infancy, deprivation of this experience at the critical period may result in an irremediable deficiency or defect. (Compare the case of the cat, White, on page 282 in Chapter 13.) However, the resulting handicap may not be apparent in the immediately ensuing stage, but may appear as an abnormality in some future stage, for which the Anlage has been established. Likewise, any teratogenic agent, such as radiation in the antenatal stages, or insult to the brain in the paranatal period, will result in a deficiency or defect which may not be obvious until the organism reaches a much later stage of development. For example, Del, one of the twin infants whom Dennis (1938) selected for the study of the effects of minimum social stimulation, was first recognizable as a cerebral palsy victim when she was in her ninth month. At that time, the infant enters a new stage of motor development and is ordinarily able to voluntarily control movements of the upper spine and is beginning to control movements of the lower spine. But in cerebral palsy the inhibitory processes which are essential for this act have been disturbed. Dennis reports that there was no sign of the hemiplegia in motion pictures which he took of Del when she was three months of age.

Margaret Mahler (1952) was able to distinguish between infantile autism and early childhood schizophrenia by taking note of the difference in the timing of their respective syndromes. She found that the autism syndrome is manifested during the early stages of infancy (before four months), but childhood schizophrenia first emerges some time between the age of two and a half and four years. The Anlage for each of these conditions belongs to an earlier stage of development, but the syndrome appears only when the organism has reached a certain stage. A similar phenomenon was quite inadvertently demonstrated experimentally, in monkeys, by Harlow (1962). Monkeys that had been deprived of normal tactile experience with their mothers and age peers in early infancy appeared normal in their childhood development, but when they reached adulthood it was discovered that they were social "monsters." They were unable to establish normal sexual relations or proper patterns of mothering. Apparently it was necessary that they experience mothering—cuddling, stroking, being held, being groomed—in order that they should be able to engage normally, as adults, in activities which involve bodily contact. Furthermore, the effects of the lack of such experience appeared to be irreversible, or nearly so.

The neat timetable of inhibition and disinhibition is too often disrupted by the operation of a teratogenic agent. Gamper (1926) was able extensively to study such a victim, an anencephalic female infant whose precocity, in certain respects, provides an especially forceful illustration of the advance preparation of a behavioral component which does not show itself in normal behavior until a later period. The normal neonate, it should be mentioned, has a functional pallidum, but the still higher brain structures only become functional in later development (Jung & Hassler, 1960). This little girl was born without a pallidum or any higher structure, and kept alive until she was almost three months of age. She had a wide repertoire of behavior, but most interesting was her ability to sit. When pressure was applied to the underside of her thighs, she would raise her head, straighten her back, and bring herself into a sitting position without any back support, although she was a weak infant. She could also cry, yawn, and stretch, would spontaneously suck her own hand, and could follow a finger by turning her head and eyes. Gamper interpreted this precocity as due to a fuller realization of the functional possibilities of lower structures when these are not restrained by their subordination to higher centers, that is, when they are not subject to inhibitory control by the latter. Jung and Hassler (1960) emphasize that "these mechanisms are not simple *reflexes* but instinctive innate patterns which are elicited by sensory sign stimuli." These coordinated acts, which will not be observed in retarded infants with greater brain development than that possessed by the Gamper child, were made possible by the relatively greater defect which still preserved the essential mechanism. A normal infant, with all of the same structures *plus* a functional pallidum, would not be able to sit up in the same manner because although the mechanisms for the act would be as well or better developed, they would also be subject to an inhibitory control which was absent in this case. When this act does appear, it will be as the result of a disinhibition due to the development of still higher structures, and hence it will appear as part of a still more advanced pattern of behavior in which it will be incorporated.

The disinhibitory release of a function involves a reorganization of the previously established balances, and hence a developmental leap. When several such leaps occur simultaneously or in rapid succession, as at the time of birth or of puberty, the entry into a new stage is obvious. Whether the release of new possibilities of behavior will be recognized as initiating a new major stage of development depends to some extent on how significant they are in terms of the culture or subculture. For example, in most middle class homes the period at which the child becomes capable of voluntary inhibition and disinhibition of the sphincters controlling elimination is readily accepted as marking a new stage. Freud responded to this when he labelled it the anal stage. But in the present American scene, with the shift of interest away from the control of body functions (the id) to the acquisition of mastery over the environment (the ego functions), some psychoanalysts have been giving more attention to the stages of development initiated by increased control of motility (Mittelmann, 1954; Mahler et al., 1959), such as standing and walking, which depend upon the inhibition and disinhibition of the antigravity muscles. Mittelmann states that motility is the dominant urge (drive) at the beginning of the second year of life and is "the dominant, or one of the dominant, means of reality testing and of integration." As another example, the advance in intellectual functioning which occurs at about 6 years of age, and which seems so decisive wherever schooling is important, fails to take place in a simple subculture like that of the canal-boat dwellers in England (Gordon, 1923) or of the Virginia hollows three decades ago (Sherman and Key, 1932). As a result, all school age children seem severely retarded by our standards.

Development does not proceed without complications, which are not unlike those of the Herbartian model, in which one idea may escape an inhibition because a second has had to resist a fresh inhibition derived from a third. Thus, some mothers successfully establish toilet training of their infants at a very young age (before eight months), on the basis of segmental controls. Later, when walking begins, this pattern of control is disrupted because the mechanisms become partly involved in the new behavior. If attention is concentrated on bowel control, the child seems to have regressed rather than advanced. Gesell and Ilg (1943) indicate that irregularities in bowel control are to be expected not only at this period, but at a number of other transitional periods when new postural and motor functions appear and need to be consolidated. The effects of genetic deficit, or of teratogenic agents that had been experienced earlier, also become manifest at the time when a new function normally appears, marking a new stage. Thus, the appearance of childhood schizophrenia after the age of two and a half years, in the children studied by Mahler (1952), must be interpreted as an indication that at this period some decisive development takes place in the normal child. Likewise, cultural-familial retardation does not become evident until the child is four years old; Kirk (1958) found that such children could not be identified at the earlier ages by physicians and social workers. This suggests that at about this time the child enters a new stage of mental development, in which the manipulation of symbols is a prominent factor. This interpretation of the course of mental development is further supported by evidence from diverse sources, including the work of Hofstaetter and of Luria, as described in the following paragraphs.

Hofstaetter's (1954) analysis of Nancy Bayley's data on intellectual development of children in the California Developmental Study, from infancy to eighteen years of age, provides a neat paradigm for identifying three stages of mental growth. He found three factors operating in time, with very little overlap between Factors I and III. Factor I is designated as *general alertness,* because of high loadings in sensorimotor tests; it was most prominent during the first twenty months and then declined in importance, contributing practically nothing to the variance from forty months on. Factor II is called *persistence,* "a tendency to act in accordance with an established set rather than upon interfering stimulation." It had negative loadings in the early period and positive loadings later, reaching its peak in the middle of the third year. Hofstaetter links it with the well-known negativism of the two-and-a-half-year-old. Factor III, which he regards as equivalent to Spearman's g and identifies as *manipulation of symbols,* is the most prominent factor after forty months, and accounts for nearly all of the variance after forty-eight months. Of course, general alertness and persistence of behavior sets do not vanish after forty months, but they evidently cease to be important controlling factors and come instead under the inhibitory and disinhibitory control of those functions which make the manipulation of symbols possible.

These relationships are demonstrated in experiments on the regulatory role of speech in the development of voluntary action, which are reported by Luria (1960a, 1960b). Luria's frame of reference is very different from Hofstaetter's, but the results dovetail neatly with his analysis and help to elucidate the inhibitory role of higher mental processes in checking impulsive behavior. He points out that for the very young child an adult's verbal instruction serves only an "impulse function," but cannot inhibit or shift the child's behavior. The child of one and a half to two years readily claps his hands on command, or puts rings on a bar, or takes them off. But, if while he is taking rings off a bar, he is asked to put one on, he is unable to do so and actually increases rather than decreases the activity in which he is engaged. Psychologists and educators have called this "negativism," and parents call it "disobedience." Hofstaetter's "persistence" seems more appropriate. It appears also in an experiment in which children of different ages were asked to squeeze a balloon when a red electric bulb lit up. For children of two to two and a half years, the verbal instruction acts as a release mechanism. They start to squeeze even before the signal, and when the signal is given, they squeeze the balloon repeatedly. The commands "enough" and "no more" only result in more energetic squeezing or, for some children, in complete inhibition. Children of this age could not learn to use their own verbal command to inhibit this overaction, but they could be trained by having a bell ring each time the ball was pressed (negative feedback). However, this persistence is easily controlled by children three and a half to four years old, who are able to regulate their reactions with their own vocal signals. Luria (1960b) describes the change as follows:

"Only by three and a half to four years of age does the process of elaboration of new connections begin to include the speech of the child himself, which at first has the character of questions addressed to the adult ('Must I squeeze when this light comes on?'), and is later converted into a rule ('for the red light I squeeze but for the green light I don't'), and by four and a half to five years it acquires all the features of mediative speech, conscious and systematized activity."

This regulatory function is clearly an expression of symbol manipulation, which allows the child to interchange sets.

The child with cultural-familial retardation resembles the normal child during the periods when Hofstaetter's Factors I and II are dominant. Because the structures which would make the higher mental processes possible are inadequately developed, such a child is unable to make successful choices and to behave in a flexible manner. On the other hand, some children who seem slow in the first years may be well endowed in these structures, which will mature later, so that they will in time demonstrate surprising intellectual growth. Retarded children as a group are most clearly deficient in respect to Hofstaetter's Factor III. Thus Thompson and Magaret (1947), who matched several hundred mentally retarded children with the Terman-Merrill standardization groups of the same mental ages, found that the retarded children were significantly lower in performance on those items which are most saturated with McNemar's first factor, which he identified as *g*.

Role of the Mother as an Inhibitory Agent. The mother, in her relationship to the child, plays different biological roles according to the stage of the child's development. Here we wish to explore her role during the infancy period.

In the infant-mother dyad, the mother or her surrogate is more than a resource for the infant's basic needs of food, warmth, shelter, and cleansing, more even than a resource for love and social learning; she is also an important resource for stimulations which are an essential aid to the infant's still inadequate inhibitory capacities. At birth the human organism is remarkably ill equipped to cope with the variations and excitations of its new environment. It is a subcortical creature, which is in danger of going into shock through overreacting to powerful or unexpected stimuli, because it lacks the means for modulation of behavior which is made possible by development of cortical control. The role of the higher structures is played by the mother; she is the child's auxiliary cortex. She does this through various acts of tactile stimulation and handling which are included in the pattern of mothering, such as cuddling, stroking, shifting positions, and grooming. These serve to reduce overreaction and to mobilize the infant's inhibitory capacity. The emotionally healthy mother performs these acts or their equivalents spontaneously. For example, the infant at birth responds to a sudden noise with the Moro reflex and startle reactions. The psychological component of the startle reaction is fright. (In German, the reaction is often called the *Shreck* [fright] reflex.) A responsive mother reacts smoothly and quickly to the stimulus of the loud noise by making gentle physical contact with the infant, with the intent to diminish its reaction. When the reaction has already taken place, she will perform any one of a number of acts which help to relax the infant, such as rocking it, stroking it, uttering soothing phrases, or placing her hand on the infant's body. McGraw (1937) found that the Moro reflex increases in intensity during the first four weeks of the infant's life, and then constantly diminishes as cortical inhibition develops, until finally only a jerk takes place. She says: "After ultimate development is achieved . . . the cortex is definitely engaged practically at the instant of the startling stimulation and cortical inquiry as to the meaning of the startling stimulation serves to restrict the nuclear aspect of the reaction" (McGraw, 1946).

Thus, although the mechanism for the reflex remains functional, with increasing maturation it is more and more effectively checked by inhibitory action. Before this development has taken place, the infant is dependent on its mother's intervention to provide stimuli which will lead to inhibition by another route.

Ribble (1944) found two prevalent reactions characteristic of a sample of 600 infants who suffered from inadequate mothering: regression and negativism. In regression there is a condition which resembles marasmus, with "lethargy and loss of muscle tone"; in negativism, on the contrary, there is "rigidity of the body musculature, the arms and legs resist extension, and the torso is arched slightly backward." She reports that the latter condition is accompanied by failure to assimilate food, breath holding, and violent and implacable screaming. Such negativism represents overreaction, and includes many components of the pattern of the startle reactions. Although Ribble interprets inadequate mothering as in sufficient stimulation, a review of her material clearly indicates that what is lacking is not stimulation as excitation, but as a source of *regulation* and *control.* For example, in 10 percent of the infants she reports the occurrence of irregular breathing which was further disturbed "by every readjustment." Handling by inexperienced nurses or mothers, as well as no handling, could bring about a "pathological degree of irregularity." In other words, the mother or nurse must perform those kinds of acts which will regulate breathing. Also, 10 percent of the babies showed exaggerated sucking activity at birth, sucking their fingers, tongue, and lips. In these infants, excessive tension was also usually noticed in the musculature of the entire body. Restriction of sucking by physically tying down the infant's arms would result in either the regressive pattern, so that the child entered a stuporous state, or the negative pattern, with spasmodic crying. However, the excessive activity could be successfully controlled by "gently stroking the head or by holding the infant in the arms for a short period at regular intervals and rocking him with a gentle rhythmic motion. These procedures reduced the . . . tension in all except a few particularly exaggerated cases. Lowering the head at regular intervals and lowering the head of the bed during sleep were also effective."

Everyone recognizes that tactile stimulation of the kind which the mother administers is somehow pacifying. Brunton referred to this as a specifically inhibitory effect in his pioneering essay on inhibition:

> The injured child which if left to itself will continue to scream for a long time may be quickly soothed by a few soft touches of the mother's hands or lips on the bruised part, with a few soft words of the mother's voice. . . . The mother's soothing tones alone might calm the child, but experience shows that they are greatly aided by the local soothing impression on the injured part. . . . I think we have here a stimulus of one kind counteracting the effect of another of a different sort, and preventing its usual results, thus giving us an instance of inhibition in the higher nervous centres, just as irritation of the frog's toe in Goltz's experiment prevented it from uttering a croak of contentment when its back was stroked (Brunton, 1874, p. 218 f.).

The point which needs emphasis is that the mother or a substitute is essential as a source of inhibition-stimulation for the infant, and that in the absence of such stimulation physical maturation alone does not suffice to insure satisfactory development of the nervous organization. Orderly auditory perception, for example, is only possible if the brain can achieve effective inhibition of most auditory stimulation. Before the infant can do this on its own, it can be helped, by tactile stimulation of a mothering sort, to inhibit other sensory stimuli more effectively. Without mothering, the infant is in danger of being overwhelmed by environmental stimulation. Lois Murphy (1961) found, in a longitudinal study of the development of coping behavior, that "infantile oral gratification is significantly related to clarity of perception among the preschool variables and negatively related to loss of perceptual clarity under stress." Undoubtedly, infantile oral gratification is itself an index of adequate mothering.

It is possible that an element of brain defect is present in the etiology of the extreme conditions of negativism described by Ribble. This would mean that such symptoms were developed by those children who, being most in need of the supplementary aids to inhibition which could be furnished by a loving mother, were getting less. Escalona (1953) and others have pointed out that the normal healthy infant evokes mothering behavior by providing clues which serve as releasers for such behavior in all human beings, but especially in adult females. The somewhat defective child may fail to provide such cues, and as a result it does not receive normal mothering support in its perceptual development. Thus its handicap is accentuated by influences which are quite properly called social, but which are parts of a vicious cycle of social influences initiated by an organic defect. It is difficult for the mother to play her part in the infant-mother dyad when the infant does not play its part, and thus some defective infants are doomed to short rations of what they need in abundance. One such sufferer may have been Del, one of the twins used by Dennis (1938) in his study of the effects of minimal social stimulation in infancy. Del had only a mild hemiplegia resulting from a birth injury, but at four years of age she was found to have an IQ of 70, whereas her identical twin had an IQ of 107. It is possible that the short rations which the two girls received during infancy had no crucial effect on the normal twin, but Del, who was defective, had a greater need for external assistance in establishing inhibitory controls.

Life Space. The inadequacy of the infant's inhibitory controls is supplemented not only by the maternal acts already discussed but also by the manipulation of the life space. It is in the examination of the life space that the field theorists have made their most important contribution to the problems of inhibition. For Lewin (1935), as the child passes through the series of developmental stages, there is an increasing differentiation and multiplication of "psychical systems." Behavior becomes more and more highly organized into hierarchical systems under the influence of a series of controls, operating at different levels. These controls are conceptualized as boundaries of psychical areas. In a series of topological models, the boundaries are represented as becoming more and more firm with increasing age, while the number of psychical systems simultaneously increases. The "segregation of areas," their organization into "hierarchical systems," and the "increase in firmness of the boundaries" can all be recognized as formulations of a hypothetical inhibition construct. The controlling boundaries are described as being weak in the child, so that they easily break down under stress, causing regression to a more primitive level of behavior corresponding to an earlier stage of development (Barker, Dembo, & Lewin, 1943).

That the character of the life space in which the infant finds himself helps to determine the ways in which he behaves is a truism; our intention here is to point out some of the features of the physical environment which can help the infant to exercise sufficient inhibitory control, or which may impede this control. Insight into this problem is furnished by the behavior of disturbed and brain-injured children.

Tony, a three-year-old, thin, and with fine, almost imperceptible movements of his hands, is called an "anxious" child by his nursery school teacher. He often can be found "hiding" in a small curtained-off hide-away under the sink. This behavior has been interpreted as a "return to the womb," in which the child may recapture the "oceanic feeling" (Freud, 1920; Fenichel, 1945). Those who hold this view suggest that the fetus in the womb enjoys a state of power, since "gratification follows upon the mere experiencing of a need" (Fox, 1954). One may well question whether the fetus has the mechanisms to enjoy this state, as one may also doubt its freedom from difficulties during this period, in view of the high rate of mortality in the womb. However, there is no question that many children like Tony are momentarily relaxed when they enter a smaller space. For any organism, there needs to be a proper concordance established between physiological capacities to cope with increased stimulation—that is, to inhibit and disinhibit the flux of stimulation—and the intensity of stimulation impinging. (Compare the analogous statement of the Freudian position by Fox, 1954.) Through each stage of its development, the child is constantly increasing his capacity to make choices and to inhibit the alternatives, but if he is thrust into a situation beyond his physiological potential he is in danger of being overwhelmed. At such times, it is a healthy act for him to retreat to a space in which the intensity of stimulation will be muted. (Compare Lois Murphy, 1961.) The brain-injured child, as compared to his age peer, has less inhibitory capacity. He tends in consequence to be impulsive and stimulus-bound. As he grows older, he often learns to withdraw, and such withdrawal cannot be considered pathological. It is a method of reducing the stimulation which his own inadequate physiological organization cannot adequately handle. In a classroom for retarded children, if the furniture is freely movable, and the atmosphere permissive, one may observe a child spontaneously turn his chair to face against the wall and so reduce what is for him excessive stimulation.

Freud (1920), in discussing the development of consciousness, states that "Protection against stimuli is an almost more important function for the living organism than reception of stimuli." He regards the sense organs as protectors against excessive environmental stimulation, and compares them to "feelers which are all the time making tentative advances towards the external world and then drawing back from it." He interprets the action of the perceptual apparatus as a "protective shield" which functions as a "special envelope or membrane resistant to stimuli."

When Tony went into his hide-away, he was establishing an added defense, an added shield against the invasion of excessive stimulation. But it is not the reduction of stimulation alone which is important. The physical size of the space is also a factor. Freud's simile of the feelers is most apt. In a larger space, these feelers have to extend themselves farther to sample the space. The very inadequacy of cortical control leads to their overextending themselves, thus leading to increased disorganization, or reduction in mastery for the child. The nursery school teacher recognizes the value of small spaces. She allows her children to play in large open playgrounds for only a limited time, since otherwise she is in danger of having a group of overstimulated children whose play is on a relatively primitive level. To develop creative play, she brings her group either into a smaller indoor room, or into a smaller outdoor yard where the children will be able to devote themselves to the easel, the playhouse, or other creative materials. Healthy children who are obviously not suffering from anxiety or any form of organic disorder delight in playing in small curtained-off areas. The Indian tepee, the underground hide-out, or cave, the table draped with a blanket, are highly attractive play spots. In them, the child experiences a feeling of secret power. And this is true, for in them he is oversupplied with the necessary inhibitory controls, which elsewhere are in short supply; he is master of his limited universe.

It would also appear that institutionalized children frequently suffer not only from maternal deprivation, but from the effects of being in too large a space and from being exposed to distant stimulation. Those who are relatively richly endowed may succeed in achieving sufficient control of their environment. (Charlie Chaplin, orphan and artist, has depicted in symbolic form the vast emptiness of the space in which he lived as such a child, and the constant hidden dangers which were lurking about him, as in the memorable scene in which he walks down a lonely road while a bear of which he is not aware trots at his heels.) Rheingold (1960) has compared the caretaking activities which occur in a normal home with those in an apparently excellent institution for foundling children. The study is concerned with maternal activities, but data are given on the location of infants and the number of adults in the room. Infants at home spend 80 percent of their time in a small room, while institution infants spend nearly all of their time in the common room which is larger than the entire apartment of the home child. During 60 percent of the time two or more adults are moving about this large room, caring for the various infants to be sure, but for only 5 percent of the time is an adult within six feet of a given child. Although this study was not concerned with behavioral development, certain data are reported which may be correlated with later development. For example, the home children slept more and vocalized more, and they spent less time with a bottle in their mouths. It is not possible to partial out the effects of mothering practices and of the spatial arrangements, but certainly the latter factor also needs to be considered in accounting for the poor showing of institutional children as a group.

Down's Syndrome. This condition (which is also called congenital acromicria) was first described by Langdon Down (1866), who unfortunately and incorrectly related it to Mongolian physical characteristics. The syndrome provides instructive examples of how an early developmental anomaly may entail serious consequences in later stages, and of how developmental pathology in the central nervous system may determine specific behavioral changes other than loss of intelligence. Recent research (Lejeune, Gautier, & Turpin, 1959; Penrose, Ellis, & Delhanty, 1960) indicates that it is associated with anomalies in the early chromosomal structure, involving faulty disjunction of the 21st or 22nd chromosome. After about five weeks of apparently normal embryological growth, abnormalities due to a defect in central growth regulation begin to appear "in manifest dyschronism and deceleration of differentiation and development (heart, hands, eyes, brain, general growth)" (Benda, 1960). As development proceeds, some phases progress normally, but others are seriously disrupted. We are reminded of Sherrington's (1951) description of the importance of timing in the development of the nervous system: "In that great multitudinous dance which we have traced, if things are to go right for the finale, the evolutions of the part figures must keep step, or certain partners may arrive late at certain places for partners who will then already have moved on."

Benda (1946) compares the developmental history of the child with Down's syndrome with a slowed motion picture, and as such it provides an opportunity to observe more easily the relationship between levels of physiological development and certain aspects of personality or behavioral patterns. At birth, though the infant may be full term, it resembles a fetus in many respects. The deceleration is uneven, affecting some organ systems more than others, and the number of organic signs varies from child to child. Some authors have therefore taken the position that the pathology of Down's syndrome is nonspecific (Malamud and Bailey, in personal communication to Masland, 1958). However, that we are dealing with a true syndrome is indicated by the fact that the signs in the syndrome are never reversed (Schmid, Lee, & Smith, 1961). The nose for example may not be depressed, but it is never beaked; the hand may not be broad and pudgy, but it is never slender. Benda (1960) finds that the abnormalities do follow a pattern which has been overlooked through failure to give "due recognition . . . to the problem of the time factor in development and developmental pathology."

Benda studied about fifty spinal cords and more than eighty brains, from patients ranging in age from two days to sixty years. He found a consistent pattern of pathology, with variations in location and degree. He concluded that "we deal here with the primary failure of the nervous system to differentiate and grow. The original Anlage does not appear abnormal, but at the same time that the other body organs failed to differentiate normally the brain was affected in a similar way. The anomalies in the cerebellum, especially the tuber flocculus, are the most striking evidence of this arrest of differentiation." Benda's published photographs illustrate the disorder in architectonics, with a persistence of infantile patterns and underdevelopment of myelination on the one hand, and on the other, a disintegration and degeneration of nerve cells and myelination which had already been normal. This failure to grow and differentiate takes place throughout the brain, but it is more severe in the cerebellum, pons, and medulla than in the cortex.

Despite this disorder, the developmental stages of the patient are more like than unlike their normal counterparts. The rhythm is slower, and some aspects of development proceed farther than others. Durling and Benda (1952) found that the growing period is approximately equal to that of the normal child, or possibly somewhat longer. About half of their sample reached their peak of development between twenty and thirty-seven years of age. In physical development, they usually reach the early stages of puberty, but do not reach full sexual maturity. There are rare instances of childbearing by women patients, but the sperms are underdeveloped in the men, and menstruation late or absent in the women (Stearns,

Droulard, & Sahhar, 1960). In mental development, they only consolidate what the normal child achieves during early childhood. The average mature individual with Down's syndrome has a mental structure which resembles that of a child approximately four years old, even when he tests somewhat higher. It is true that his abilities are much more expanded, and he can do things which are not possible for a normal six-year-old, but he cannot reason on the abstract levels as well as the child of four or five, and he is outstandingly rigid and stubborn.

Roy is a 19-year-old boy with classical stigmata of Down's syndrome, and an IQ of 45 on the Stanford-Binet. He is extremely polite, in fact courtly in his behavior, especially towards women, bowing deeply, kissing their hands, and saying: "You are beautiful." This he learned from a moving picture seen when he was 12. He plays the accordion, is able to do second grade and some third grade school work, and is very proud of his spelling. On occasion he will successfully perform three-place subtractions. This is obviously a meaningless exercise for him, since he cannot make simple change, although he does use public transportation and makes purchases at reliable stores. He insists on tying his shoelaces and his necktie and buckling his trouser belt too tight. In warm weather he suffers from this, but someone else has to loosen these items for him. He was informed one day that he would be taken to "college" (for a demonstration visit) on a Thursday. Somehow he formed the idea that Wednesday was the day. No one could persuade him differently, even after the hour for the appointment had passed. (He can read time.) On both Wednesday and Thursday, he persisted, "The Doctor say he take me on Wednesday, at 10 o'clock. *I* know. When I know, I know."

This stubborn assertion by Roy is almost like a declaration that what he lacks is not the ability to form associative bonds. And indeed, his first demonstration visit to college, which had been a high point in his experience, had taken place on a Wednesday of the previous semester! Perhaps it was easier for him to retain this association than to set it aside, to make way for another.

In teaching these patients academic subjects, progress for brief periods seems most rewarding, but disillusionment follows when it all has to be done over again. Something of the same sort may happen with the normal child, but the great difference in degree permits better analysis of the phenomenon in the retarded child.

The rote learning which such a child accomplishes deteriorates, perhaps because of interfering associations, in the absence of insight learning. Insight learning, however, requires a higher degree of structuralization, with more active checks and balances based on inhibitory functions. Rote learning is like the building of an adobe house, in which only the simplest form of balance is employed to keep one brick on another. An overly ambitious adobe house will collapse. Insight learning, on the contrary, is like a structure in which the principle of thrusts and counterthrusts has been applied, by incorporating pillars and crossbeams into the structure. The higher the level of inhibitory controls, of thrusts and counterthrusts, the higher the level of structuralization which can be achieved, as seen in the Gothic cathedral or the modern skyscraper where the "rote" material of brick on brick assembly serves only to provide a curtain or protector from the elements, but plays no supporting part in the structure.

In their social development, these patients contrast sharply with autistic children, whose mothers complain that they cannot get close to them. Here the reverse is true. These children are outstandingly sociable. They are usually affectionate, cuddly, and amiable. They are fun-loving, enjoy dances and all kinds of parties, and are protective of one another. Further evidence of their social responsiveness is that they have a delightful ability at mimicry. This picture of the patient with Down's syndrome is drawn from individuals living in the community. But even in the institution, their mimicry and affectionate nature are clearly evident and often mentioned (Benda, 1946). Butterfield (1961) describes a 36-year-old patient newly admitted to an institution who, with a mental age of five (IQ 28, on the Stanford-Binet), was able to "play the piano" (as Roy played the accordion), do housework for his mother, write legibly, pay bills, and run errands. This was interpreted as overachievement in terms of the expected level of performance with this intelligence, but this is questionable. All of this behavior is possible for a normal five-year-old boy who has been coached for many years, as this patient had been, by a devoted teacher (his mother). Our patient, Roy, was trained for over ten years on early school work. What is remarkable is that the personality of these patients remains healthy. It is precisely for this reason that they furnish such good material for understanding the full potential of an early stage of functioning. Just as the anencephalic infant studied by Gamper can be used to illustrate the capacity for motor behavior which is ordinarily inhibited by later developments, so here there is an opportunity to witness the fuller development of the potentials present at an early developmental stage, when they are not brought under the inhibitory control of more developed processes.

Earlier in this chapter, reference was made to a factor analysis of childhood intellectual functioning by Hofstaetter (1954). It will be recalled that Factor III, which was identified with Spearman's *g*, began to come into prominence during the fourth year, while Factor II, called "persistence," disappeared at about that time. Factor II was related by Hofstaetter to the "negativism" of the two-and-a-half-year-old. The combination of stubbornness and ritualism in patients with Down's syndrome, along with their low level of conceptual thinking, places them at the mental stage comparable to that of a normal child below four years of age. An interesting confirmation of this is furnished by Benda's analysis of their ability at mimicry. The talent of mimicry is quite marked in these children; it also occurs in other forms of severe mental retardation where the personality remains healthy, such as microcephaly. These children go through all the gestures of playing pool, bowling, or doing a square dance, like a group of playful clowns. A.K., a seventeen-year-old patient with Down's syndrome, has a rather flattering way of saying, "Ahhhh! Yesss!" to a speaker, as though he were congratulating him on making a very neat point. Benda reminds us:

> Everyone familiar with child psychology knows that mimicry is the outstanding characteristic of a normal child between two and four. Time and again parents are delighted and proud to see their infant child observe certain peculiarities of his surroundings and copy them with great facility, but discover that the child is quite unable to do the same thing a year later. The faculty of mimicry is a most important asset in early childhood, and no normal infant would learn to talk or eat and behave without an inborn aptitude for mimicry. The faculty of mimicry in the mongoloid is, therefore, not a character trait of this condition, but a manifestation of his protracted infancy (Benda, 1960, p. 67).

A stage of development which lasts for approximately two years in the normal child, and which is terminated by the achievement of inhibitory controls which actually check such free mimicry, is here prolonged into adolescence. The child with Down's syndrome may learn many complicated acts by rote, but he stays on a level in which persistence and mimicry are dominant. Because of inhibitory deficiencies, he is unable to advance in plasticity of behavior. If he were to do so, the factors leading to such persistence and mimicry would first have to come under the control of the processes needed for symbol manipulation. These processes, which would make possible his entry into the next stage of intellectual development, with its greatly increased plasticity of behavior, are either absent or they cannot be released for functioning. However, this serves to clarify what happens in the normal child. In the fourth year, as the ability to manipulate symbols manifests itself, it precipitates a reorganization of the child's mental structure, and with it, of his personality structure. In the new structure, mimicry and persistence are brought under the inhibitory control of higher thought processes. Certainly, mimicry is not completely suppressed in any of us, but it occupies a greatly reduced position in the more intricate patterning of symbolic functions in the average individual.

It is often supposed that the social development of these patients reaches a higher level than their intellectual functioning. But there is a real question whether this, too, is not just the fuller expression of a social stage which belongs to the psychosexual development of a child of three to four years, a period when the dependency needs of the oral stage are still freely expressed, along with the aggression and withholding of the anal stage, while the phallic stage with its concern for others is just beginning to become manifest.

Another intriguing aspect of the functioning of the child with Down's syndrome is the marked and sudden alternations in his level of alertness and muscle tone. Benda (1960) reports that babies of three to six months have fought so strenuously against being X-rayed, that three people were needed to hold them down. And yet the outstanding characteristic of the baby with this syndrome is his flaccidity! Ingalls (1952) reproduces two photographs of a one-year-old child, taken minutes apart. In the first, there is a happy and bright looking youngster, and in the legend the mother is quoted as saying, "Hope." In the second, there is the classical picture of a droopy, dull-looking child with protruding tongue; here the mother says, "Mongoloid." This alternation is typical, although those acquainted with these children only through the literature and the usual published photographs know them only as sluggish and retarded, walking on a wide base or sitting like vegetables. When seen in the community, they can be observed to alternate between moments in which their apparent intelligence is even below the tested score, giving rise to the erroneous designation of "idiot," and those in which the level appears to be much higher than expected, leading their parents to believe that school authorities have unjustly excluded their children from educational advantages. The following observation of Jan, a 9-year-old girl with devoted parents, attending a special school, is typical.

Jan was found sitting on the corridor pavement near the doorway of her schoolroom, with her legs thrust before her, eyes glazed, jaw hanging, and tongue protruding. When greeted by P, the visiting psychologist, there was no response. Five minutes later, she slowly hoisted herself and came running to the psychologist. With a lively gleam in her eyes, she started to swarm over P, kissing and demanding affection. She spied the carom table out in the courtyard, dragged P to it and dislodged the child who was there, grabbing the cue stick from him. She then proceeded to show off her skill at this game, approximating with clownish grace the movements of a billiard player. Jan approximated the skilled movements, but of course did not perform them. These children have great difficulty in simple acts of hand coordination.

These sharp alternations of innervation and enervation, as also of attention and inattention, as if these were all-or-none states, suggest not only that the inhibitions needed for finer modulations are defective, but also that the inhibitions needed to prevent the discontinuance of an act, under the stress of fatigue or in a difficult or conflict situation, are inadequate. This is another example of the "rigidity" which Lewin (1935) described as characteristic of the feebleminded, their inability to be in two "psychical areas" at the same time. But this still does not explain the tremendous strength which these patients sometimes exhibit, in spite of a generalized state of hypotonia. Here, a parallel may be drawn with the development of prehension in normal children. The neonate has a grasp reflex so powerful that it can sustain its own weight, but it cannot voluntarily release its grasp, although it cries in obvious discomfort throughout the act (McGraw, 1940). When cortical development has progressed to the point that the child can inhibit the grasp reflex, he also loses the power to sustain his weight. The hypotonia of Down's syndrome implicates the cerebellum, which is consistent with Benda's finding of extensive cerebellar pathology. Cerebellar pathology in man gives rise to grave disturbances of skilled movements, and an enduring hypotonia (J. D. French, 1960). The hypotonia presumably arises from a failure of facilitation, but defective inhibition is also indicated in the poor muscle coordination and the lack of feedback during the periods of heightened muscular tonus. The normal infant can crawl or climb a flight of stairs more easily than descend. This is also true of the child with Down's syndrome, even when as well developed as Roy, who walks up a flight of stairs with relative ease, placing his feet alternately on the treads, but descends cautiously, placing two feet on each tread before proceeding to the next. Much greater inhibitory control is needed to modulate the pull of gravity when working with it, than to maintain a tonic pull against it. The car is not much in need of brakes when going uphill, but it must have them when going downhill, or court disaster.

Prevalence of Organic Defect. Much recent evidence indicates that it is the rule rather than the exception for anomalies in brain development or some degree of brain injury to be present in each individual. For most, this defect, like the imperfections which the Japanese potter exploits to give greater meaning to his art object, only lends greater individuality to their basic personalities, though it may also plague their surgeons if a need for surgery should arise. Kawi and Pasamanick (1959) hypothesize that there is a "continuum of reproductive casualties" extending from fetal deaths to behavior disorders and reading difficulties. Mild symptoms are so common in infants that pediatricians tend to disregard them, and even neurologists usually depreciate their importance. Tremors, slight choreic movements, sudden spasms, even seizures, are expected to pass with no residue of ill effect. However, minor injuries which are unnoticed in infancy may result in a degree of stress which has noticeable consequences in a later period. Stuttering, awkwardness, impetuosity, and undue anxiety are only some of a long list of possible consequences. The more severe insults to the brain are recognized as cerebral palsy, aphasia, epilepsy, or character and personality disorders. In all of these, a breakdown in the normal processes of inhibition and disinhibition may be accompanied by more or less loss of intellectual potential. When lesions of any extent are present, more knowledgeable techniques than uninstructed mothering are necessary to supplement the inadequacies of the growing child's system of inhibitory controls. Chemotherapy, physiotherapy, psychotherapy, and educational therapy all play their parts. The form which the disturbances take depends, of course, on the affected areas of the brain, and the child's developmental stage (Pevzner, 1961).

Seizures are the clearest indication of inhibitory defect. Approximately 15 percent of those in institutions for the mentally retarded have convulsive disorders (Yannett, 1945), and this does not include those who have histories of rare seizures. Nevertheless, it is not the frequency of convulsive behavior which should surprise us so much as the fact that it does not occur more often. As Jung (1954) states it, it is appropriate to wonder "why all normals are not epileptic. Why the enormous synaptic powder barrel we carry in our heads does not explode in a fit, although the potential energy for epileptic discharge is certainly present in all of us." The implication is that convulsions do not occur under normal conditions because of the effectiveness of ongoing inhibitory processes. If this is true, then convulsions would be expected much more frequently in childhood, first because of the immaturity of the neural processes which control behavior, and second, because of the recurrent reorganization of patterns of control, which makes the child more vulnerable to stress as it moves from one developmental stage to the next. This is indeed the case. Epilepsy is predominantly a childhood and adolescent disorder. Convulsions are so common in infancy and childhood illnesses that some pediatricians take the attitude that they are the equivalent of a chill in an adult—and perhaps a chill is a minor convulsion. Douglas Thom (1942) found that 7 percent of children have one or more convulsions during their first five years of life; in the large Craig Colony for Epileptics in New York, the highest incidence of epilepsy occurred in children under five (Wallin, 1949), and Lennox (1960) reports, from a survey of many hundreds of case histories, that the onset of seizures occurred in 38 percent of the cases, whether grand mal or petit mal, before the patient was five years old. The onset of seizures occurred after the age of twenty-nine in only 1 percent of petit mal cases and 8 percent of grand mal cases. Gibbs (1958) states that EEG abnormality is largely age determined, the locus shifting in a way which helps to demonstrate the restructuring of cortical activity which takes place with age. For example, occipital spikes are the most common focal abnormality of infancy, but they disappear in 40 percent of the cases by the time the child is ten. Of the remaining cases, half develop a focus in the occipito-temporal or mid-temporal areas, and this in turn tends to disappear by the age of fifteen. Gibbs finds that the mid-temporal lobe focus is the most prevalent form in the school-age child. It is the children with this focus who usually show aggressiveness and hypermotility. It is also interesting that mice which are subject to audiogenic seizure are most susceptible during infancy and tend to outgrow this behavior as adults.

Lennox (1960) quotes a statement by Russell that "It is simpler to think of all people as epileptics and regard the matter as one of thresholds." This position is tenable, whether susceptibility is determined in large part by a genetic factor, or whether, as Gastaut and Fischer-Williams (1959) state, 95 percent of all epilepsy is of the symptomatic type, based on an "anatomically recognizable cerebral lesion."

Clinically, epileptic attacks tend to occur under two types of situations, overstimulation and understimulation. The first is well known. Individuals subject to attack are particularly prone to them under conditions of stress, fatigue and surprise—even pleasant surprise. On the other hand, Lennox (1960) states that "vacancy of mind is fuel for seizures of all kinds." Boredom will induce seizures in petit mal patients; sufferers from epilepsy claim that they can ward off an attack if they can keep busy with an intellectual task; and seizures are common during sleep, when cortical activity is greatly reduced. Gibbs and Gibbs (1947) found seizure discharges, as shown by EEG records, were twice as frequent during sleep as in waking periods. All types of seizure discharges were more common during sleep, but "discharges of the psychomotor types are particularly prone to be absent awake–present asleep."

Forms of Palsy. A lesion in any part of the brain results in some form of cerebral paralysis (palsy). The term cerebral palsy is ordinarily used to designate what might better be called motor palsy, that is, those disorders arising from lesions of the central nervous system above the spinal level which show themselves in impairment of locomotor and manipulative control. It is useful to have a similar inclusive term to designate impairments of those abilities involved in integrating perceptual units and utilizing them in communication. We shall use the term *perceptual palsy* in this sense. Thus, in perceptual palsy, the child may be handicapped in receiving, storing, or using sensory information, although the sensory organs themselves are intact. Perceptual palsy, like motor cerebral palsy, takes different forms depending on the locus of the lesion, its extent, and the developmental age at which it occurs. The aphasias are the forms of perceptual palsy which have been most intensively studied clinically. In parallel manner, the term *visceral palsy* might be applied to a third group of disorders, affecting the regulation of the vegetative system. Such disorders can be identified in the panic or "catastrophic response" which Goldstein (1942) finds characteristic of the brain injured, or in the sex offenses and other primitive responses which occur in the partial epilepsies (that is, epilepsy without loss of consciousness). Neurovegetative symptoms are common in all forms of epilepsy, but Lennox (1960) points out (following Penfield, 1930) that such symptomatology can be central in origin and result in an epilepsy in its own right. Lesions of the "visceral brain" or limbic system, as contrasted with the neocortex, generally lead to disturbances of emotional behavior and the biological processes (MacLean, 1955). These three different forms of palsy do not occur singly, since all parts of the brain function interdependently, and a lesion which interferes with integration in any area of behavior will have repercussions in the others.

Motor Cerebral Palsy. The interruption in the normal processes of inhibition and disinhibition can be observed unmistakeably in motor palsy. The very effort of its victim to control his movements backfires, by imposing still greater burdens on his already inadequate inhibitory apparatus. The unfortunate plight of the stutterer, whose greater effort leads only to perseveration of the bit of speech which had served all its purpose on its first activation, is too well known. The athetoid child, when he attempts to walk, gets involved in wide windmill-like thrashings of his limbs; and the child with ballism, when he undertakes to lift his arm, will not only fail to keep this movement within limits, but will also kick with his leg (Jung & Hassler, 1960). Incidentally, these all point to the validity of Mercier's argument that (in the words of William James, 1890) "no muscular contraction, once begun, would ever stop" without a special inhibitory process.

The normal child controls his movements merely by attention to the goal. The palsied child who must pay attention to the units of behavior is in the position of the centipede in the fable, whose feet got so badly tangled after he had been asked how he could manage so many of them all at once. The palsied child has intact spinal reflexes, but the brain lesions have disrupted their orderly sequential performance by disinhibitory release and subsequent inhibition, and his effort to integrate these acts on a level of awareness leaves him as confused as the centipede. The normal infant also had difficulty in achieving control of his motor system, but for him maturation and the auxiliary controls of good mothering suffice. The cerebral palsied child needs more skilled assistance. His inadequate inhibitory and disinhibitory controls can be supplemented by the ministrations of a physiotherapist, through a planned program of so-called muscle reeducation. This is essentially a program for the establishment of cerebral control over muscle action, by a process of substituting intentional inhibition for automatic inhibition. It is instructive to examine some of the steps in muscle reeducation from this point of view. The procedures discussed in the following paragraphs constitute the now classical Phelps method, as described by Egel (1948).

Relaxation: Here the child is taught what *not* to do. He is instructed to tense a muscle, to recognize this state, and then not to do it. It is an effort to teach inhibition of action, and this inhibition may be supported by the therapist's use of light strokes, warm water, or chemotherapy.

Passive action: The therapist puts the muscles through the pattern of movement without the child's active participation in the act, but with his attention focussed on the muscle which he is to contract. The therapist points to the muscle involved in each movement. The purpose of this process is to have the child learn how to bring this muscle under voluntary control. In a field of general inhibition—that is, relaxation of all muscles—the designated one is to be disinhibited. The slightest little twitch is reinforced by the therapist's drawing attention to it. This is repeated over and over to establish it.

Active assisted movement: After the child has acquired the ability to contract the muscles needed to perform the pattern, two facilitators of the intended act are brought to awareness: the pull of gravity, and the parallel action of the corresponding muscles of the other side of the body. After the child has learned to master the movements with the assistance of gravity, attention is turned to those muscles which are needed to resist gravity. Great care is taken to avoid the slightest fatigue, since this would diminish the inhibitory control while an effort is being made to establish it.

In spasticity there is likely to be what is called "overflow"—that is, the opposite side is likely to perform the same act. If the child attempts to take a spoon to his mouth with his right hand, the left hand will also go to his mouth. Clearly, the normal inhibition of contralateral actions is defective. A substitutive inhibition is established by giving the other hand a function of its own. In eating, the child will be instructed to hold his dish; in writing, to steady his paper.

Another type of control is provided by the use of braces. These serve not only as supports and for the correction of deformities, but also to restrict inappropriate movements. Angle joints restrict the plantar flexion of the foot in walking; knee caps prevent flexion; recurvatum straps serve to prevent hyperextension of the knees. These devices are of general value to the athetoid child, to prevent involuntary movement. The victims of cerebral palsy usually wear these aids with surprising willingness, for although they would be regarded as burdens by the normal child, to him they are tools of mastery.

A most interesting aspect of the management of motor palsy, which emphasizes the importance of stages of development, is the use of highly skilled acts to control behavior after the child has reached ten years of age. The child who had difficulty in writing may then be taught to type, and the child who stumbled in walking may be taught to ride a bicycle or do ballet dancing. This is possible because at this age the child enters a new stage of development, when additional inhibitory controls become available. Teachers of the piano, for example, know that children under ten have difficulty in coordinating the two hands, while after that age even the beginning student can do this with relative ease. The importance of these higher controls becomes obvious in later life, when a great dancer may still perform with skill despite arthritis, or a painter like Goya can continue to paint his masterpieces despite parkinsonism.

Perceptual Palsy. The diagnosis of perceptual palsy is difficult. It has been confused with sensory defect, familial mental retardation, emotional disturbance, and psychosis. There is considerable reluctance to diagnose organicity in the absence of positive neurological signs, although such signs have motor and not perceptual character. Strauss and Lehtinen (1947) and Werner (1944) have paid particular attention to children with visual perceptual difficulties. Strauss and Lehtinen selected for special study children with no apparent motor involvement but a history indicating possible brain damage, who were exhibiting difficulties in learning and adjustment. On the basis of psychological tests they concluded that the difficulties were largely determined by the child's limited ability to form perceptual patterns. The point of departure for this work was the theoretical position previously developed by K. Goldstein (1939). This syndrome has come to be known as "the exogenous child." Strauss proposed that perceptual tests be used to diagnose organicity even in the absence of the classical neurological signs, but this suggestion meets with considerable opposition. (Cf. Sarason & Gladwin, 1958.) Tests useful for this purpose include flicker fusion, various forms of figure-ground discrimination, the Bender Gestalt Test, the Marianne Frostig Developmental Test, the Ellis Visual Designs, and the Marble Form Board. Strauss and Kephart (1955) emphasize the importance of the developmental process for a theoretical understanding of the brain injured child. They state that besides recognizing that "the organism operates as a whole . . . we must also consider the important question of the effect of the injury upon the development which is in progress and the effect upon the organism which will eventually result from the deviation of this development."

Actually, a high proportion of children with perceptual palsy also have either the usual neurological signs, or such signs of visceral palsy as belching, precipitate voiding, and failure of the bowels to evacuate; and they are typically hyperactive. Whenever hypermotility is present, brain injury can be suspected. Goldenberg (1955) found that the method of approach in making a design, as on the Marble Form Board, is a more sensitive psychological test of brain injury than the finished product. In contrast to a normal child, the brain-injured child, even when he completes the design correctly, will jump abruptly from one part of the board to another without completing a logical sequence. It should be remembered that, to a lesser degree, impetuous behavior is characteristic of the normal child. The many tragic accidents which occur because of the suddenness and unpredictability of the acts of children attest to this. No experienced guide will tolerate a young child in rattlesnake country, because the child's sudden movements elicit the snake's attack. (Wildlife is cued to respond swiftly to abrupt changes in visual patterns.)

Many children who are at first suspected of being deaf are actually victims of what has been identified as receptive aphasia. The child who receives auditory stimulation but is unable to organize it into stable perceptions is actually much worse off than the deaf child who does not have to contend with a dysfunction. Myklebust (1957) makes the point that the congenitally deaf child organizes his world and becomes "an integrated symbolic organism" with greater ease and greater facility than the child with aphasia. Anyone who has watched a child of three or four years receiving instruction in lip reading cannot but be impressed by the capacity these children have to sit still and focus attention for long periods of time on the instructions which they are receiving. This attention span is far greater than that of the normal hearing child, and may be a consequence of the exclusion of auditory distraction. The normal child must actively inhibit these external auditory stimuli and the activities which they arouse, when attending to either specified auditory stimulation or any other sensory stimulus. The deaf child must of course exercise central inhibition over reactions to discomfort and to competing visual stimuli. He is probably more highly motivated than the normal child to inhibit extraneous stimuli in order to master his environment. This too indicates a relatively intact and healthy central nervous system. For the aphasic child, the situation is far more complex. For him, in contrast to the normal child, there is a loss of inhibitory capacity in the area of lesion, and as a result there is a tendency to overaction. The child with receptive aphasia is also typically distractible and impulsive. He is not a welcome pupil at the school for the hard of hearing. Myklebust, following Strauss, speaks of these children as being "disinhibited," meaning thereby that they show a lack of inhibition.

There is in receptive aphasia an inability to perceive auditory structure, to separate the auditory figure from the background of sound. A child so afflicted may appear to be deaf under most circumstances, yet puzzle his parents because he occasionally responds to some faint sounds such as the tinkle of the distant ice-cream vendor's bell, or the sound of the lid being placed on the cookie jar in another room. These children also experience a very loud sound as painful. It might be supposed that a soundproof room which excludes all extraneous stimuli would be ideal for directing attention to given sound patterns, but pilot studies have demonstrated that such is not the case (Myklebust, 1957). Actually, it should not be expected. The same finding has been made for treatment of disturbances in organization of visual figure-ground fields. It is desirable to reduce extraneous stimuli, but not to eliminate them. The epileptic has seizures when he is deprived of sufficient stimulation, and the normal adult may have a psychotic episode when deprived of outside stimulation. It must be remembered that the aphasic child is a hearing child. Inadequate as his inhibitory controls may be for the modulation of auditory stimulation—as is seen by his overreaction to very loud sounds—they are not altogether absent, and it is in this function that learning must take place. It is not hearing which is his problem, but the patterning of sound, and the elimination of all extraneous sound does not give him the opportunity to practice the function in which he is deficient.

Visceral Palsy. Just as it is incorrect to speak of cerebral motor palsy in the singular, so it is true that there are several forms of visceral palsy. These range from severe chronically disabling organic lesions to temporary states which result from what we may call, with some extension of the usual meaning of the term, biochemical lesions. This phrase describes the reversible malfunctioning of the central nervous system which can be induced for experimental purposes by the application of selected biochemicals (Russell, 1960). The various substances which are released in states of fatigue, anxiety, or emotional excitement act in much the same way, causing a paralysis or overaction of normal functioning which may also be called a biochemical lesion, without undue strain on the meaning of that term. The origin of such lesions may be emotional or pathological, and their effects may induce motor or perceptual palsy as well as visceral palsy. They can be recognized in such temporary states of perceptual palsy as "narrowing of the field," "blocking," and "perseveration." The fatigued driver fails to see the warning signal in his line of vision; the anxious student reads his examination question over and over without perceiving its meaning. Fear may give rise to "freezing," or to defecation. Biochemical lesions of a more malignant form result from various errors of metabolism, as in galactosemia and phenylpyruvic oligophrenia. Any child who suffers from palsy can be expected to have special difficulty in coping with his environment and his impulses in periods when he must carry the added load of a temporary biochemical lesion arising from emotional frustration or the like. Therefore psychotherapy of a supportive kind will often be highly effective in reducing his dysfunction.

Visceral palsy may be either primary or secondary. Goldstein's "catastrophic response" is an example of visceral palsy as a secondary effect, while Penfield's (1930) "diencephalic autonomic epilepsy" or the visceral seizures of childhood described by Lennox (1960) are primary manifestations. Visceral palsy is evident in the partial epilepsies, for which Gastaut and Fischer-Williams (1959) list the following symptoms: "abnormal epigastric abdominal and precordial sensations, with reactional gestures: chewing, salivation, deglutition, and imperious needs to urinate or defecate, as well as disorders of attention, anxiety, fear, anger, etc." On the basis of these symptoms, these authors implicate the rhinencephalon and the diencephalon in the seizures found in psychomotor epilepsy. They note that these formations have the lowest convulsive threshold of all cerebral structures. While neurological findings are likely to be negative in the intervals between attacks of psychomotor epilepsy and the EEG signs of epilepsy may be absent, behavior disorders are common (Gastaut, 1953). The possibility exists that children with behavior disorders involving distractibility, anxiety, fear, anger and bed wetting–the last of which was found by Michaels (1955) to be the most common symptom in delinquency–are, even in the absence of a positive EEG, victims of minor damage to structures in or closely connected with the rhinencephalon and the diencephalon. The overaction of these structures will often be a consequence of interruption of inhibition normally exerted by higher structures with which they are intimately connected.

Among the children suffering from various aspects of visceral palsy are the hyperkinetic, emotionally overreactive children who are poor learners even without being mentally retarded. They often come from good homes, and therefore their difficulties cannot be attributed to sociocultural factors. Their emotional overreaction may be expressed in sudden rage, overaggression, or even overaffection; in addition, enuresis, soiling, or compulsive eating are often present. These are the children who are so "familiar to educators, maybe nauseatingly familiar when we consider what teachers say about them" (Burks, 1958). These victims of palsy are the "very bad children," the discipline problems who "refuse to learn." Lois and Willy provide two contrasting examples.

Lois is a nine-year-old, hyperactive, "mischievous" child who, when seen by the psychologist, had already been excluded from two schools and was about to be excluded from a third. She was a premature Rh negative baby born to an Rh positive mother; the mother states that birth was induced because the mother had developed severe eclampsia. The nurse commented on Lois' hyperkinesis even while she was in the incubator. As an infant she was unable to assimilate milk and was fed on a concentrated protein diet. She is an obviously bright child as judged by her conversation and test results. For example, she gave three human responses of high form level to the first Rorschach card; to the last, she said "Wow! Fourth of July." On the WISC she had a weighted score of 13 on Similarities, but 5 on the Picture Completions. Most interesting is her overaffection. This is a most serious problem, as she cannot be trusted to go to school unattended. She readily makes new friends with men, women, or children, hugging and kissing them, and often wanders off with them.

A very different child belonging to this same category is Willy. At 5 years of age Willy had no friends at all. His kindergarten teacher and his classmates found him "repulsive" because of his compulsive eating. He raided the children's lockers for their snacks, and ate garbage out of the waste can and chewing gum off the sidewalk. At the start of the testing session he led the examiner a merry chase through the Health Clinic room, where he turned up the flame on a hot water heater, switched on the sterilizer, then swirled into the bathroom to open all the water taps and flush the bowl. He was finally quieted, and the Rorschach was administered to him lying on a couch. The protocol revealed both his explosive character and his potentially good intelligence. Willy was then seen at a child guidance clinic for six months, until the psychiatrist decided that progress was not sufficient to justify continuance. Three years later Willy was excluded from another elementary school when the principal found that the teacher (a naive one who had not read the case record) was suffering from a nervous breakdown precipitated by Willy. At this time an EEG study was made. (It had been recommended after the first examination, but the clinic had not accepted the recommendation then.) The record showed "indications of psychomotor disturbance."

From these histories alone it might be imagined that both of these children were compensating, in different ways, because they had been deprived of affection. However, the indications in both cases were against such a supposition, and this kind of explanation is also definitely excluded in the following case.

Robin, a 15-year-old Negro boy who reads on a fourth grade level, is another difficult behavior problem. His parents are devoted to each other, and were hopeful that their son would be a credit to their race. Yet periodically the boy does outrageous things. His teacher says that Robin is sometimes very good and polite, then all of a sudden he breaks loose. When he was 8 his mother sought advice. Robin was reported to have rushed into the school auditorium while a class play was in rehearsal, flipped down all the aisle seats, making a great clatter while he hallooed at the top of his lungs. He become "ugly in mood," fighting and kicking at the teacher. He was diagnosed by the school psychologist as severely emotionally disturbed due to the "over ambition" of his mother. Robin had an undiagnosed illness when he was 9 years old. He was rushed to the hospital, had convulsions, ran a high fever and was lethargic for several days. At this time it was learned that he had had repeated seizures up to the age of 4½. The pediatrician had assured his mother that he would outgrow them. He has had no more seizures since then, but periodically becomes involved in some antisocial behavior. He is always most contrite: "I don't know why I do it, I don't want to. Something just happens." (Cf. Geleerd, 1945.)

Walter (1950) states that the EEG's of "very bad children" have more signs of immaturity than those of good children, so that the record of a 12 year old can be mistaken for that of a normal 5 or 6 year old. He suggests that this results from unusually slow development of some cerebral functions, which shows itself, for example, in a persistent theta rhythm; as a consequence, the child is unable to cope with his environment. Goldstein's explanation, in terms of the "catastrophic response," is essentially similar. However, it seems probable that in cases such as these, it is not *any* anomaly or *any* lesion which is responsible for these behavior disorders, but rather lesions of the limbic brain specifically. There is a basic similarity between these cases and the syndrome that Gastaut describes as partial epilepsy. It would seem that here is a special type of deficit in inhibitory control, which involves paleocortical and subcortical structures rather than the neocortex. Consequently, these disturbances are not inconsistent with intellectual capacities of superior and even genius level. Such brilliant children, who have the possibility of attaining a higher level of cortical control, more easily succeed in stopping short of antisocial acts. Van Gogh was apparently such a victim of visceral (or partial) epilepsy: for a time he was able to impose a discipline upon himself through the superb cortical control which is also expressed in his art.

Psychotherapy has been found to be of limited value in treating children, like Willy and Robin, with severe behavior disorders. However, the amphetamines have proved most helpful (Lindsley & Cutts, 1940; Lindsley & Henry, 1942; Walter, 1950; Lennox, 1960).

Early Infantile Autism. In "early infantile autism" there are signs of both perceptual and visceral palsy. The syndrome of this disorder was first identified by Kanner (1943), who characterized it as "an inborn autistic disturbance of affective contact." Kanner (1957) states that these children "appear feebleminded because of emotional interference with the unfolding of cognitive potentialities." In the past, some neurologists diagnosed these children as deaf, because of their failure to respond when spoken to. Many practising psychiatrists today regard the condition as a deep emotional disturbance or a psychosis occasioned by cold, rejecting mothers. Margaret Mahler (1952) doubts this latter hypothesis, and finds that the evidence suggests the presence of constitutional or organic factors: "It seems that such basic damage to the ego which results in infantile psychosis occurs in children who have a hereditary or constitutional Anlage for it, or in whom an intrinsic factor is present. There *are* infants with an inherently defective tension-regulating apparatus which probably cannot be adequately compensated by either the most qualitatively or quantitatively efficient mothering." This intrinsic factor, we suggest, may be found in lesions in both the limbic system and the higher structures necessary for cognitive functioning.

The symptoms of this disorder include extensive disorganization of communication functions which are ordinarily ready to function during infancy. Touch is acutely involved, but so are the natively organized patterns of response to other human beings. Dennis (1938) found, for example, that the twin infants who were deprived of usual social stimulation still smiled at their poker-faced attendants. The autistic infant does not so smile: it fails to respond overtly or appropriately to the signals for the release of the earliest social behavior. The autistic child has an agnosia for signs which are ordinarily responded to by the healthy child. Mahler says: "In autistic infantile psychosis there are no signs of affective awareness of other human beings. Behavior which would point to affective perception of ministration coming from the mother—from the outside world—is absent. In the anamnesis of these children one finds descriptions of the earliest behavior which betray that there was no anticipatory posture at nursing, no reaching out gestures and no specific smiling responses" (1952).

She quotes one mother as saying: "He never greeted me when I entered, he never cried, he never even noticed when I left the room," and another: "I never could reach my baby." Like the child with receptive aphasia, who overreacts to a loud noise, these children overreact to social cues which are forced upon them through tactile stimulation. The case of Lotta demonstrates the failure to communicate and the overaction to social tactile stimulation:

> At the age of three-and-a-half, Lotta had no language, no gestural communication, no hand, mouth, and eye integration. She neither fed nor handled herself, and she showed a terrified startle reaction at any chance touch *of* or *by* another person. . . . However, Lotta's habits were compulsively neat, her motor and manipulative skills were age adequate, her knowledge of, her memory for, her static environment were phenomenal (Mahler, 1952, p. 290).

In summarizing her discussion of the "function" of autism, Mahler states: "In short, it seems as though these patients experience outer reality as an intolerable source of irritation, without specific or further qualification."

In the treatment of the autistic child, care must be exercised in the early stages not to express affection through human contact. While the warmth of the hand, gentle stroking and cuddling were seen to be inhibitors of muscular tension for the normal child, the exact opposite occurs with the autistic child. This is analogous to the increased motor discoordination of the cerebral motor palsied child when he attempts to control his movements, and the aphasic child's violent reaction to very loud sounds. The partial successes which have been achieved in the treatment of autistic children suggest that the unexpressed functions are present, but lesions interfere with their normal exercise, so that the cues for normal social communication lead to either overaction or failure to react. Their avoidance of social symbols is most intriguing. Benda (1952) describes children who will pick blocks and cars out of a play box and leave the dolls and animals alone. "Even if able to express themselves so that one may have an idea of what is going on inside of them, they will use blocks as symbols of animals or men, rather than use dolls for expressing their thoughts." Adult patients with brain injuries sometimes exhibit perceptual agnosias for surprisingly precise categories of phenomena. Nielsen (1951) describes one patient who could perceive all animate objects but none that were inanimate, and another who could recognize inanimate objects, but not the animate. The autistic child has a comparable defect. He responds to nonsocial stimuli with competence, but can handle the social only by responding to it as if it too were inanimate. "The autistic child shoves away the *hand* that is in his way as he would a wooden block" (Mahler, 1952).

Along with the perceptual signs, there are the very strong indications of visceral palsy. Lotta, for example, was extremely reactive to visceral pain, had daily struggles over constipation and a "vulvovaginitis followed the first signs of her beginning to touch herself." On the other hand, when she accidentally burned her mouth with an automobile cigarette lighter she showed no reaction to pain.

The panic responses of these children, when there is any change in an expected pattern, are startling. Their rote memory is phenomenal. When they make a pattern of objects, no matter how haphazard it may seem to be, it is remembered accurately. If anyone disturbs this pattern, they will go into panic.

Lily, a beautiful girl of five, with autism, finally made contact with her nursery school teacher. Each morning she had to be greeted with the set phrase, "Good morning, Lily. I am very, very glad to see you." If even one of the very's was omitted or another added, she would start to scream wildly. As soon as the expected salutation was given, she became calm.

This overaction to what might evoke a minor disturbance in a more normal ritualistic child suggests that those central processes involved in the mediation of the expression of rage, fear, and anxiety are too easily and too totally disinhibited.

Benda (1952) presents a group of cases of children with early infantile autism, in all of which there is evidence of brain injury. He considers the possibility that there are three causes of autism: psychological trauma, childhood schizophrenia (psychosis), and injuries to the central nervous system. These injuries are possibly caused by asphyxiation, which, he says, produces a very characteristic syndrome of lack of awareness and disturbances of orientation.

Schain and Yannett (1960) studied 50 children at Southard School who met Kanner's criteria of early infantile autism. They discovered to their surprise that these children as a group differed from Kanner's in one important respect: 42 percent of them had histories of seizure. Since the selection of the children had been carefully governed by

Kanner's criteria, they suggest that either rare seizures are commonly overlooked, or physicians reject the diagnosis of autism when seizures also are present. They also suggest the possibility that the limbic system is the site of the cerebral abnormality which accounts for both the susceptibility to seizure and the severe affect disorder.

There are interesting parallels between the "stubbornness" of the child with Down's syndrome and the "demand for sameness" of the autistic child. Both may be regarded as ritualists, and although the store of things remembered is scant for the child with Down's syndrome as compared to that of the child with infantile autism, in both cases what these children remember they retain with great tenacity, and usually as a result of a single exposure. The combination of feats of memory and ritualism is also prominent in the misnamed idiot-savant, and K. Goldstein (1959) suggests that these children should also be regarded as cases of infantile autism. He reports the case of a boy who could play the piano quite well, but it had to be the same piano, in the same room. In the case of the child with Down's syndrome, we suggested that mental development was arrested at about the four-year stage. Can this hypothesis be applied to the autistic child, who is often characterized as "intelligent?" We believe it can be. Even though the autistic child may learn to read, may perform well on the piano, and do complicated arithmetic manipulations, he is remarkably deficient in his ability to manipulate symbols, which is a different ability from that of identifying symbols, or naming symbols. Even the use of "yes" and "no," or how to apply the first person pronoun to themselves, is learned with great difficulty. Such a child will say, "He went home," when speaking of himself. This behavior can be interpreted as the result of a specialized developmental arrest.

A similar combination of memory and ritualism, though less pronounced, is often seen in normal three-year-olds, even in those who are destined to become superior adults. Parents are amazed at their ability to correct the slightest deviation in a bedtime story, and sometimes they will select as their very own a particular glass or spoon which to the uninitiated appears identical with its mates, and they will tolerate no substitution. This apparently phenomenal memory for detail usually passes (like the talent for mimicry which was discussed earlier) when the child becomes a four-year-old. We therefore suggest the hypothesis that the rigidity of the autistic child, like that of the child with Down's syndrome, is due to the fact that brain structures which are essential for the manipulation of symbols, and which ordinarily emerge during the fourth year, fail to become properly functional. However, in the case of the autistic child, with his more nearly intact brain, a high level of performance in respect to retentivity (as well as normal performance in many other respects) is possible. If this is true, then the autistic child provides us with another example (analogous to the Gamper child) of precocity in lower functions, due to the fact that they fail to come under the inhibitory control of the higher function which fails to develop.

The problem why autistic children behave as they do is among the most intriguing in the whole field of personality study. Whatever solutions are finally reached, it would seem that they must include an evaluation of the nature of the inhibitory controls which are intact, as well as of those which are defective.

The present chapter was written as an exercise to test the fruitfulness of the inhibition construct in a particular area—mental retardation and mental defect. Inhibition was found to have implications regarding the relation of the child to its social environment, particularly its mother, as well as to its physical environment. By employing the construct, it was possible to arrive at an integrated conception of the sources of various symptoms and personality characteristics which are associated with different forms of mental handicap, such as impetuosity, seizures, motor and perceptual palsy, rigidity, infantilism and autistic behavior. These results offer promise of new insights if not new pathways in the fields of personality, genetic psychology, and, of course, clinical psychology.

THE INFLUENCE OF DRUGS ON BEHAVIOR 15

For those who are accustomed to think of behavior primarily as a habit structure, the predictable alteration of behavior which results from the administration of certain drugs poses a difficult problem. The use of drugs to influence mood and performance is as old as the practice of medicine. The practical knowledge of intoxicants, aphrodisiacs, and sedatives has prehistoric roots. Homer knew enough of their possibilities to tell how the enchantress Circe used one drug to tame mountain lions and wolves, so that they behaved like mastiffs, and another to make men lose the memory of their homes, and how Ulysses withstood her potion because he had first taken a "potent herb" which—in modern terminology—antagonized its effects. These legendary events are close enough to recognizable effects of known drugs to suggest that the Homeric account may not have been a pure figment of imagination, but rather a poetic overstatement of actual experience. In various parts of the world, men discovered the use of plant alkaloids (caffeine, cocaine, mescaline, etc.) to induce euphoric moods; it is fitting that in India, the home of the Nirvana concept, physicians learned the use of the powdered root of *Rauwolfia* to bring their disturbed patients a different form of release, which we now call tranquilization. Modern pharmacology has assembled this scattered knowledge, enriched it with a host of artificial derivatives, but has only begun to understand how it is that the drugs bring about these varied effects. An appreciation of the role of neural inhibition in the control of behavior has provided the first rational basis for interpretation of some of these phenomena.

The key was given long ago: *in vino veritas.* It is immemorial tradition to loosen men's tongues with alcohol, and modern "truth serums" only continue this tradition with refinement of method. Anstie provided an additional hint when he observed that the effects of chloroform and hashish, as well as those of alcohol, could be interpreted as due to interruption of higher controls over lower functions. In earlier chapters, we have seen how, again and again, in the work of Bernard, Heidenhain, Wedensky, Sherrington, and others, the effects of drugs provided clues as to the existence of an inhibitory process. The theory of chemical transmission of nerve impulses provided scant help so long as the process of transmission was looked upon as simply a means of producing excitation, but the concept of adrenergic and cholinergic divisions of the autonomic nervous system did bring partial order into the confused picture of pharmacological effects. However, it is only the attainment of an understanding of central synaptic inhibition, along with increased knowledge of the regulatory influences exercised by centrencephalic and brain stem structures, which has led to heuristically valuable hypotheses, the investigation of which may be expected to lead not only to a better understanding of drug effects, but to a better understanding of the organization of behavior in general.

For our purpose, the most important general conclusion which arises out of this whole body of observations is one which does not depend on any particular effect, but on the repeated observation that many drugs are quite specific in their action, taking effect on one part of the nervous system rather than on another. If only the contrast between cholinergic and adrenergic mechanisms were involved, the drugs could be neatly catalogued into several groups, and rated according to the intensity of their effects on these mechanisms. Actually, pharmacologists are confronted by a medley of paradoxical results, whose major importance for us is that they imply the existence of a very elaborate chemical differentiation of the nervous system. In this respect, McIlwain (1959) writes: "Nervous structures of a variety of functions are closely packed in the brain. Localization of the action of given cells is largely determined anatomically, but where such elements are closest, chemical specificity becomes more important."

Our purpose in including a brief summary of the effect of drugs on behavior within the scope of this book is solely to indicate the probable significance of such chemical specificity for the general organization of behavior, which will be discussed in the next chapter. The great variety of drug effects provides supporting evidence for the conclusion that the number of different transmitter substances is much greater than the four or five that have so far been isolated, and also that the receptor sites of synapses are of different kinds, some being more sensitive to one transmitter, some to another. These distinctions provide the neural basis for differentiated response mechanisms which are largely independent of "connections" in the traditional sense. On the other hand, the task of identifying such response systems is complicated by the fact that the somatic and behavioral effects associated with a given transmitter substance can be offset by interference with any part of the cycle of events involved in the formation and removal of the transmitter substance, and that the drugs themselves interact, antagonizing and supporting one another in ways that are at present rarely understandable. In this medley of effects, those that can be regarded as taking place specifically at inhibitory synaptic sites, to cause either the activation or the blocking of such sites, are only one class among many, but they constitute an essential class, the understanding of which would contribute a great deal toward forming a clearer picture of the nervous control of behavior.

The reader will recall that the implications of synaptic inhibition for understanding the specificity of drug action were briefly discussed in Chapter 5, and they were illustrated by the mention of several theories of LSD action—theories which differ in detail, but which all agree that the effects of this most potent drug, as well as those of several other drugs which exercise similar effects in lesser degree or tend to antagonize the effects of LSD, must all be sought in the details of synaptic inhibitory processes. The present chapter will make no effort to consider drug effects on that fundamental level. It merely presents the position that a major goal of pharmacological research must be to arrive at the operational definition of chemically differentiated action systems within the nervous system, and that coordinated behavioral studies can then demonstrate the participation of these subsystems in different patterns of behavior. In both phases of this interdisciplinary program, the concept of synaptic inhibition plays a key part.

It is important to recognize that the number of kinds of synapses is greater than the number of presently known transmitter substances. Domino (1958) points out that there are many anatomically distinguishable varieties of central synapse, and for only a few of these is the transmitter substance known with some degree of certainty. Furthermore, it has been known for some time that cholinergic synapses include two types, the nicotine-sensitive and the muscarine-sensitive. Trouton and Eysenck (1961) express the distinction between these as follows: "Preganglionic nerves and nerves to voluntary muscles are cholinergic (nicotinic) whereas the postganglionic fibres and the sympathetic fibres to sweat glands are cholinergic (muscarinic)." However, Anichkov (1961) states that recent Soviet research has found that the "cholin-receptors of the central synapses, as well as the peripheral ones" include both types. The fact that different synapses respond differently to these two alkaloids implies that they also respond differently to some as yet undiscovered nuances of physiological stimulation. The successful distinction of these systems, and an analysis of the expressive behaviors associated with each, would almost certainly deepen our understanding of the patterns of emotional experience, which have been so resistant to orderly arrangement on a phenomenological basis. This is but one example of the manner in which neuropharmacology may contribute to psychological understanding.

Wikler (1957) opens his excellent review of the pharmacology of behavior with this quotation from Claude Bernard: "Les poisons constituent un moyen d'analyse des proprietés nerveuses, des sorted de scalpel physiologiques beacoup plus délicats et plus subtils que les scalpels ordinaires." The greater delicacy of the physiological scalpel, even in these days of microtechnique, is due to the fact that it cuts out functions, as the surgeon's scalpel cuts out tissues. Another important advantage of chemical lesions is their reversability—a circumstance which permits us to be more ruthless in experimentation. (The pharmacologist does not mind playing Circe to a human subject, producing an experimental madness, nor does the subject object to the experience, if it is only a transient one.) The reader will recall how Bernard himself, with curare as his "scalpel," approached the discovery of an invisible functional barrier placed between the conductile tissue of the nerve and the contractile tissue of the muscle; and he will not need to be reminded of the need to consider, in relation to each drug, whether it does not gain its effect by directly or indirectly influencing a synaptic process. From this point of view, the literature of experimental pharmacology represents an enormous accumulation of evidence, if such evidence were needed, on the importance of inhibitory processes. More relevant to our immediate problem, however, is that it also demonstrates in detail a fact already hinted at by the different concentrations of various neurohumors in different parts of the brain: to wit that these parts are by no means equipotential, any more than the eye and the ear are equipotential and capable of vicarious functioning in respect to light and sound. It seems that the doctrine of specific energies must receive its final statement in terms of the chemistry of the nervous system.

The limitations of anatomical and electrophysiological analysis, by contrast with the pharmacological, appear, for example, in the work of W. R. Hess (1957). His goal was to study the "functional organization" of the diencephalon, and his technique was the careful observation of behavioral effects resulting from electrical stimulation of precisely determined structures, with currents of varying intensities. However, he would not only obtain opposite effects within the same general area, but sometimes there would be a combination of effects (such as pressor and depressor effects on blood pressure, in a diphasic pattern) belonging to different response patterns. He concluded that such an area "includes a variety of fibers belonging to different systems, so that the electrical stimulus, *acting in a nonselective fashion,*" produced the inconsistent responses. In contrast to this, we shall see later that different chemical substances applied to the same point in the brain can evoke distinctive effects. It is of course true that in many instances drugs also will have confused and inconsistent effects, particularly when they are introduced into the blood stream or administered in other ways which bring them into contact with many different structures of the nervous system. However, such instances are challenges to further pharmacological research which will produce substances capable of differentiating the effects joined together in this manner.

Before we look at the investigations themselves, it will be convenient to have in mind a general classification of the so-called psychoactive drugs, with some rough indications of the kinds of effects commonly associated with them. That any such classification is tentative appears from the fact that F. M. Berger (1960) gives brief summaries of ten different proposals for the classification of the "tranquilizers," all published during the years 1957 and 1958. He himself proposes a classification based on chemical structure, which is shown in Table 4. This table also gives some indication of one

TABLE 4. The Effect of Various Classes of Compounds on Certain Functional Units of the Brain

	Cortex	Hypothalamus	Limbic System	Reticular Formation
Phenothiazines	Not affected	Stimulated	Not affected or stimulated	Slightly depressed
Rauwolfia alkaloids	Not affected	Stimulated	Stimulated	Slightly depressed
Diphenyl-methanes	Slightly depressed	Stimulated	Not affected	Slightly depressed
Propanediols	Not affected	Not affected	Depressed	Not affected or slightly stimulated
Substituted amides	Depressed	Not affected	Depressed	Depressed

SOURCE: F. M. Berger, in Uhr & Miller, *Drugs and Behavior*, 1960, p. 99. By permission of John Wiley & Sons, Inc.

of the most important facts emerging from neuropharmacological research: that a given drug not only varies in potency from one part of the brain to another, but it may even produce effects in one part which, on the surface at least, seem opposite in character to those it produces in another part.

Although any attempt at a brief summary characterization of the typical effects of each class of drugs is sure to be partly misleading, it can nevertheless serve as a frame of reference for what follows. Perhaps the error will be less serious if we try to describe the effects of one prominent member of each class, rather than of the class as a whole. A typical phenothiazine derivative is chlorpromazine. This drug blocks the adrenergic system; it produces sedation and potentiates the action of other sedatives and of analgesics and anesthetics. The derivatives of the *Rauwolfia* root include reserpine, which inhibits sympathetic centers in the hypothalamus; it, too, produces sedation; and, in many instances, it has a serotonin-like effect. Derivatives of diphenylmethane include azacyclonol (Frenquel). This substance does not produce sedation. Unlike chlorpromazine and reserpine, it does not block the performance of conditioned reflexes. However, it prolongs the action of barbiturates and other hypnotics (that is, of substituted amides), and it antagonizes effects of serotonin. The substituted propanediols have their effects primarily on the striped muscle system rather than on the autonomic system. One member of this group is meprobamate, which is primarily a muscle relaxant, but serves also to relieve anxiety and to increase tolerance for frustration. Finally, the substituted amides are not tranquilizers in the narrower sense of that term, since their primary effect is to produce sedation of intellectual and sensory functons by depressing cortical activity, whereas the use of tranquilizers aims at control of emotionality without intellectual sedation. This group includes the barbiturates and other hypnotics, drugs which were used for sedation before the introduction of tranquilizers. A typical member of the group is pentobarbitol.

Berger goes on to classify the stimulants or antidepressants into three groups: analeptics, monoamine oxidase inhibitors, and acetylcholine precursors. The analeptics (that is, drugs classified as having restorative or strengthening effects) are a broad group which share the characteristics that they antagonize drugs which depress the central nervous system, but they may differ in other important respects. A very important member of this group is amphetamine. Iproniazid is a drug which interferes with the action of the enzyme monoamine oxidase, which destroys serotonin. Finally, diethylaminoethanol (Deaner) is thought to gain its antidepressant effects by helping to overcome a deficiency in the production of acetylcholine, when such exists.

The data concerning the influence of drugs on behavior derive from three principal types of research: clinical, behavioral, and electrophysiological. However, problems which are of special interest to clinical workers tend to orient most research on psychoactive drugs, by whatever method. The leading clinical problems are: (1) the relation of schizophrenia to deficiency or imbalance in the supply of neurohumors, and particularly of serotonin; (2) the production of "model psychoses" by the use of LSD, mescaline, and other psychotogenic drugs, to facilitate the study of psychotic-like processes in thinking, and discover other drugs which antagonize these effects; and (3) the efficacy of tranquilizers and other drugs in overcoming various forms of emotional disturbance, including manic excitement, anxiety, and depression.

Woolley and Shaw (1954) advanced the suggestion that a relative deficiency in serotonin might be the cause of schizophrenia and other mental disorders. The suggestion grew out of their observation of side effects attendant on the use of serotonin to relieve hypertension. It precipitated intensive research efforts, and a proportionately extensive literature, from which it seems safe only to conclude that either deficiency of serotonin or its imbalance with respect to one or more other neurohumors does contribute to intellectual disturbance. (Cf. Woolley, 1958; Marrazzi and Hart, 1957.) The nature of the inconsistences may be briefly illustrated. Canali and Grisoni (1957) found that injection of serotonin in humans, in concentrations which did not have any detectable influence on the EEG's of normal subjects, eliminated the abnormal features of the EEG in most epileptic patients, particularly those suffering from focal epilepsy. Subsequently, elevation of serotonin level has been credited with reducing the incidence of epileptic seizures (Santanelli et al., 1961), which is consistent with the above result, but it has also been blamed for increasing their incidence, specifically in cases of artificial focal epilepsy in cats (Wada, 1961).

While we await more detailed neurophysiological explanation of the way in which serotonin and other substances achieve the effects attributed to them, we cannot overlook the fact that the general conclusions reached by clinicians, based on their experience in the therapeutic use of tranquilizers, suggests that these drugs are somehow influencing a balance of inhibitory and excitatory processes, as Pavlov would define them. Hoch summarized such experience as follows:

What kind of patient responds to a tranquilizing drug? It is the general opinion that excited, overactive, aggressive, tense, and anxious patients benefit most from chlorpromazine or some of the Rauwolfia preparations. Driveless, apathetic patients without tension respond far less. Patients with a tendency toward motor discharge and those who have symptoms which could be classified as over-reactive are the most influenced. Those patients where over-reaction is not present do not respond well. This is especially marked in patients suffering from depression who do not respond too well to the drugs, whereas in the manic phase of their sickness the drugs are very effective. . . . The clinical impression is that [these drugs] do not sedate uniformly every psychic function. . . . The clinical investigations indicate that the tranquilizing drugs are selective sedatives which especially affect anxiety and tension, but do not affect some other emotional mechanisms such as depression (Hoch, 1958, pp. 340, 342).

Ayd (1957) also states that "the most favorable cases for chlorpromazine and reserpine therapy are the hypomanic and manic states," and warns that states of depression may be only enhanced, or indeed precipitated where a disposition to depression exists.

These statements of clinical experience suggest that the function of these drugs is somehow to fortify deficient inherent inhibitory capacity in the central nervous system, and that when such inherent inhibitions are in fact preponderant (as in some depressions) the drugs only intensify the illness rather than tending to remedy it. Such a viewpoint is in general agreement, of course, with Pavlov's (1927) interpretation of the effects of administering bromides to dogs that were overexcitable—not to diminish excitability, he points out, but to strengthen internal inhibition—and of administering caffeine to dogs that were overinhibited.

The degree to which such effects depend on the modification of different kinds of synaptic inhibitions remains to be investigated by experimental procedures. Evidence of drug effects may be sought either in the recording of neural events, usually by electrophysiological techniques, or in the modification of overt behavior. We shall look first at some electrophysiological studies.

One important investigation of this kind was Brazier's (1958) study of the effect of barbiturates on the cortical response to a single flash of light. (The reader may wish to bear in mind that the barbiturates include such anticonvulsant drugs as dilantin, triadone, and phenurone, which are used for the treatment of some forms of epilepsy, and the effect which is to be described may therefore have some relevance to the therapeutic value of these drugs.) Forbes and Morison (1939) had shown that the cortical response to a single flash of light consists of a double discharge, which implies that the excitation of the cortex takes place by two different pathways, one of which conducts more rapidly than the other, presumably because it involves fewer synapses. Brazier discovered that the effect of a moderate depth of barbiturate anesthesia was to reduce the intensity of the primary response by about 30 percent, but almost to double the amplitude of the secondary response. The result, she says, "suggests a 'release' effect as though *at this stage* of barbiturate anesthesia some inhibitory system . . . has been put out of action by the drug." She also points out that this interpretation is consistent with the known fact that under pentothal anesthesia the cortical response to auditory stimulation is augmented. She therefore draws the conclusion that "a state of anesthesia does not require that sensory impulses should be prevented from reaching the cortex. A disruption of the balance between inhibition and activation at a subcortical level of integration would appear to determine whether incoming sensory impulses receive the elaboration necessary for 'awareness.'"

Bradley (1958) obtained evidence on the site of action of a number of widely used drugs by observing their effects on the electrocortical activity of conscious intact cats and two kinds of acute preparations: those with *encéphale isolé* (that is, with transected medulla but connections still intact between the cerebral hemispheres and the brain stem) and those with *cerveau isolé* (a condition in which the transection is higher, which results in a "sleeping" brain, as discussed in the next chapter). All the drugs used showed their characteristic effects on the brains of intact animals, some drugs also influenced the *encéphale isolé* preparations, and some of these also influenced the *cerveau isolé* preparations. These and other findings led Bradley to conclude that some drugs (including amphetamine and the barbiturates) act directly on the reticular formation, that the cholinergic drugs act more diffusely, and that still other drugs (including LSD-25 and chlorpromazine) "appear to have little direct action on the reticular formation but seem to have an action related to the afferent input into this system." It will be seen that this classification according to site of action cuts across the distinction between excitant and antiexcitant or inhibitant effects. The evidence that some psychoactive drugs have their effects largely on subcortical afferent pathways is extremely important.

In another investigation, Bradley (1957) made microelectrode recordings of single unit activity in the reticular system, by means of electrodes chronically implanted, so as to permit repeated observation of the response of the same unit to a variety of influences. Most of the units studied showed "convergence," that is, they were responsive to stimulation of more than one sensory modality. He was then able to observe the effects of injections of adrenaline or of acetylcholine on the rate of activity of such units, both spontaneously and in response to peripheral stimulation. The effect of acetylcholine might be either to increase or to decrease the activity of the unit being studied, more commonly the former. Adrenaline, too, might have either of these effects, but there were also a good many instances of "no effect." Also, it is worthy of note that instances of decreased activity, after injection of adrenaline, were much less frequent in the medulla than in the mesencephalon. For any given unit, the nature of the effects produced by acetylcholine and by adrenaline might be either similar or dissimilar. The effect of chlorpromazine on reticular units was to decrease both the spontaneous activity and the responsiveness to peripheral stimulation; the addition of a barbiturate would then cause complete cessation of response, something which was never observed to happen with barbiturates alone.

There are many other studies of the same general type, but we shall mention only a few. Thus, Rothballer (1956) found that the slow, tonic system of afferents from the brain stem reticular formation was adrenaline-sensitive, and that it could be blocked by chlorpromazine, which did not block the faster-acting phasic system of afferents from the thalamus. On the other hand, Killam and Killam (1958) reported that chlorpromazine "markedly raised the threshold for behavioral arousal from the diffuse thalamic projection system," while somewhat elevating the cortical response to stimulation of the brain stem reticular formation. It has been pointed out (Schneider, 1958) that contradictions such as this may result from the use of different sources of stimulation, since it may happen that a drug which blocks afferentation resulting from ordinary pressure on the footpads of an anesthetized cat, for example, may not block pain arising from a mild electric shock applied to the foot.

As a final example of research using the techniques of electrocortical recording, we shall mention a study by Marrazzi and Hart (1957). These workers stimulated the visual cortex of the cat in one hemisphere, and measured the response evoked transcallossally, at the corresponding point of the opposite hemisphere. This response was suppressed when adrenaline, noradrenaline, LSD, or serotonin had been introduced previously into the blood stream. Such suppression did not occur following injection of chlorpromazine, reserpine, or azacyclonol. The response was enhanced by acetylcholine. Serotonin was particularly powerful as a suppressor agent, and this is one piece of evidence among many which Marrazzi uses to support his contention that it is a natural synaptic inhibitor.

This sample of studies combining pharmacological and electrophysiological techniques demonstrates the feasibility of constructing a functional chart of the nervous system—which will necessarily be far more complex than existing neuroanatomical charts—on the basis of differences in responsiveness to the effects of various drugs. However, the value of such a chart would depend on the correlation of these findings with behavioral data. Therefore we turn now to a consideration of pharmacological research of a behavioral nature. The scope and variety of research in this field is indicated by the almost forty chapters in *Drugs and Behavior*, edited by Uhr and Miller (1960), which are devoted to concise summary statements of experimental work. Most of these chapters deal, not with single studies, but with extensive programs. The review article by Trouton and Eysenck (1961) includes almost 600 references, yet it is not difficult to discover important omissions. With this wealth of available material, our selection of examples must be arbitrary. It is guided by the intention to suggest how such studies can help in defining response systems, rather than to display the effects of drugs as such.

Feldberg and Sherwood (1953) developed a technique for injection of drugs directly into the ventricular system by means of a permanently implanted cannula. Thus, in intact animals, drugs were brought into direct contact with central organs of the brain rather than being introduced through the blood stream. Later, Sherwood summarized observations made of the effects of various drugs with this technique.

> To summarize the effects quite briefly: With acetylcholine, a high-pitched cry was elicited, a retching, and then an akinetic state lasting for about a minute; then the cat was depressed or subdued. In large doses, a prodromal seizure was provoked, followed by a catatonic state lasting a very short time, approximately 6 or 8 minutes.
>
> With epinephrine, a condition somewhat similar to nembutal anesthesis was produced, and the animal was fully relaxed.
>
> With atropine there was increased liveliness, apparent well-being, swift, beautifully coordinated movements, a continuous readiness to be petted. . . .
>
> Injections of *d*-turbocurarine will produce seizures. Between seizures, this drug will produce a state of excitement and, if we can infer it, acute anxiety. An interesting point is that this episode seems to be covered by amnesia, because no matter how often this is done to a cat, he will never fight against the injection. . . .
>
> Hexamethonium produces a kind of weakness. The cat lies down and is inactive. It isn't actually sleeping, and we are not certain whether he won't move or he can't. The decamethonium compound produces spastic rigidity. It lasts quite a short time, about a half hour, but while the cat is standing in his cage, if he is given a shove, he falls over like a wooden soldier, with both legs straight out (Sherwood, 1955, p. 92 f.).

Since the excess of acetylcholine was observed to produce catatonia in the cats, cholinesterase was tried for the treatment of catatonic human patients, with good success, not only in activating the patience but also inactivating thought processes.

In recent studies, investigators have generally selected specific components of behavior for observation, and in most cases they have observed the effects of drugs on the performance of learned responses which could be elicited with regularity in control animals. The value of this device can be seen by comparing the results obtained by Feldberg and Sherwood, who were left wondering whether some of their cats would not move or could not, with the result of a similar experiment by John and coworkers. John, Killam, Wenzel, and Tschirgi (1959) used the Feldberg-Sherwood tchnique to inject GABA into the ventricular system of cats. Some of these animals were first trained in a battery of tasks, which they performed on signal. In the trained animals, injection of GABA caused a brief ataxia and a marked diminution of activity, as well as "a marked and unusual tendency to purr" and "noticeably fewer instances of fearful or aggressive behavior" for several days following. However, there was no loss in the performance of the learned tasks. In other words, motor activity is suppressed or discoordinated, while "affiliative" functions are facilitated and hostility decreased; but there is no apparent loss of intellectual function. The ataxia and flaccidity were even more marked in the untrained animals; they would lie down, breathing deeply and slowly, with pupils dilated, and occasionally engage in sustained vocalization.

One excellent example of the manner in which drugs may serve to "excise" functions temporarily, is provided by Hess's research on the determinants of the imprinting process in young water fowl. E. H. Hess (1959) formulated the hypothesis that the decisive condition which terminates the critical period for imprinting in these birds is the maturation of unlearned fear responses, which then interfere with the approach behavior essential to imprinting. It would follow from this hypothesis that susceptibility to imprinting, which ordinarily declines rapidly after reaching a peak at about sixteen hours after hatching, could be extended by the use of tranquilizers which control the development of emotionality. Hess (1960) then studied the effects of meprobamate, nembutal, and chlorpromazine. None of these drugs interfered with the performance of imprinted responses which had been acquired prior to administration of the drug. Emotionality was effectively controlled by meprobamate and by chlorpromazine, but not by nembutal. With respect to fresh imprinting, the results with chlorpromazine sustained the hypothesis, since at twenty-four hours these animals imprinted far more successfully than controls, showing no significant decline from the optimal level at sixteen hours. On the other hand, birds that received meprobamate at twelve hours showed almost no imprinting at fourteen to sixteen hours. Hess reasoned that this was due to the muscle relaxant effect of this drug, since it is known that effort expended in following the object to be imprinted is an important factor in imprinting. He therefore did a new series of experiments in which he compared control animals, those receiving meprobamate, and others receiving carisoprodol, which is an effective muscle relaxant that does not possess tranquilizing properties. As expected, carisoprodol proved to be even more effective than meprobamate in preventing imprinting.

Our interest in Hess's series of experiments is not in the specific findings, but in the clear way in which they demonstrate the possibility of isolating different response mechanisms, and thus assessing the degree of their involvment in a given kind of behavior. Notice that in the course of this investigation Hess used four drugs: One sedated without eliminating emotionality; a second eliminated emotionality without reducing muscular tonus; a third reduced muscular tonus without eliminating emotionality; and a fourth reduced both emotionality and muscular tonus. Since the drugs were absorbed through the blood stream into the body as a whole, it is evident that such different effects must be based on chemical differentiation of the neural structures involved in these different kinds of behavior. Reduction of emotionality results from depression of sympathetic functions, probably by an influence exerted on parts of the hypothalamus.

Norton (1957) has attempted to demonstrate the relationship between certain major forms of adjustive behavior and neural systems which can be isolated by particular drugs. She defined five major behavioral patterns, and constructed rating scales for each pattern. The patterns chosen were *sociability, contentment, excitement, defensive hostility,* and *aggressive hostility.* Working with hamsters, cats, and monkeys, she constructed different rating scales for each. For example, *defensive hostility* was measured in hamsters by defecation, kicking, squeaking, defensive rearing, and rolling over; in cats by growling, hissing, flattening ears, withdrawing, and crouching; in monkeys by withdrawing, urination, baring teeth, pulling back, and opening mouth. Using these scales, she then observed the effects of chlorpromazine on all three kinds of animals, and of LSD and amphetamine on hamsters and cats. Under chlorpromazine, *sociability* increased and *defensive hostility* decreased for all species; *excitement* was increased in the cat and the monkey, but decreased in the hamster; *aggressive hostility* was increased in the cat and decreased in the monkey. These results are only suggestive, because very few animals were tested; nevertheless we are reminded, by this difference between the cat and the monkey in respect to *hostility*, that these two animals also exhibited very different emotional responses after amygdalectomy (see page 118). Amphetamine markedly decreased the *sociability* of both cats and hamsters, and increased the *excitement* of both. It also reduced the *contentment* of cats, making one wonder whether perhaps the scale for measurement of contentment in the hamster was less successful. The pattern of response to LSD resembled that to amphetamine, but in addition it increased the *hostilities* of cats and hamsters, the latter quite markedly.

The components of Norton's scales are unlearned expressive behaviors, but it is also possible to test the differential effects of the same drug after first training the animal subjects in several different habits, serving different drives. Along this line, a number of investigators have trained the same animals in instrumental and conditioned avoidance responses, and studied the influence of drugs on performance.

Majkowski (1961) describes how the contrary effects of adrenaline and chlorpromazine can both contribute to better performance of conditional avoidance responses and simple discriminations. In this study (which is another phase of a collaborative research with Jasper already mentioned in Chapter 11), cats were first trained by pairing a click with a shock to the forepaw, delivered after a three-second delay. After the animals had reached a criterion of at least 90 percent correct response, the auditory cortex and surrounding areas were extirpated, and the animals were then retrained. In the postoperative training, some animals showed a low proportion of conditioned responses, with good discrimination. These animals are said to belong to the "inhibitory type." Others gave a high proportion of conditioned avoidance reactions, but their ability for differentiation was poor. These are said to be of the "excitatory type." Adrenaline was administered to animals of the first group, and chlorpromazine to those of the second. The adrenaline-treated animals increased their proportion of positive avoidance responses from 60 to 80 percent, before treatment, to 93 to 96 percent, with treatment, without showing any loss of discrimination. When adrenaline was discontinued, the percentage of response again fell to

65 percent. Optimal doses of chlorpromazine, administered to three "excitatory type" animals, enabled them to reach a high level of discrimination, with correct response on about 90 percent of trials; but still larger doses caused a decrease in the number of positive conditioned reactions. Majkowski's interpretation is that improvements in performance by both "types" was the result of manipulation of "the balance of excitation and inhibition in the brain stem's reticular formation."

Brady (1957) trained both monkeys and rats in bar-pressing, until they attained steady rates of bar-pressing in order to obtain liquid reward. He also subjected them to occasional electric shock punishment, which was preceded by an auditory signal, which thus became a conditional stimulus for anxiety, since no opportunity for escape was provided. He found that after such training, the undrugged animals would perform steadily until the signal for punishment was heard, then check their responses during the period of anxious waiting for the shock, then resume at the old rate immediately after it had taken place. The effect of reserpine was to produce a generally lower rate of response, but animals so treated did not check their responses, or did so to only a minor degree, when the signal for punishment was sounded. Ray and Marrazzi (1961) trained rats to obtain food by bar-pressing whenever a tonal signal indicated its availability. This adaptive response was eliminated by LSD-25. A small dose of chlorpromazine protected the animals against this effect, although a large dose would enhance it. This is in line with Marrazzi's theory that the two drugs have similar effects, although one is far more potent than the other. Therefore a non-depressant dose of chlorpromazine may still be sufficient to preempt many of the synaptic sites on which LSD must exert its action.

Another valuable technique is that of Olds, who first establishes consistent response-rates for self-stimulation with electrodes implanted in specific portions of the brain, and then observes the influence of various drugs on these rates of response. Studies utilizing this technique will be described on page 370.

Finally, we must mention two programs of research which are concerned with the testing of specific hypotheses concerning the influence of chemical events in the cortex on behavior: one dealing with the relation between acetylcholine and adaptability, the other with that between introversion and inhibition.

Since acetylcholine is an important central synaptic transmitter, there can be little question that any serious disturbance in its metabolism or utilization would necessarily interfere with nervous control. Peterson (1949) found that topical applications of acetylcholine to the motor cortex of the nondominant hemisphere in rats that exhibited clear handedness preference in reaching for food, resulted in a switch of handedness in about half of the animals. Pointing out that enforced practice is another means of inducing a change in handedness, Peterson speculated that the application of acetylcholine might be a neurochemical equivalent of practice. The possibilities suggested by such an approach have been pursued by Krech and his collaborators, in a series of experimental papers which have sought to correlate strain differences and individual differences in cortical cholinesterase (ChE) activity with adaptiveness to learning situations. Interpreting these results, Rosenzweig, Krech, and Bennett (1958) state: "Cortical ChE activity level provides a measure of the readiness of nerve impulse transmission in the central nervous system; the relative ease of nerve impulse transmission is correlated with capacity for more adaptive behavior; a spatial Preference Score in our maze is indicative of a more adaptive animal; therefore, one might expect a positive correlation between level of ChE activity and a spatial Preference Score."

In previous chapters, we have seen more than sufficient evidence to warrant dismissal of the notion that "relative ease of nerve impulse transmission is correlated with capacity for more adaptive behavior." However, near the end of their article, after considering the work of Hernández-Peón and Scherrer on habituation (see page 365), Rosenzweig et al. offer another hypothesis, to the effect that "central initiation of afferent habituation may require a given rate of ACh metabolism," so that an animal with a relatively low rate of cortical ChE activity would be slow to initiate the brain stem stage of the habituation process, and thus exhibit more "stimulus-bound" and therefore less adaptive behavior. Although these hypotheses are tenuous, seem to ignore the equally important synaptic inhibitory processes, and face the difficulty of some inconsistencies in their own experimental data, it remains true that adequate ChE activity is an essential of flexible behavior, for the reason that if the minute transmitter-quanta of excitatory acetylcholine are not promptly metabolized, some form of perseverative response is the inevitable result. (The reader will recall that Feldberg and Sherwood observed catatonia as a consequence of heavy dosage with intraventricular injections of acetylcholine, and that they recommended cholinesterase as a possible therapy for catatonia.) Russell (1958) has also found that reducing ChE below a critical level interferes with behavioral efficiency, although his work does not suggest that relatively minor variations can be of importance. Chow and John (1958) made an experimental test of the Krech-Rosenzweig-Bennett hypothesis that administration of anticholinesterase drugs would cause rats to shift from "visual hypotheses" to "spatial hypotheses" in maze-running behavior; the outcome was negative.

Eysenck (1957a) seeks to relate the dimension of introversion-extraversion, to which he gives very fundamental importance in his system of personality, to the relative strengths of inhibitory and excitatory tendencies. In his statement of this hypothesis he seems to identify *inhibition* with *reactive inhibition,* and in the experimental testing of various deductions drawn from the hypothesis, he and his coworkers limit themselves to comparing the effects of sodium amytal, used to favor inhibitory predominance, and dextroamphetamine, to favor excitatory predominance. Although it is not possible to quarrel with this experimental limitation, there can be no justification for stating conclusions in terms which seem to apply to inhibitory processes generally. In the original statement of his hypothesis, Eysenck (1957a) said: "extraverted behavior patterns are produced by excessively strong reactive inhibition and/or excessively weak excitation, while introverted behavior patterns are produced by excessively weak reactive inhibition and/or excessively strong excitation." Hence he postulated that depressant drugs would produce extraverted behavior patterns, and stimulant drugs would produce introverted behavior patterns. A concise summary of a dozen tests of deductions, which of course depend in part on his prior delineation of introvert and extravert behavior patterns, is given by Eysenck (1960). The results are consistently favorable to the hypothesis. However, it is difficult to reconcile such oversimplification with the same author's sophisticated awareness that "drugs have numerous different sites of action and . . . it would be surprising if the basis for a fundamental difference in personality were located in a precise region of the central nervous system" (Trouton and Eysenck, 1961). Does Eysenck nevertheless suppose that the effects of a single drug, sodium amytal, which produces cortical depression, can be used to characterize behavioral effects of "inhibition" generally?

We have been concerned in this chapter with showing how the study of the effects of drugs on behavior can help to delineate chemically distinctive response mechanisms in the central nervous system. In the next chapter we shall meet with some further instances of such chemical specificity of response systems in the brain, and we shall attempt to draw some conclusions regarding the nervous organization of behavior.

THE ORGANIZATION OF BEHAVIOR 16

We never seem to tire of the platitudes that an organism's behavior must be studied in relation to its environment, and likewise in relation to the physiological state of the moment. This chapter deals with some consequences which arise from an implication of these platitudes: that each act must be considered in relation to the acts that have preceded it, and to the other acts that might have taken place in its stead. These are essential parts of the physiological state, and they are in the most literal sense the behavioral environment of the act itself. It is from them that the act must be differentiated, by a many-sided process of inhibition, if it is to move from a potential to a readiness, and from readiness to performance. It is not surprising, therefore, that the careful analysis of any area of behavior seems always to reveal a polarity in the mechanisms involved. One cannot study flexion without extension, movement without posture, sleep without waking, digestion without evacuation, love without hate. It seems as if there is a principle underlying the organization of behavior which is very like Newton's third law of motion, that "action and reaction are equal and opposite." The mechanism of every act includes its behavioral counterpoise.

One very fundamental expression of this principle is in the wave nature of brain potentials, which we have assumed (see page 128) to result from the interplay of excitatory and inhibitory phenomena in the cortex. More obvious are such other rhythmic phenomena as those of circulation and respiration, and all the great variety of rhythmic acts which comprise the locomotor behavior of almost all motile organisms. The ciliary beat of protozoa, the waves of contraction which are seen in the earthworm, the side-to-side motion of a fish's tail, are all instances in the same catagory as the antagonistic muscular actions involved in vertebrate walking. When these acts are regarded solely from the excitatory standpoint, it seems as if their integration must depend on the existence of special mechanisms for sequential timing of their components, but they can be more parsimoniously envisaged as the inevitable outcome of the simultaneous activation of two response systems, each of which tends to inhibit the other. It is not difficult to imagine an arrangement which would have such an outcome. For example, let us assume that the excitation is an ongoing process, but each inhibitory process is relatively short-lived, perhaps because of cyclic exhaustion and replenishment of the transmitter substance involved. Then activation of *A* involves inhibition of *B*, but as inhibition of *B* loses its effectiveness, the *B* apparatus passes into a stage of activation, which similarly involves inhibition of *A*. This inhibition becomes exhausted in its turn, so that the first phase of this recurrent cycle reappears. This is only one of many hypotheses which might be constructed; it is intriguing in part because it suggests that although inhibition is not to be explained as a kind of fatigue, as had long ago been suggested by Verworn and others, it is possible that this kind of disinhibition might be so explained.

The dependence of rhythm on the inhibitory effects of neurohumors is not limited to these rapid forms of alternating action. It also includes a number of other kinds of alternating behavior, occurring in diurnal or even in seasonal rhythms. Among these are the rhythm of sleep and waking, the rhythm of sexual behavior, and perhaps also the rhythm of hunger and satiety. We shall consider first the contrast between sleep and waking, that is, between a generalized readiness for responsive behavior and the lack of such readiness.

There are, in general, two opposite ways of conceptualizing the phenomenon of sleep: as a torpid state from which the organism must be roused to a state of reactivity, or as a protective device which periodically dulls the normal reactivity of the organism. The opposition of these views appears most clearly when they take the form of an assumption, in the first case, that some sort of arousal mechanism must operate to keep the organism from falling into sleep, and in the second, that some sort of sleeping center must be activated if the organism is to enter a state of somnolence. The two points of view can be synthesized in a conception which regards neither sleep nor wakefulness as more normal than the other, but sees the organism rather as oscillating between both states, with a periodicity imposed by both internal and external factors.

We recall that Pavlov regarded sleep as a widespread cortical inhibition. However, most modern theories consider that it has a subcortical origin. These theories derive from the work of Mauthner (1890), who pointed out that the victims of a sleeping sickness which was then epidemic regularly showed lesions of the central gray substance in the neighborhood of the third and fourth ventricles. Mauthner argued that since normal sleep is regularly accompanied by dreams, the essence of sleep cannot consist in a cessation of function by the cerebral cortex; neither does sleep entail any reduced functioning of the peripheral nervous system and the sense organs. It must therefore consist, he reasoned, in an interruption of both centrifugal and centripetal pathways in the ventricular region indicated by the pathological lesions. This interruption he attributed in the normal case to the diurnal accumulation of fatigue products. Later Economo (1926), having fortuitously been provided with a fresh abundance of similar material by a new epidemic of encephalitis lethargica, revised this theory. From an analysis of the symptoms of the illness he argued that sleep is a primary and not a secondary symptom, that is, that sleep did not result from a mere interruption of sensibility, but that "in this region there must be situated a *center* where a *regulation* of sleep takes place—a true *sleep regulation center.*" He also concluded that "*Awakening would then occur as a result of disinhibition.*" Furthermore, Economo considered that the sleep produced in this manner consisted, on the one hand, in a "brain sleep" resulting from inhibition of the thalamus and the cerebral hemispheres, and a "body sleep" resulting from inhibition of vegetative centers.

A similar distinction was made later by Kleitman (1939), who writes of a "wakefulness of necessity," which depends very largely upon afferentation from the viscera, and a "wakefulness of choice," which is based upon habit. The first has a short cycle of several hours, and is responsible for fluctuations in level of alertness during the day and in depth of sleep during the night, while the second has the longer diurnal cycle. However, whereas von Economo spoke of two kinds of inhibition imposed on a normally reactive organism, Kleitman speaks of two kinds of wakefulness or arousal of an otherwise inert organism. Both agree that sleep is a complex phenomenon, which does not have a single explanation.

Experimental support for the sleep center theory was provided by W. R. Hess (1929a, 1929b), who reported that electrical stimulation of the posterior hypothalamus, and the walls of the third ventricle, produced drowsiness and sleep.

A new approach to the problem of sleep and wakefulness was opened up when H. Berger, in 1929, drew attention to the potential value of records of the brain's gross electrical activity as recorded in the electroencephalogram (EEG). Soon it was known, thanks to the work especially of Adrian (1947), that the activity of a relaxed wakeful brain is characterized by wavelike changes in electrical potential at a frequency of about eight to twelve per second (alpha waves); that increasingly deep sleep is characterized by slower waves of greater potential (delta waves, four to seven per second, and in the extreme case, theta waves, less than four per second); and that sensory alertness is characterized by a condition which is now called *desynchronization* and shows itself in high frequency low voltage waves of considerable irregularity. The sleeping pattern also includes intermittent bursts of short sequences of rapid waves, which are called *spindles* because of the appearance of their graphic record when, in the ideal case, they start with low voltage, build up to a fairly high voltage, and then decline again, all in the space of about two seconds. The knowledge of these patterns of electrical activity makes it possible to describe a brain as "awake" or "asleep" even when it is cut off from the musculature so that observable somatic movements are eliminated.

Taking advantage of this, Bremer made observations on a *cerveau isolé* preparation, that is, on a cerebral cortex which was cut off from the lower portions of the nervous system by a transection just above the third cranial nerve. Bremer found that although the cortex of a spinal animal shows normal alternations of sleep and wakefulness, the *cerveau isolé* is always "sleeping," despite the presence of afferentation through the optic and olfactory nerves. He argued that sleep is simply the quiescent state of a brain which is deprived of most afferentation, because a steady influx of sensory data from the body itself is needed to maintain a state of wakefulness.

This theory of Bremer's is in harmony with what may be called the old-fashioned view that an otherwise inert brain needs to be stirred to activity, as opposed to the newer view that the brain is in constant danger of becoming overreactive and needs to be subdued. In describing his earlier findings, Bremer (1953) says: "My interpretation of this electrographic and ocular syndrome was that it was the expression of a state of rest of the diencephalon and cortex, resulting from the interruption of the continuous stream of ascending impulses that normally activates their constituent neuronal net-works, and determines the waking state. Freed from all disturbing influences, the cortical and diencephalic neurones were left to their fundamental automatism, and to their natural tendency to beat in synchronism"—that is, in the pattern of deep sleep.

Then, interpreting this as the truly spontaneous activity of the brain, he continues: "The main physiological significance of the spontaneous activity of the cortex cerebri . . . seems thus to be the necessity for the continuous maintenance of a subliminal excitation of subordinate aggregates of neurones, reducing to a minimum their reactional inertia and insuring the coordinative subordination of all parts of the nervous machinery."

In other words, the conflict which Bremer sees is not one between excitation and inhibition, but between excitation and inertia. In his own words (Bremer, 1954): "The physiological process of falling asleep may be explained, without necessary recourse to the hypothesis of a hypnogenic center, by the cumulative deactivation (defacilitation) of the encephalic neuronal networks resulting from synaptic fatigue and favored by a reduction in the exteroceptive and proprioceptive sensory afflux."

Bremer's theory has proved untenable, despite the fact that at first glance it seems to be supported by the evidence of sensory deprivation experiments. Moruzzi and Magoun (1949) demonstrated that stimulation of the reticular formation results in arousal of the cortex, pointing to the possibility that it is not the sensory influx per se, but the indirect arousal mediated by sensory collaterals of the reticular formation, which is responsible for wakefulness. This theory was put to direct test by Lindsley and his coworkers (Lindsley, Bowden, & Magoun, 1949; Lindsley, Schreiner, Knowles, & Magoun, 1950). They found that if the classical sensory afferents to the brain are interrupted, but the diffuse afferents from the reticular formation are spared, the latter suffice to induce wakefulness, whereas if the reticular afferents are interrupted, and the classical sensory pathways are spared, the brain will "sleep." It is therefore necessary to conclude that sensory influx per se does not activate the brain, but can do so only in conjunction with reticular activation. This activity is ordinarily mediated by collaterals of the sensory afferents which enter the reticular formation. Obviously, these facts are consistent with the hypothesis we have stated that the reticular arousal is disinhibitory. This hypothesis makes it understandable why no amount of sensory excitation per se can suffice to arouse the brain.

If we ask why this should be so, a rather clear answer emerges: sensory input immediately rouses local inhibitory feedback (which we have designated as Heidenhain inhibition) which is not merely a protection against overwork of the elements, but a protection against overresponsiveness of the organism generally; and added evidence on this point appears in the fact that if strychnine is applied locally to any sensory area, thus blocking the inhibitory synapses in that area, then sensory stimulation via the corresponding modality leads easily to convulsion. For example, if the visual area is strychninized, then photic stimulation easily produces convulsion; if the auditory area, then sound produces convulsion, etc. The function of the reticular innervation must therefore be to overcome or at least to modulate this local cortical inhibition, and it seems most plausible that it should do this by a disinhibitory rather than by a directly facilitatory effect.

In a recent statement of his views, W. R. Hess (1954) declares that it is necessary to recognize the existence of two systems, one of which tends to produce arousal while the other tends to produce a sleep-like state. He designates the first, which corresponds to the ascending reticular arousal system of Moruzzi and Magoun, as "ergotrophic," and the second, which includes his sleep center, as "tropotrophic." "While the arousal system prevails in the waking state and the inhibitory center during sleep, neither is in absolute control except in extreme conditions such as deep sleep after exhaustion or maximal activation, in attack or defence. In normal circumstances, the state of alertness—and consciousness—fluctuates between these extremes and keeps adjusted to the needs of the situation." (See also W. R. Hess, 1957.)

Lindsley (1952) has also described a continuum of behavioral states extending from strong excited emotion to coma and death, through all the degrees of sleep and wakefulness. From a purely formal point of view, it may seem acceptable that these should be described as stages in a single continuum of arousal, but it is important to recognize with Hess that at every stage in this continuum there are two contrary tendencies in operation—the tendency to arousal on the one hand, and the tendency to quiescence on the other. One is as real as the other, and although the two processes are opposed they are also in a sense independent, since they involve activity of different units. Nor is it unreasonable to suppose, following the lines of Pavlov's neurophysiology, that there is an essential difference between the kind of alertness which results from a balance of strong tendencies toward both arousal and quiescence, and that which results from a balance of weak tendencies toward arousal and quiescence. One can readily imagine, for example, that the strong system could be able to maintain its balance in the face of an overload of stimulation which might overwhelm the weak system. In any case, there seems to be abundant evidence that the sleep-arousal polarity rests upon the mutual interaction of opposing processes, and not on the greater or lesser activation of one.

Nauta (1946) not only found evidence for the existence in rats of a sleep center in the anterior hypothalamus and a waking center in the posterior hypothalamus, but he also showed that the influence of the sleep center is indirect, by way of the waking center. A schematic representation of the action of such hypothalamic centers, upon cortical inhibitory elements, is shown in Figure 6. Although one might wish that sleep could be described more simply than as a de-disinhibition, the actual relationships involved are not more complex than those we are compelled to assume in other instances.

It is interesting to compare this view of sleep with that of Pavlov. Pavlov described sleep as an inhibition which originates in the cortex, and spreads to embrace subcortical structures. Instead,

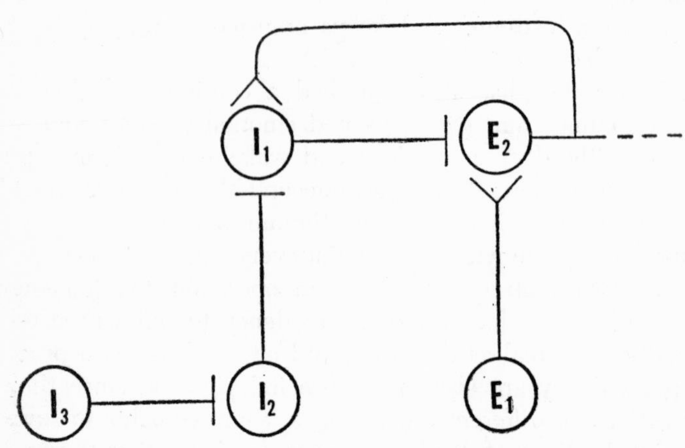

Figure 6. Schematic representation of hypothetical action of hypothalamic centers of sleep and waking. E_1 (thalamic) excites E_2 (cortical). Negative feedback from I_1 (cortical) tends to reduce the frequency of discharge of E_2. The discharge rate will increase if I_2 (hypothalamic waking center) is also active, since it tends to inhibit I_1. This disinhibiting effect can be eliminated by activity of I_3 (hypothalamic sleep center). The arousal effect of the reticular formation is similar to that shown here for the "waking center," and would be initiated by collaterals of the E_1 axon.

sleep seems to be primarily an effect of subcortical regulation of cortical inhibition.

The event of waking does not take place all at once throughout the cortex. Rather, the pattern of alertness appears first in a circumscribed area, and then spreads to other areas. This appears clearly in EEG records of animals that are awakened on signal—of a cat, perhaps, which is awakened by the sound of a click that has become a conditioned signal for electric shock. Rowland (1959) tells how he and his co-workers had their attention drawn to this phenomenon of specific arousal:

"We were recording the waves of a sleeping cat during some intermittent wall-pounding occasioned by extensive renovations in the adjoining room. The animal had long since grown accustomed to this racket and slept through it undisturbed with no change in the encephalograph records. During a quiet interval one day another cat in the laboratory emitted a soft mew. The brain waves of our experimental animal immediately changed from the sleep pattern to the alert pattern. Some 10 seconds later the animal raised its head and looked toward the other cat."

In this anecdotal account, there are three points to be noted. First, there is the phenomenon of habituation, shown in the fact that the cat could sleep, in the fullest sense of the word, despite loud noises which would have kept it awake if it had not experienced them for some time without meaningful consequence to itself. Second, there is the specific arousal to a much less intense stimulus, but one which has ecological significance to the animal. This behavior is like that of the sleeping mother who is awakened by her infant's cry. Finally, we must take note that the behavioral alertness followed after a latency of about ten seconds, a period during which the pattern of alertness spread from the auditory area, where it originated, to other parts of the cortex.

This chance observation led to experimental study, including the following demonstration by Gluck (which is also described by Rowland). A cat which had been trained to recognize a series of clicks as a danger signal which was ordinarily followed after two minutes by an electric shock, would be roused by the clicks from sleep; but if it had also been trained to recognize that when the clicks were followed by a certain tone, there would be no shock, then he would stir but gently—encephalographically speaking—and fall back into deep sleep with no overt response when the "all clear" signal followed the clicks.

It is important to recognize that such alerting may be quite specific, rather than generalized. Hernández-Peón, Scherrer and Jouvet (1956) showed that the sight of a mouse in a bottle would not only alert the visual cortex of a cat, but simultaneously depress its response to auditory stimulation. In this case, of course, we are dealing with the increased alertness of an already wakeful animal, that is, with the phenomenon of alpha suppression by desynchronization, in the visual cortex, accompanied by return to the alpha pattern in the previously desynchronized auditory cortex. We must think, in other words, not in terms of a generalized opposition between single mechanisms of sleep-relaxation and arousal-alertness, but rather in Pavlovian terms, of a ubiquitous conflict between mechanisms of excitation and inhibition, in which at any given instant one process gains the upper hand in some areas, and the other in other areas. To understand behavior, we must penetrate beyond the relatively obvious contrast between the generalized inhibition of sleep and the generalized state of wakefulness. In the waking animal, the succession of stimuli, controlled and uncontrolled, internal and external, provides a constant interplay of arousals which take many forms. In addition to the relatively diffuse arousal which originates in the brain stem reticular formation, and the area-specific arousals which are mediated by thalamic pathways, we must recognize also the existence of function-specific arousals. Although these are more difficult to demonstrate, they may in the long run be more important than either general or area-specific arousals. The alerting effects of stimulation of the hypothalamus and other parts of the visceral brain are probably of this nature.

The technique of electrical stimulation is even at its best a very inadequate method for exploration of functional systems, which have specific chemical sensitivities. Fisher (1956) demonstrated the possibility of carefully controlled intracranial chemical stimulation of specific sites by the use of implanted cannulas, serving a function analogous to that of permanently implanted electrodes. He described some of his results as follows: "Males having no adult contact with females, young, or paper have responded to chemical stimulation [of different loci] with integrated maternal behavior [which includes the use of paper as nest-building material] on the first trial. . . . Testosterone has ostensibly elicited both sexual and maternal patterns. . . . The data strongly suggest selective chemical action within the central nervous system. Further work may demonstrate that differential sensitivity to specific physiological change by functionally organized areas of the nervous system is a basic principle of neural function." We shall look at another important application of this technique shortly, and must expect that in time its results will overthrow many present notions.

When we look for specific instances of behavioral polarity, we find that the clearest example is provided by some recent experimental tests of an hypothesis which was first stated by Anand and Brobeck (1951), that the lateral hypothalamus contains a "feeding center" and the ventromedial nucleus a "satiation center" which has an inhibitory effect on eating. Wyrwicka and Dobrzecka (1960) studied the effects of electrical stimulation of these areas by implanted electrodes, using goats that had been trained to obtain food when hungry by placing the left foreleg on a food tray. Their results confirm the Anand-Brobeck hypothesis. When the lateral hypothalamus is stimulated, animals that have already been satiated with food will nevertheless perform the learned act to obtain more food, and eat what they thus obtain. Stimulation of the satiation center, on the other hand, causes even hungry animals—or animals that were hungry up to the moment of stimulation—to forego eating. However, there are two different types of behavior that appear under this latter condition, depending on the particular point which is stimulated.

Stimulation of some medial points caused a defensive start and the display of "fear and restlessness which lasted for several minutes after the withdrawal of the stimulus." In this case we are dealing with a kind of negative response which antagonizes feeding, but is not simple satiation. The stimulation of other medial points leads to rejection of the food without any defensive reaction, and in these cases the animal not only resumes eating as soon as the stimulation has ended, but often does so with renewed vigor, displaying the "rebound" phenomenon which is a good indicator of the cessation of an active neural inhibition. This inhibitory function comes out quite clearly when it is used against a background of simultaneous stimulation of the feeding center. When already satiated animals are set to eating by stimulation of the latter kind, and inhibitory stimulation (that is, stimulation of the satiation center) is then applied, the eating becomes less intense and may stop altogether; then when the inhibitory stimulus is discontinued, the rebound phenomenon is likely to appear.

Lissák (1955) also reported that stimulation of different areas of the hypothalamus would either inhibit or activate a conditioned feeding response, the latter effect taking place, on appropriate stimulation, even when the animal was satiated and therefore did not respond to the external conditional signal. Similarly, there are other points which either inhibit or facilitate a conditional defense response. Even prior to conditioning, stimulation of any hypothalamic point tends to produce a general orientation response. Lissák also draws the bold conclusion that "primary completion" of the conditional reflex must take place in the hypothalamic region; but this statement is followed by an editorial comment that "the editorial staff does not yet believe there is sufficient basis" for such a view.

Another exploration of the hypothalamic feeding center was performed by Grossman (1960). Using Fisher's technique (in rats), he implanted a small cannula into the feeding center of the lateral hypothalamus and stimulated this point by releasing minute quantities of crystals of acetylcholine and of norepinephrine, thus selectively activating either the cholinergic or the adrenergic system. When norepinephrine was used, the previously satiated animals would nevertheless consume a fair quantity of dry food during the next half hour. They would also take a very small quantity of water, but this was evidently only secondary to their eating of the dry food, because if the same experiment is tried in a cage in which water but no food is available, they will investigate the water but not drink any measurable quantity of it. When stimulated at exactly the same point with acetylcholine, the animals consume no food, but drink large quantities of water. When strychnine is used, no consummatory behavior appears. Very minor deviations in the placement of the cannula suffice to eliminate the effects which have been described. In control experiments, Grossman (1961) found that administration of cholinergic and adrenergic blocking agents would interfere with these effects in expected ways, supporting the interpretation that they were directly dependent on the activity of the chemical substances.

Considering these experiments together, we see that feeding, as an element of the behavioral repertoire, is imbedded in several different behavior-pairs or polar opposites. First, we have the contrast between feeding and satiation as originally postulated. Second, there is conflict between feeding and fear, an observation which is consistent, for example, with the behavior of animals in the open-field test and in many other situations where either novelty or punishment causes the appearance of anxiety and the consequent cessation or nonappearance of eating behavior. Third, in the feeding center itself, there is the differentiation between eating and drinking, which depends on the opposition of cholinergic and adrenergic mechanisms at virtually the same site. When an animal chooses not to eat, there may be at least three kinds of motivational influence: satiation, fear, or felt need for liquid. It is an established fact that any one of these inhibits the feeding mechanism, but it is not established that there is any neurological state which can be described as a mere absence of feeding motivation, not accompanied by one of these active inhibitions.

These results remind us inevitably of those obtained by Olds with the technique of self-stimulation through implanted electrodes. Olds (1956) defined an area centering on the hypothalamus and involving most of the rhinencephalon or "visceral brain" as well as some other structures, within which mild electrical stimulation has either a positive or a negative reward value. That is, when the electrodes are located at some points the animal will work to obtain stimulation, and when the electrodes are located at other points, the animal will work to avoid stimulation. The positive reward area seems to be more extensive than the negative reward area, with occasional ambiguities where one passes over into the other. However, since electrical stimulation is being used, it is clear that what are being mapped out are areas of preponderant function; and we must therefore consider the possibility that both functions actually overlap through a great part of this area, each being associated with a different neurohumoral process. The response rate which is customarily achieved varies greatly from point to point, indicating that some points provide more motivation than others, as would be expected. In general, stimulation of the posterior hypothalamus (which is preponderantly sympathetic in function) provides higher response rates than that of the anterior hypothalamus (which is preponderantly parasympathetic in function). Gelhorn (1957) points out that "the sympathetic functions of the posterior hypothalamus are released under conditions in which the parasympathetic functions of the anterior hypothalamus are diminished," with a regularity which indicates "the validity of the principle of reciprocal innervation for the regulation of autonomic processes at the hypothalamic level."

Olds (1958) recognized the possibility that he was not dealing with a single reward system, but with a multiplicity of reward systems associated with different sources of motivation. To study this problem, he selected two physiological drive states which he could vary experimentally—hunger, which can be readily manipulated by deprivation; and sex, which he manipulated by using castrated male rats and injecting testosterone to cause a rise in androgen level which would then be followed by a decline. Thus he was able to determine how the response rate with a given electrode placement would vary under conditions of high or low hunger drive, and high or low sex drive. He found that "in places where hunger causes the greatest rise in self-stimulation rates, androgens cause a depression; and in places where androgens cause the greatest rise in self-stimulation rates, hunger causes a depression." He concludes that there appears to be "a localized hunger-reward system within the regions studied differentiated from a localized sexual-reward system." However, the evidence points to the further conclusion that these two systems somehow oppose one another, so that the strong activation of one inhibits the activation of the other.

Olds, Killam, and Eiduson (1957) studied the influence of various drugs on these response rates, and their results provide one of the most dramatic demonstrations of the local specificity of drug actions. Reserpine, in a dose which has no effect on the response rate when the electrodes are placed in the septal region, causes a very pronounced reduction in rate of response when the electrodes are in certain portions of the posterior hypothalamus. (The reader will recall that excitation of the posterior hypothalamus leads to a general excitation of sympathetic as against parasympathetic functions.) Chlorpromazine gives quite different results: the same dose which brings about virtually total suppression of response with the electrodes fairly deep in the posterior hypothalamus, produces almost no effect in another nearby area. Most striking of all is the interaction between LSD and serotonin. In the septal region and in the extreme posterior-ventral hypothalamus, LSD by itself would produce brief but almost total suppression of self-stimulation; the prior administration of serotonin would completely prevent this effect, and when brom-LSD was used there would be no suppression. With the electrodes placed in the subseptal region or the middle hypothalamus, serotonin did not antagonize LSD, and brom-LSD had an effect even stronger than that of LSD.

Results such as these show how futile it is to think of the nervous system as composed of homogeneous units, which have different effects solely according to their positions and interconnections. It is evident that units of different function are often located side by side, exerting influence upon one another. These patterns of interaction are far too complex to be reduced to a simple formula of opposition between excitation and inhibition. Within each system there is some sort of chemical affinity; and between the systems there is a chemical antagonism, more or less intense. Probably the activation of any system is more or less antagonistic to any other. But apparently the most direct and irreconcilable antagonism is that which is exercised between the two members of a pair of opposite tendencies, each of which represents the behavioral counterpoise to the other. Take the many systems together, and we must assume that it is far from sufficient to speak of cholinergic, adrenergic, and serotonergic mechanisms. However, these are a beginning, and they show us the direction which our thought must take. Probably there are many kinds of excitation, and many kinds of inhibition.

We shall not consider in detail any other behavioral polarities, but examples will readily occur to the reader. Beritov (1957) states that Rozhansky—the man who more than anyone is responsible for the Pavlovian theory of sleep—described twenty-four pairs of "complex biological reflexes." Unfortunately, we have been unable to find the source for this statement. However, Rozhansky's pairs are said to include waking-sleeping, swallowing-vomiting, thirst-hydrophobia, acquiescence-wariness, and libido-frigidity. There is little reason to doubt that the same kinds of evidence could be marshalled for some of these pairs, if not for all, as that which we have reviewed in the case of eating-satiety. For example, Law and Meagher (1958) found evidence of a sex-inhibiting as well as a sex-facilitating system in the hypothalamus.

Moreover, facts such as those reviewed in this chapter inevitably suggest the hypothesis that all the activities of the integrated organism including those patterns of action which develop in the course of experience, must be organized according to the same principle—that is, that the tendency of any stimulus to elicit a given response, whether by excitation or by disinhibition, will always be accompanied by the simultaneous strengthening of inhibitions of other responses. This is an extension of Freusberg's principle (which might also be called the principle of specificity of response evocation) that inhibitory controls normally operate to prevent simultaneous activation of opposed response tendencies. The hypothesis is related to the assumption which Beritov makes, that the excitation of any central nerve cell results in the diffuse inhibition of neighboring cells, a process which permits propagation of the excitation along specific pathways, to remote areas. It is also similar to the suggestion made by Milner (1957) in his elaboration of Hebb's cell assembly hypothesis, that the firing of a long-axon cortical cell will, by way of its collaterals, which terminate on short-axon cells, cause inhibition of neighboring long-axon cells.

We may also suppose that the generalized inhibition of incompatible responses will be accompanied by the partial disinhibition of related mechanisms, belonging to the same general response system, thus establishing a "set" for their activation. Such an arrangement might also provide a basis for the integrated performance of the sequential elements of a chain response.

Under this hypothesis, the innate system of paired response patterns, the "complex biological reflexes" of Rozhansky, represent a scaffold on which the entire structure of behavior is supported. It is these pairs which directly give meaning to all experiences and all actions in most animals. Even in man, they are perhaps the basis on which we construct such concepts as truth and falsehood, justice and injustice, near and far, up and down, large and small, sad and glad. It is not the necessity of logic which compels us to build our concepts in this manner, but behavioral necessity, the fact that reciprocating relationships are basic to all the operations of the nervous system. This conclusion is in harmony with the opinion expressed by Osgood (1962). Based on extensive research dealing with factor analysis of meaning and utilizing his semantic differential technique, Osgood's studies have now been carried out in many different languages, in all parts of the world, and have consistently revealed the same factors of *evaluation* (good vs. bad), *potency* (strong vs. weak), and *activity* (fast vs. slow) which first appeared in the analysis of word meanings as indicated by Princeton students —who are thus shown to be members of the human race at large. This leads Osgood to conclude that these dimensions of meaning have biological foundations. It seems not at all impossible that they might be related to generalized systems such as the serotonergic, cholinergic, and adrenergic mechanisms—that is to say, that the "meaning" of a word depends to some extent, and often very largely, on the degree to which it excites a biological class of responses.

The picture which is thus given of the living organism, is of a complex of mechanisms which are not only incessantly active, but are also incessantly engaged in competitive rivalry. However, this rivalry takes place in neurochemical terms, at the synaptic or intracellular level. Consuming very little energy, it serves to keep activity in bounds while permitting the organism to remain at a high level of reactivity. If we reserve the word *conflict* to represent instances in which there is actual excitation of effector units involved in incompatible responses, at a level sufficient to produce at least a minimal overt response, then we may say that such mutual inhibition serves to reduce conflict. Indeed, we may say that *organized* behavior is characterized by the effective inhibition of incompatible responses, so that such responses (like the tail-flips of Retzlaff's fish) are never overtly manifest at the same time, and that behavior is *disorganized* to the extent that the absence or breakdown of inhibitory controls permits the simultaneous activation of incompatible responses, that is, to the extent that it is *conflictful.*

The adaptive organism must have sensitive reactivity, but it must also have regulative control. In the developing organism, in its embryonic stages, the appearance of each new potential for action must be accompanied by the mobilization of an effective inhibition for that potential. The same principle must apply to the acquisition of each new behavior potential in interaction with the environment. Otherwise, the unbraked activity of the organism would quickly run it to exhaustion and breakdown while the medley of responses, all interfering with one another, would fall short of effectiveness. Everywhere in the nervous system, so long as the organism is intact, the physiologist's delicate probe—the microelectrode—finds the units ceaselessly discharging. We call this "background activity" or "neural tonus," but it is held to these limits only by the fact that portions of this activity are pitted against other portions, in a balance of inaction which is somewhat like the successive phases of imbalance which constitute normal locomotion. The essential processes of the organism, each with its own systole and diastole, form a contrapuntal harmony, in which inhibition and counter-inhibition are in constant interplay with excitation and counter-excitation.

Upon this foundation rise the coping mechanisms, the apparatus of locomotion and manipulation, of eating and sex, of fighting and building: a great wealth of adjustive acts which are all held ready but all held in check, each restrained by all the others, and most especially by its opposite number, its behavioral counterpoise—as the flexion by extension, as inspiration by expiration, so also the grasp by the letting-go, the lying down by the standing up, eating by satiation, all constantly ready, all constantly inhibited. In the behavior which appears out of this balanced inaction, each act is the momentary release of one element from the inhibitions which have been placed upon it, and each act at once upsets in some measure the equilibrium of all the others, and thus makes it easier for some, more difficult for others, to escape the inhibitions by which they are held in check.

In terms of automational control, each organism is a multipurpose machine which must be capable of switching its part mechanisms on and off as different demands arise, within and without. In the development of these controls, it is only natural that there should be some master switches included, so that the shift from one type of behavior to another shall not depend on the nearly simultaneous operation of a million little synaptic switches, independent of one another. These master switches apparently consist of generalized neurohumoral controls, and they are of double-throw design, that is, the activation of one pattern entails the simultaneous inactivation of another. In sum, the organism may be described as a pattern of mutually inhibitory response dispositions, and the excitations which lead to any overt response must do so by effecting critical disinhibitions which interrupt this balanced state of affairs.

CHOICE AND CONFLICT 17

When is an organism "in conflict"?

Applied to human beings, the phrase clearly suggests the behavior of persons who are torn by conflicting motives, or who waver uncertainly between different means for achieving an objective, and who in consequence of their "divided minds" fail to perform to the best of their ability in the service of either motive, or in the execution of either course of action. In other words, *conflict implies some arrest or difficulty in the process of choice.* We would expect that any useful definition of conflict should help us to understand behavior of the kind that we have been describing. If a definition of conflict states conditions which are compatible with the orderly and efficient performance of adaptive responses, we must assume that it has omitted something that is essential to conflictful behavior. With this criterion in mind, we shall consider some contemporary definitions and theoretical formulations of conflict. We cannot attempt to review all phases of this problem in the short space of a chapter, but we shall try to show how the concept of inhibition, as something more than merely the conceptual opposite of a positive response tendency, leads to a more fruitful statement of the problem.

In their *Comprehensive Dictionary of Psychological and Psychoanalytical Terms*, English and English (1958) define conflict as "the simultaneous functioning of opposing or mutually exclusive impulses, desires, or tendencies; or the state of a person when opposed impulses or response tendencies have been activated." No alternate definition is given, to suggest that there is anything but unanimity among psychologists on this matter. Psychoanalysts, field theorists, ethologists, and S-R behavior theorists all agree that conflict is the consequence of the opposition of response tendencies. Only one notable exception comes to mind: Pavlov's discussions of conflict do not deal with a supposed opposition between tendencies to different forms of response, but with the "collision" between inhibitory and excitatory processes relative to the same response. It is true that Anokhin (1958) attempts to erase this lack of harmony, by stating that whenever Pavlov describes a situation in which such a "collision" is taking place, there is also an actual opposition of response tendencies. Nevertheless, it is clear that Pavlov's theoretical formulation of conflict was in terms of the adequacy of inhibitory control, and not in terms of incompatible excitations.

Lewin (1935) defined conflict as "a situation in which oppositely directed simultaneous acting forces of approximately equal strength work upon the individual." Most readers will recall his analysis of three types of situations involving these oppositely directed forces, in which he points out that the conflict is minimal if the two forces are both positive valences directed toward different goals, and that it is nonexistent if they are both negative valences, unless some barrier—which Lewin himself acknowledges to be a symbolic representation of an inhibitory force—helps to define the situation. It is only the third type of situation, in which positive and negative valences attach to the same object, that is inherently conflictful. Surely, the logical conclusion from this analysis is that Lewin's initial definition of conflict, which applies equally to all of these situations, must be faulty. The existence of "oppositely directed simultaneous acting forces" may be a necessary condition of conflict, but it is not a sufficient condition.

Miller (1944) says that "conflict is produced by competition between incompatible responses." But what does incompatible mean? A sneeze and a smile are incompatible, but the smile can offer very little competition, once the sneeze has been initiated. Turning the eyes to the right and turning the eyes to the left are incompatible, but the behavior which involves both responses, as in reading a page of print, is not therefore conflictful. Conflict may be severe when we keep our eyes directed to one side, while we are conscious of some attractive but socially forbidden target on the other. The ruddering action of a fish's tail has two incompatible forms; but they function smoothly together in the normal pattern of swimming; and when the occasion for a sharp turn arises, one excludes the other effectively enough to avoid all semblance of conflict.

The incompatibility thesis is stated most circumspectly by Berlyne (1960): "When a stimulus, external or internal, that is associated with a given response occurs, we shall say that the response is *aroused,* whether or not it is actually performed. . . . When two or more incompatible responses are aroused simultaneously in an organism, we shall say that the organism is in conflict."

To spell out the implication: whenever stimuli associated with two or more incompatible responses occur, conflict results. It is a necessary corollary, which Berlyne accepts, that any complex organism is, at least in its waking state, in almost continual conflict. Conflict, according to this view, is simply choice from another aspect—one does not exist without the other.

By thinking consistently in terms of this definition, Berlyne is led into a strange error which highlights its misleading nature. Every student of psychology remembers that both Miller and Lewin agree that the conflict which results from tendencies of approach to different goals is easily resolved, when no other complicating factor is present. Nevertheless, Berlyne mistakenly declares: "Lewin and Miller have shown why conflicts between approach tendencies should be more serious, and resolve themselves with greater difficulty, than either conflicts between avoidance tendencies or approach-avoidance conflicts." Indeed, if it were true that the source of conflict is simply the opposition of incompatible response tendencies, then Buridan's ass might have starved, and it would be in order for Berlyne thus to "correct" Lewin and Miller.

There is a particular reason which leads us to doubt the adequacy of the definitions that have been cited, and the whole point of view which they represent. The discussion in the preceding chapter led to a description of the organism as "a pattern of mutually inhibitory response dispositions," that is, a system of tendencies to incompatible responses. If the opposition of response tendencies is inherent in the integrated organism, it would be strange indeed that this should also be the sufficient cause for conflict. Even if we put aside the special topics discussed in the last chapter, and think in terms of behavioral motives in the most general sense, is it not true that "oppositely directed simultaneous acting forces" are characteristic of all individuals, including the best integrated, and that the person in conflict is one whose behavior has somehow been disrupted by the effects of such oppositely directed forces, rather than merely one who harbors them? Should not the definition of conflict help us to isolate the *reasons* for such disruptive activity, rather than naming conditions which are perfectly compatible with integrated, conflictless behavior?

At this point, it will be useful to digress a little, to consider a parallel whcih exists between the scheme for the organization of behavior which was developed in the preceding chapter, and the scheme by which Herbart explained the movement of ideas in consciousness. The reader may recall that William James, after stating his hypothesis that neural "drainage" is the basis for learning, appended a footnote in which he declared: "This brain-scheme seems oddly enough to give a certain basis of reality to those hideously fabulous performances of the Herbartian Vorstellungen." (See page 56 for the complete note.) In the same way, we also feel the need to pay respect to that amazing metaphysician, because our hypothesis regarding the relationships among behavioral acts and their physiological origins, although it was written without a thought of Herbart, is similar in certain essential respects to his account of the relationships among ideas and of the circumstances which determine their emergence into consciousness. But it is not simply a matter of acknowledging a debt which concerns us. The fact of this parallel implies that there is a logical necessity underlying this schema, since it was possible for Herbart to deduce it without experimental evidence. It is important for us to understand the nature of this necessity, as a guide to our further thinking.

Herbart said that if the succession of ideas in consciousness is to be explained by characteristics of the ideas themselves, which he conceived as enduring entities, and not by outside forces acting upon them, then it must depend on the resistances which they offer to one another, that is, on inhibitions. Without such inhibitory effects, they would all have to share consciousness together, in proportion to their strengths, and there would be no movement of ideas. Translating this argument into behavioral terms, one may say that if the organism has a variety of response mechanisms available for activation in a given situation, each associated with a quantitatively definable reaction potential, then the fact that one of these responses is performed rather than all attempted together, each with a vigor proportional to its own reaction potential, must be due to inhibitory relationships among them.

This argument tells us nothing about the nature of the inhibitions. It only tells us that just as for Herbart's ideas, so also for the behavioral acts with which the modern psychologist is concerned, it is by no means true that the few elements which appear overtly (like the few ideas that appear in consciousness at one time) are the source for all the inhibition of the great number of elements which do not appear. At each moment, all of the response tendencies, including those which remain below the behavioral threshold, are engaged in many-sided inhibitions, from which one or another may be released sufficiently to permit it to rise above the threshold, that is, to become realized in action. Thus, "singleness of action," which Sherrington said it is "the specific office of the nervous system to perfect,"—like the unity of consciousness which Herbart emphasized—rises from a background of subthreshold rivalries. Conflict is not the necessary outcome of these opposed tendencies.

The many manifestations of synaptic inhibition which have been discussed in this book are all ultimately based on the same original and logically deducible need: to provide a means by which an organism can behave in a manner which is both versatile and unified. This unity must be effected either by the intervention of something external to the response mechanisms themselves—that is, by a physiological surrogate for the faculty of *will* which Herbart rejected as unnecessary—or by inhibitory relationships among the response mechanisms. Without inhibitory restraints for readied responses, only a sluggish organism, or one with a very limited repertoire of response, could survive. Without disinhibitory release of responses, those inhibitory restraints would be shackles interfering with effective action. Although it is true that the *possibility* of conflict is created by this complex interplay of response mechanisms, conflict in the behavioral sense is not a necessary outcome, any more than breakdown is the necessary consequence of the fact that a machine has many parts.

One source of confusion, of course, is that the word "conflict" is a synonym of "opposition," and therefore it seems logical to assume that "opposed response tendencies" imply conflict. But if we are interpreting conflict in the sense of "behavioral disorganization" this is no longer true. There are many instances of behavior in which opposite response tendencies are collaborative, rather than in conflict. It would not be possible to wave an admonishing finger, or to play a violin vibrato, without the simultaneous activation (as well as the nonsimultaneous disinhibition) of antagonistic muscles. Hunger and thrist, or love and aggression, need likewise be no more in conflict than two woodsmen at opposite ends of a two-handled saw. Even when opposed response tendencies are not reciprocating collaborative parts of a larger pattern, conflict may be prevented by the fact that one is commonly (as expressed by F. H. Allport, 1924) prepotent over the other. The behavioral effect of prepotency is to obviate conflict, and it is clear that the physiological basis is neural inhibition. As Freusberg (1875) stated the matter, inhibition is an expression of "the remarkable characteristic of the central organ, *which does not allow its separate parts to be excited by different causes at the same time.*"

Inhibition is the means which the organism has discovered to achieve the unity of action essential to survival. Conflict represents a breakdown in Freusberg's "remarkable characteristic," a failure of the nervous system to maintain unity of action when incompatible responses are being "aroused," in Berlyne's use of that term. But it is not a necessary consequence of such multiple response arousal.

Freusberg reached his conclusion largely from a consideration of the spinal reflexes of the decapitated frog. Earlier, Pflüger (1853) emphasized that the reactions of the spinal frog were not completely predictable, but included an element of choice, which he regarded as evidence for a "spinal soul." For Lashley, in one of his last papers, the essentials of choice are still presented in the frog's struggle to wipe away a drop of acid.

> Voluntary action is usually defined as a choice between two foreseen, alternative actions. This is beautifully illustrated by the spinal frog. If a bit of acid is placed on the midline of the rump, the preparation responds by alternate jerking of the hind legs; incipient wiping movements. Finally the motor system of one leg performs the complete wiping reflex, while the other is extended. Here is foresight; we often see a man making such tentative actions while he is reaching a decision, and his verbal debating (foresight) about it is only a substitute for other alternative actions. After the period of indecision, of vacillation, the spinal frog also reaches its decision. Save in the complexities of the alternatives, the procedures are the same (Lashley, 1958, p. 7).

However, it is misleading to compare the vacillations of the decapitated frog with those of cortical man, as if they were two points of an uninterrupted continuum. The intact frog, in the same situation, would reach the bit of acid with the first wipe of one leg, while the other was extended, its wiping action inhibited. In other words, the conflict in the spinal frog's behavior arises in this instance from inhibitory insufficiency, which has as a result that for a while both legs try to perform the act, and neither succeeds. The man's "verbal debating" of alternative courses of action is not necessarily a sign of conflictful vacillation. It can be effectively performed only because the man can inhibit one course of action, including its verbal expression, while considering the probable outcome of the other; he would be in conflict if he were occupied simultaneously or at least intermittently with the imaginary performance of several courses of action, in a way that would make it impossible for him properly to evaluate any: that is, if he also experienced inhibitory insufficiency, relative to his need for control.

To choose relevantly, it is necessary to hold all other considerations in abeyance. Recognizing this, Lashley points out that when a "system in tonic activity" dominates the brain, other systems are not readily activated. Intense stimuli or those of special meaningfulness may break through, but "the great mass of afferent excitation is excluded. This blocking might be either an active inhibition or the pre-emption of neurons which might otherwise be included in the blocked system. The phenomena of attention demand some such hypothesis." Lashley prefers to think in terms of an organization of neurons excited at subthreshold levels. We, of course, favor the other alternative which he suggests: active inhibition is required to permit orderly choice behavior, and it is therefore the basis for the reduction of conflict.

If one criterion of conflict is impairment or loss of efficiency, then we must distinguish between *conflict* on the one hand, and *competition* or *rivalry* of responses on the other. The latter terms do not carry the same connotation of disorganization. Thus defined, conflict is not a matter of opposed responses or response tendencies, but of failure in the inhibitory control of such tendencies, leading to simultaneous disinhibition of incompatible activities. A major determinant of conflict is therefore the individual's inhibitory capacity. The same "opposed response tendencies" which might create an intolerable situation for one person might present no difficulty at all for another. There will, of course, be important individual differences in the areas in which such difficulties arise. Nevertheless, it is permissible to use the term "inhibitory capacity" in much the same way in which we commonly speak of "intelligence," as a quantifiable characteristic of behavior which is a composite of many specific abilities. Just as of two persons, the one with lower intelligence may still excel in some of the abilities which enter into the composite, so in the same way, the individual with higher overall inhibitory capacity may have less control in some particular area of behavior. Whether generalized or specific, conflict is always a matter of choice pathology, which is dependent on the faulty integration of response tendencies, and not merely on their number and their strength.

What we have been saying of "responses" applies to the emotional responses with the same force as to those by means of which the organism copes with its environment. Here, too, ease of disinhibition is the principal factor which determines the prevalence of one or another type of responsiveness.[1] Pathological anxiety, or aggressiveness, or hypersexuality are the expressions of instability in the normal tonic inhibitions of these behaviors. The role of the limbic structures in such disturbances is considered by MacLean (1955). In a figure which is strongly reminiscent of Plato's allegory,

[1] Accordingly, the definition of temperament in terms of "relative ease of arousal of unlearned response patterns," previously stated by one of the authors (Diamond, 1957), should be revised to read: "relative ease of disinhibition of unlearned response patterns."

he likens the relations of the limbic lobe and the neocortex to those of horse and rider, two creatures "very much alive to each other and to their environment, yet communication between them is limited." The "patient and sympathetic horseman" must try to learn why "the horse may shy and bolt for reasons at first inexplicable to the horseman," in an effort to reduce this maladaptive overresponsiveness.

If conflict were only a matter of the opposition of response tendencies, then degree of conflict would depend on the characteristics of such tendencies. Pursuing this point of view, Berlyne (1960) says: "Degree of conflict must surely increase with (1) the *nearness to equality in strength* of the competing response tendencies, (2) the *absolute strength* of the competing response tendencies, and (3) the *number* of competing response tendencies." He considers the possibility that "degree of incompatibility" may be a fourth determinant, but decides that it can probably be reduced to the other variables. He offers experimental evidence, such as the fact that response times are prolonged when the individual is given a free choice of several possible responses rather than just two. However, such evidence does not go to the heart of the problem, which is not whether these are some of the determinants of the degree of conflict, but whether they include the principal determinants, under the conditions of motivated adaptive behavior. To us it seems that their influence is relatively slight, almost trivial. Even in the laboratory, the entire history of reaction experiments supports the expectation that individual differences will greatly overshadow differences due to such treatments; that is, for some individuals it will matter only a little that the number of alternative responses is increased, and for others the effect will be enormous. In other words, the degree of conflict will not be fixed by the number and characteristics of incompatible response tendencies, but by characteristics of the process of choice among them. Again we emphasize: incompatible response tendencies set the stage for possible conflict, but they are not the sufficient condition for conflict.

If conflict arises simply from opposition of response tendencies, then, as Berlyne says, "the simultaneous instigation of conflicting chains of events will result, at least initially, in blockage, mutual impediment, and, in short, the absence of definite response. . . . If two responses are activated simultaneously and with about equal strength, the most likely outcome is that each of them will succeed in inhibiting the other so that neither will come to fruition." Berlyne also recognizes that "the launching of one piece of adaptive behavior is generally accompanied by the inhibition of structures that might bring other response processes into play," but he apparently does not interpret this as a means by which conflict is frequently excluded even when nearly simultaneous and nearly equal instigation of responses occur. For him, the shade of Buridan still walks.

Maier's (1949) experimental study of frustration throws interesting light on the supposed relationship between degree of conflict and the relative strengths of simultaneous response tendencies. In the early trials in the jumping situation, faced with a discrimination problem of only moderate difficulty and before any marked preference has been established for a particular response, the hunger-motivated animals will respond without much hesitation, and there is no reason to say that they are in conflict. After many trials with an unsolvable problem, the repeatedly punished rat may develop a great reluctance to jump at all; when forced to do so (as by air blast) it responds with an invariable position response, or "abnormal fixation." It is now in conflict, although on a superficial analysis one might say that the response tendencies are now quite unequal, since one response is consistently performed rather than the other. But does this mean that the tendency to the "preferred" response is really stronger than the other? Not at all; the animal may even show, in the length of time spent in postural orientation toward each window, a preference for the response which it never performs! The fixated response is not one which has a stronger response tendency associated with it, but the one which is more readily disinhibited. The situation is quite justly compared to that of the neurotic individual who is strongly motivated to some action, but also strongly fears it, or circumstances attached to it. But after all, do we not all, in our normal everyday behavior, spend most of our time in doing the things that are easily done, rather than in doing the things toward which we are strongly motivated? What a distortion of reality it is to suppose that our acts arise as the resultant of tendencies to respond in different ways, without considering the factor of ease of disinhibitory release! The frustration situation, in which the lack of correspondence between positive motivation to response and behavior is made conspicuous, serves to emphasize this fact, but the situation is not really so completely different from "motivated behavior" as Maier supposes.

The problem of frustration has received a very different treatment from Brown and Farber (1951), who state a theory which has recently been further elaborated by Brown (1961). Writing in the general context of Hullian behavior theory, they conceive of frustration as a hypothetical state of the organism which is brought about whenever two competing habit strengths are jointly activated by drive. It is explicitly recognized that the competing tendencies may be tendencies to two different responses, or excitatory and inhibitory components relating to the same response, but these two situations are not regarded as essentially different. In either case, frustration manifests itself as an increase in drive, or in new interoceptive stimuli. Since a multiplicative relationship is assumed to hold between drive and habit strength, relatively small differences between the two habit strengths become magnified by the increase in drive. On the other hand, the new internal stimuli produced by the frustration state tend to elicit behaviors which have previously been associated with such stimulation, or unlearned species-specific behavioral tendencies such as the "displacements" described by the ethologists, which will be discussed below. Such stimuli therefore lead to forms of response which tend to be maladaptive, because they are independent of the external stimuli which initiated the response tendencies giving rise to the frustration and having little likelihood of removing those stimuli.

Considered solely as an explanation of the disruptive and maladaptive effects of conflict, this theory has much to commend it; but again it fails to meet our criterion, that conflict (or frustration) shall not be defined as the outcome of conditions which are compatible with orderly choice behavior. Brown and Farber explain too much, because the scheme they present is one which will lead to ever more complex configurations of excitatory tendencies, throwing the organism deeper and deeper into maladaptive conflictful behaviors. The real problem, after all, is not the explanation of conflict, but to understand why the richly responsive organism is not hopelessly in conflict due to the continual opposition of incompatible response tendencies. The answer to that problem is inhibitory choice, and the answer to the problem of conflict, in its many forms, is then nothing more than a recognition of the many ways in which the mechanisms of choice can fail to serve their purpose.

Some interesting examples of behavior arising from simultaneous incompatible response tendencies are those reported by the ethologists in their studies of the innate response patterns of birds and fish, and especially of the courtship, nesting, and territorial defense patterns. Hinde and Tinbergen (1958) state: "Recent studies of both fishes and birds have shown that a threatening animal has two incompatible tendencies: to attack its rival and to flee from it. Similarly a courting bird has three incompatible tendencies: to attack, flee from, and behave sexually toward its mate. The nature of the behavior shown at any stage of the courtship depends on the strengths and relative strengths of these conflicting tendencies."

The competitive rivalry of such incompatible response tendencies is said to give rise to three types of display movements: intention movements, which are abbreviations of the original activities; displacements, which are apparently irrelevant activities; and redirection activities, which are comparable to the "displaced aggression" that has been described by Miller (1948). However, it is of the greatest importance to remember that each of these activities may be highly ritualized, showing sometimes minute nuances of difference from one species to another, and that because of this ritualized character they are able to function as signals to other members of the species, who are rivals or partners in the social setting for the behavior. They serve as releasers for the IRM's (internal release mechanisms) by which innate responses in these other individuals are disinhibited (Tinbergen, 1951).

In describing this behavior, the word *conflict* is frequently used. For example, Tinbergen (1960) writes: "But what makes the gull take up a certain posture? The controlling elements in the immediate situation in which a gull strikes one of these postures can be summed up in a single word: conflict. . . . The bird is in the grip of two mutually opposed impulses: to attack or to escape. . . . In such states of inner conflict the impulse to attack may also be redirected against inanimate objects or displaced by some irrelevant activity such as the nest-building head flick in the gull or the lighting of a cigarette in man."

So it goes on, but we also read: "Somehow in the course of evolution these 'involuntary' expressions of inner conflict between two incompatible response tendencies acquired value as signals. . . . Once a given posture acquired such a value, it is apparent that it tended to become quite clearly differentiated from the movement in which it originated."

Is it correct, however, to describe as conflictful the highly ritualized actions which are carried out with strict uniformity by all members of a species (or at least by all those of a given sex), and which have become "clearly differentiated" actions having their own functional significance and a definite survival value, as in reducing or even totally eliminating the actual physical combat between members of the species? While accepting the correctness of Tinbergen's basic position, that these display movements have arisen, in the evolutionary sense, out of the conflict of incompatible response tendencies, must we not at the same time recognize that conflict is absent or greatly reduced when they have evolved to the point of constituting "clearly differentiated" signalling behavior which is no longer disruptive? This differentiated behavior must depend on the particular patterns of neural activity which have been developed for the inhibition of these incompatible responses.

The conflict of incompatible responses does exist at times, particularly in behavior which is not species-specific, and it can be extremely maladaptive. Dilger (1962) describes the nesting behavior of lovebirds, which are a genus of parrots. The more primitive species tuck small strips of nest material among their feathers, and thus transport six to eight pieces at a time to the nest site. The more recent species build more structured nests of larger materials, and transport these one at a time, in their bills. In the laboratory, Dilger observed hybrid birds which had inherited dispositions to both patterns of nest building. He describes these birds as "completely confused," since they never succeeded in carrying material to the nest site except in their bills, but originally engaged in long sequences of abortive tucking behavior, using the method of bill-

transport only about 6 percent of the time. "It took two years for them to learn to diminish actual tucking activity to any great extent," and even after three years they would still resort to it occasionally. Dilger remarks that although they have never once been successful in transporting materials in their plumage, their attempts to do this are becoming more efficient at the same time that they are becoming less frequent!

There can be no doubt that the behavior of these hybrid birds can be properly described as conflictful, although the degree of conflict has been progressively reduced by the gradual suppression of the ineffectual response. So, too, in the threat postures and courtship behavior of normal birds and fish of many species, as described by Tinbergen, Hinde, and others, conflict exists only to the extent that there is uncertainty in the behavior sequence. Those invariable ritual acts which appear to be the survivals of conflictful behavior which may be assumed to have existed in the evolutionary past of the species, have now lost the character of conflict, but represent instead adaptive responses which are mediated by inherited relationships among incompatible responses. The degree of conflict which exists, in the individual case, is not so much dependent on the number or the strength of the incompatible response tendencies present in the situation, as on the degree to which readily disinhibited "displacement" activities are available in the behavior repertoire.

Liddell's extended research on conditional responses established under stress illustrates many of the facets of choice pathology. Recently, Liddell (1959) has related his conditioning procedures to the background of "self-imposed restraint established through training in the conditioned animal." A basic procedure is to expose the animal to a signal followed by shock. No discriminative choice among stimuli need be required. After some training, the animal adopts the posture of "self-imposed restraint" while awaiting the signal, and it is possible occasionally to observe a "vigorous positive conditional reflex which is not signal-bound but which suggests a vivid hallucinatory reaction." Animals that have been subjected to "graded doses of traumatic experience" sometimes show far more general loss of control. For example, Liddell mentions that when a photographer approaches a flock of sheep grazing, the entire flock may take flight in one direction, while "an experimentally neurotic ewe . . . flees in the opposite direction. Her damaged gregariousness menaces her survival. When dogs gain access to our flock at night, it is one of the neurotic sheep that they kill." Similarly, the majority of these neurotic ewes may abort or fail to establish adequate maternal-neonate relations. Many other examples might be cited to illustrate effects which Liddell believes are due to a "chronic or self-perpetuating state in which there is faulty control of emergency reactions." The point is that the neurotic loss of control affects not only the behavior in the conditioning stand, but also affects mechanisms of adaptation which are usually considered species-specific modes of responding. There is an evident choice pathology even in situations which would not be expected to involve conflict. Apparently the prolonged periods of "self-imposed restraint" influence the general background of neural activity, including the inhibitory controls of many other behaviors. Yet the shock delivered is so weak as to be scarcely detectable to the human hand, and what seems to be most punitive in the experimental situation is its monotony. The effects described take place even more rapidly in the young or newborn animal, and therefore it is difficult to conceive of them as resulting from the competition of either "learned" or "innate" response tendencies. They are obviously comparable to instances of pathological anxiety in humans.

We shall turn for our last example to human behavior, but we shall not take it from either the laboratory or the clinic. Any day on a playground, you can hear one youngster say to another, "I'll choose you! Odds or evens?" The election made, the two boys simultaneously thrust out a hand, with either one or two fingers extended, to make a total that is odd or even. In this way, they are introduced to the problems of game strategy, which have occupied so many mature minds in recent years. Let us say that Tom, thus challenged, chose *odds,* thrust out one finger on the first try, and found his maneuver had been unsuccessful; his opponent also extended one finger, and won on *evens.* For the second trial, Tom, if he is very simple minded, may react perseveratively, again with one finger. If he is just a little less simple, he thinks: "I'd better change," and he extends two fingers. If he is a moderately complex youngster, he says to himself, "He thinks I'm going to switch, so I'll fool him, I'll put out one finger again." Or if we are dealing with a pair of very bright boys, Tom may say to himself, "He thinks I wouldn't do the obvious thing and switch, so he expects me to put out one finger again, but I'll fool him, I'll do two." And so on, through cycles of expectation and counter-expectation, each of which involves added elements of inhibition.

All this must transpire quickly, for Tom must make his choice in the short space of time in which the two boys draw back their hands, and then simultaneously thrust them forward again. As they complete this gesture, the suddenly outstretched fingers are a symbolic expression of what Lloyd Morgan called "the faculty of the forked way." It is the faculty of the reacting organism to deny some of its potentialities, in order better to realize others. When we cannot make this choice, we are like the beheaded frog struggling to wipe away the bit of acid, and making ineffectual movements with both legs, where either might do the job.

CONCLUSION

As we end our labors on this book, we are painfully aware that the volume of research on the problems of inhibition is growing at a pace which makes it impossible for us to keep abreast of it, let alone synthesize it successfully; and that the possibilities of application are infinitely broader than we have been able to illustrate by our efforts in that direction. How many tempting paths have been left unexplored, how many fascinating facts have been left unreported! And not without conflict! Nevertheless, we can hope that we have directed the attention of some readers to the importance of inhibition for psychology, and to the perspectives which applications of that concept offer for the development of psychological theory.

Making use of the concept of inhibition does not by itself guarantee quick and easy solutions for long-standing difficult problems, nor does it provide insurance against error. Above all it holds forth no promise for simple answers. Quite to the contrary, it seems to compel an advance to greater complexity in theory construction, to a picture of behavior in which each act emerges from complex interactions, and there is no room anywhere for relationships as simple as the S-R bonds of what we may term theories of response excitation.

One of the lessons which emerge from the history of the concept of inhibition is that the principle of parsimony in theory construction has not been an unmixed blessing. If it has prevented error at times, it has also stood in the way of progress at other times. As the role of theory construction in science has changed from an emphasis on explanation to an emphasis on hypothesis, the restraining influence of an injunction against the multiplication of entities has lost its old importance. The scientist of the twentieth century is aware that his theories must invite and withstand experimental test. He must not fear complexities, and rather than adhering to an ideal of parsimony he must boldly face the problem of what is the proper level of complexity for a theory which is to deal adequately with the phenomena he wishes to explain, so that he may match his theory to the phenomena in this respect. The technique of factor analysis has been recommended as able to perform this service in some of our research, by determining the minimum number of variables which must be used in the description of a given psychological domain (Thurstone, 1947). Anyone familiar with the general trend of factor analytic studies will recognize that we are more often in danger of oversimplifying than of overcomplicating our hypotheses. Useful theory must always be simpler than reality, in the sense that it abstracts certain relationships out of the complex of events in which they are imbedded. But sometimes the passion for simplicity exceeds the passion for meaningful structure, and, after sweeping away the dust, we also try to sweep away the pattern of the carpet, because it is too involved for our perceptual grasp. Surely, something of this sort has happened again and again in the long history of the concept of inhibition, since there has been such reluctant acceptance of the implications of experimental results which disturbed the simpler picture of the nervous system. What ingenuity was expended in attempts to prove that, on the neural level, inhibition did not take place, and on the psychological level, that such hypotheses as "repression" were without justification!

To speak out against parsimony is almost like taking a stand in favor of sin, but it would probably not be difficult to discover similar examples in other fields of science, in which theoretical progress has been checked by refusal to accept nonparsimonious theories which have subsequently proved sound. If theory must not multiply entities without necessity, neither must it deny existence to those that are indispensable. Whatever the need of the past to "inhibit" uncontrolled speculation, experimental and conceptual techniques have reached a level where each added degree of complexity, in dealing with phenomena that are themselves complex, is more to be welcomed than shunned. The concept of inhibition, with all that it implies regarding the interaction of systems and structures in the nervous system—or, on another descriptive plane, among the component parts of behavior—pushes us toward this needful complication of psychological description and hypothesis.

Our second general conclusion relates to the role of inhibition in the evolution of behavior. The study of inhibition provides forceful illustration of the principle that the structure which evolves in the service of one need often gives rise to new potentialities for further development. Since all behavioral choice rests on inhibition, it is all an outgrowth of the primitive needs which first gave rise to an antiexcitatory process. These primitive needs are of two kinds. One was suggested by Freud (1920), in his conjecture that the primitive organism must somehow be shielded from the hazards of excessive environmental stimulation. Support for this point of view may be found in the fact pointed out by Schneirla (1959), that the locomotion of many lower organisms is not concerned with positive orientation toward food and the like, but with withdrawal from sources of intense stimulation. As sensitivity to environmental stimulation is heightened, the need for such protective inhibition increases, leading to the inhibitory modulation of afferent activities. This leads in the vertebrates to such mechanisms of interaction, between the brain stem and higher brain centers, as have been considered in earlier chapters. When any such apparatus has been developed to a fair degree of complexity, it provides a basis for experiential modification of behavior generally, through processes which we designate as "perception" and "attention," but which consist essentially of modulation of the intensity of the components of stimulation.

The other type of primitive inhibitory need is for adaptive cessation of otherwise automatic activity. Such activities may be initiated and sustained by purely local, non-nervous processes, but if they are to be checked by negative feedback, something like nervous communication is necessary. Inhibition was therefore no late development in nervous control, which appeared alongside of excitation as a further development in already elaborate nervous systems. A purely excitatory nervous system could not evolve beyond a very rudimentary stage without introducing unsupportable new difficulties into the life of the organism.

Once inhibition arose as a nervous function, it created novel possibilities for enrichment of the behavioral repertoire. As the capacity for response inhibition increased, organisms were enabled to advance to new levels of sensitivity to environmental influence, and they could acquire new means of responding to the same situation with different elements of their behavioral repertoire, and different combinations of those elements. Later, the inhibited response could be utilized as a kind of rehearsal, a process which led to the development of thinking. A comparative survey of the role which inhibition plays in animal behavior, done with some thoroughness, should clarify the main lines of this development. However, it seems highly probable that the capacity for all forms of behavioral plasticity, including thought, had its beginnings in the primitive needs for filtering intense stimulation and for response cessation.

Physiological research on inhibition dealt first with those forms which serve the need for response cessation, and later with those which are involved in control of central activity and afferentation. The principles of inhibition which emerged from our historical survey include the following:

Neural impulses sometimes serve to relax muscles (Bell). . . . There exist cerebral structures capable of inhibiting spinal reflexes (Sechenov). . . . Action often comes about by release from such inhibition (Anstie). . . . This release is often effected by the inhibition of an inhibition (Brunton). . . . Activation of one response normally precludes activation of competing responses (Freusberg). . . . Local inhibition is essential to keep cortical activity in bounds (Heidenhain). . . . Perceptual selectivity is an inhibitory process (Wundt). . . . Coordination of rhythmic responses is due to reciprocal inhibition of the components (Sherrington). . . . Sensory impulses undergo tonic inhibitory modulation (Head).

Three additional concepts arising from modern neurophysiological research contribute to the development of a total picture of the manner in which inhibitory processes participate in behavior:

The nervous system is a complex of chemically differentiated subsystems (Dale). . . . The mechanism of inhibition is synaptic hyperpolarization (Eccles). . . . Cortical arousal is mediated by reticular activation (Magoun). (We venture to restate this last in the hypothetical form, that local cortical inhibition is subject to disinhibitions of reticular origin.)

To understand plasticity in behavior, it is necessary to avoid the overemphasis on "learning" which has been characteristic of most behavior theory. The ability to form associations, and the still higher ability to attain understandings, can only arise where there already exist a number of mutually inhibitory ways of responding to the same stimulation. What appears in one context as chemical differentiation of the nervous system, in another context as the interplay of systems in the hippocampus and other limbic structures, in still another as the rivalry of opposed response tendencies, is everywhere the expression of the inhibitory mechanisms which extract unity and moderation from diversity and potential self-destructive excess. When these controls are defective, or temporarily inadequate to the stress placed upon them, various pathologies of choice appear, but much more impressive is the degree of behavioral unity which is achieved from moment to moment, despite the constant rivalry of potentially incompatible actions, by a nervous system which, when it functions well, is able to exclude maladaptive conflict without suppressing spontaneity or unduly restricting the organism's spectrum of choice.

REFERENCES

Bracketed dates are original dates of publication for items seen only in later editions or in translation, as noted. Bracketed titles are translations of Russian titles. Entries preceded by an asterisk have not been verified directly, but have been well authenticated otherwise.

Abramson, H. A., 1955 (Ed.) *Neuropharmacology.* Trans. Second Conf. New York: Josiah Macy, Jr. Foundation.

Abramson, H. A., 1957 (Ed.) *Neuropharmacology.* Trans. Third Conf. New York: Josiah Macy, Jr. Foundation.

Abramson, H. A., 1960 (Ed.) *The use of LSD in psychotherapy: Transactions of a conference on d-lysergic acid diethylamide (LSD–25).* New York: Josiah Macy, Jr. Foundation.

Abramson, H. A., & Jarvik, M. E., 1955. Lysergic acid diethylamide (LSD–25): IX. Effect on snails. *J. Psychol.,* **40,** 337–340.

Ach, N., 1905. *Über die Willenstätigkeit und das Denken.* Göttingen: Vandenhoeck, Ruprecht.

Adametz, J. H., 1959. Rate of recovery of functioning in cats with rostral reticular lesions. *J. Neurosurg.,* **16,** 85–97.

Adams, D. K., 1931. A restatement of the problem of learning. *Brit. J. Psychol.,* **22,** 150–176.

Adams, D. K., 1933. Three theories of learning. *J. gen. Psychol.,* **8,** 485–497.

Ades, H. W., 1959. Central auditory mechanisms. In Magoun, vol. I, 1959. Pp. 585–613.

Adey, W. R., 1959. Recent studies of the rhinencephalon in relation to temporal lobe epilepsy and behavior disorders. In Pfeiffer & Smythies, 1959. Pp. 1–46.

Adrian, E. D., 1947. *The physiological background of perception.* Oxford: Clarendon.

Adrian, E. D., 1954. The physiological basis of perception. In Delafresnaye, 1954. Pp. 237–243.

Allport, F. H., 1924. *Social Psychology.* Boston: Houghton Mifflin.

Allport, G. W., 1937. *Personality: a psychological interpretation.* New York: Holt.

Amantea, G., 1921. Über experimentelle beim Versuchstier infolge afferenter Reize erzeugte Epilepsie. *Pflüg. Arch. ges. Physiol.,* **188,** 287–297.

Amassian, V. E., & Waller, H. J., 1958. Spatiotemporal patterns of activity in individual reticular neurons. In Jasper, 1958b. Pp. 69–108.

Anand, B. K., & Brobeck, J. R., 1951. Hypothalamic control of food intake in rats and cats. *Yale J. Biol. & Med.,* **24,** 123–140.

Anichkov, S. V., 1961. Highlights of Soviet pharmacology. *Ann. Rev. Pharmacol.,* **1,** 21–28.

Anokhin, P. K., 1958. *Vnutrennee tormozhenie kak problema fiziologii.* [Internal inhibition as a problem of physiology.] Moscow: Medgiz.

Anokhin, P. K., 1961a. Discussant; pp. 351–352, in Delafresnaye, 1961.

Anokhin, P. K., 1961b. Electroencephalographic analysis of cortico-subcortical relations in positive and negative conditioned reactions. In Kline, 1961. Pp. 899–938.

Anrep, G. V., 1923. Irradiation of conditioned reflexes. *Proc. Roy. Soc. London,* **94B,** 404–426.

Anstie, F. E., 1864. *Stimulants and narcotics.* London: Macmillan.

Arieti, S., 1959 (Ed.) *American Handbook of Psychiatry.* New York: Basic. 2 vols.

Aristotle. *Nicomachean ethics.* D. P. Chase (trans.). New York: Dutton, 1911.

Aristotle. *On the senses and sensibility.* J. I. Beare (trans.). In *Great Books of the Western World,* vol. 8. Pp. 673–689.

Ashby, W. R., 1960. *Design for a brain* (2nd ed.) New York: Wiley.

Ayd, F. J., Jr., 1957. A critique of tranquilizing drugs. In Garattini and Ghetti, 1957. Pp. 548–555.

Ayrapet'yants, E. Sh., [1952]. The principle of temporary connections in the physiology of interoception. In *Central Nervous System and Human Behavior,* 1959. Pp. 113–138.

Bain, A., 1855. *The senses and the intellect.* London: Parker.

Bain, A., 1859. *The emotions and the will.* London: Parker.

Baldwin, M., 1960. Electrical stimulation of the mesial temporal region. In Ramey & O'Doherty, 1960. Pp. 159–179.

Balvin, R. S., 1956. *Decision-making in a situation involving stationary probabilities and providing several alternatives for maximization.* Unpublished doctoral dissertation, Univer. of California at Los Angeles.

Barcroft, J., 1938. *The brain and its environment.* New Haven: Yale Univer. Press.

Barcroft, J., and Barron, D. H., 1937. Movements in midfoetal life in the sheep embryo. *J. Physiol.,* 91:329–351.

Bard, P., 1950. Central nervous mechanisms for the expression of anger in animals. In Reymert, 1950. Pp. 211–237.

Bard, P., & Mountcastle, V. B., 1947. Some forebrain mechanisms involved in expression of rage with special reference to suppression of angry behavior. *Res. Publ. Ass. nerv. ment. Dis.,* **27,** 362–404.

Barker, R. G., Dembo, Tamara, & Lewin, K., 1943. Frustration and regression. In Barker, Kounin, & Wright, 1943. Pp. 441–458.

Barker, R. G., Kounin, J. S., & Wright, H. F., 1943. *Child behavior and development,* New York: McGraw-Hill.

Bass, A. D., 1959 (Ed.) *Evolution of nervous control from primitive organisms to man.* Washington, D.C.: A.A.A.S.

Bass, M. J., & Hull, C. L., 1934. The irradiation of a tactile conditioned reflex in man. *J. comp. physiol. Psychol.,* **17,** 47–66.

Beach, F. A., 1948. *Hormones and behavior.* New York: Hoeber.

Beer, Th., Bethe, A., & Uexküll, J. v., 1899. Vorschläge zu einer objektivierender Nomenclatur in der Physiologie des Nervensystems. *Biol. Centbl.,* **19,** 517–521.

Bekhterev, V. M. [1928] *General principles of human reflexology.* London: Jarrold, 1933. Trans. from 4th (1928) Russian ed.

Bekhterev, V. [1910] *Objektive Psychologie.* Leipzig: Teubner, 1913.

Bell, C., 1823. On the motions of the eye, in illustration of the uses of the muscles and nerves of the orbit. *Phil. Trans.,* **113,** 166–186, 289–307.

Benda, C. E., 1946. *Mongolism and cretinism.* New York: Grune and Stratton.

Benda, C. E., 1952. *Developmental disorders of mentation and cerebral palsies.* New York: Grune and Stratton.

Benda, C. E., 1960. *The child with mongolism (congenital acromicria).* New York: Grune and Stratton.

Berger, F. M., 1960. Classification of psychoactive drugs according to their chemical structures and sites of action. In Uhr and Miller, 1960. Pp. 86–105.

Berger, H., 1929. Über das Elektrenkephalogramm des Menschen. *Arch. Psychiat.*, **87**, 527–570.

Beritashvilli, I. S., 1960. Discussant; pp. 34, 209–210, in Jasper and Smirnov, 1960.

Beritoff, J., 1927. Über die individuell-erworbene Tätigkeit des Zentralnervensystems. *J. Psychologie u. Neurologie,* **33,** 113–335.

Beritov, I. S., 1948. [General physiology of the muscular and nervous systems (2nd ed.)] Moscow: Akad. Nauk. 2 vols.

Beritov, I., 1957. The development of the physiology of the central nervous system in the Soviet Union in the last 40 years. *Sechenov J. Physiol., USSR,* 43, 941–955.

Beritov, I. S., & Roitbak, A. I., 1955. [On the nature of the process of central inhibition.] *Zh. vyssh. nervn. Deital.,* **5,** 173–186.

Berlyne, D. E., 1960. *Conflict, arousal, and curiosity.* New York: McGraw-Hill.

Bernard, C., 1857. *Leçons sur les effets des substances toxiques et médicamenteuses.* Paris: Baillière.

Bernard, C., 1858a. *Leçons sur la physiologie et pathologie du système nerveux.* 2 vols. Paris: Baillière.

Bernard, C., 1858b. Sur une expérience relative a l'influence que les nerfs exercent sur les glandes. *Compt. rend. Soc. Biol.,* **10,** 29–30.

Bernard, C., 1864. Études physiologiques sur quelques poisons américains: le curare. *Rev. deux Mondes,* **53,** 164–190.

Bernstein, J., 1902. Untersuchungen zur Thermodynamik der bioelektrischen Ströme. *Pfl. Arch.,* **92,** 521–562.

Bethe, A., 1897. Vergleichende Untersuchungen uber die Functionen des Centralnervensystems der Arthropoden, *Pfl. Arch.,* **68,** 449–545. Summary trans. by W. W. Norman, in *J. comp. Neurol.* (1898), **8,** 232–238.

Bethe, A., 1897–1898. Das Centralnervensystem von Carcinus Maenas. *Arch. mikr. Anat.*, **50**, 446–546; **51**, 382–452.

Bianchi, L., 1922. *The mechanism of the brain and the function of the frontal lobes.* Trans. by J. H. Macdonald. Edinburgh: Livingstone.

Biedermann, W., 1887. Beiträge zur allgemeinen Nerven- und Muskelnphysiologie: XX. Über die Innervation der Krebsschere. *Sitzber. Akad. Wiss. Wien (Math.-naturw. Kl.)*, 95:7–40.

Biedermann, W., 1888. Beiträge zur allgemeinen Nerven- und Muskelnphysiologie: XXI. Über die Innervation der Krebsschere. *Sitzber. Akad. Wiss. Wien (Math.-naturw. Kl.)*, 97:49–82.

Biryukov, D. A., 1958. Landmarks in the development of the theory of reflex activity. *Sechenov J. Physiol.*, **44**, 71–77.

Boring, E. G., 1950. *A history of experimental psychology* (2nd ed.) New York: Appleton-Century-Crofts.

Bowditch, H. P., & Warren, J. W., 1890. The knee-jerk and its physiological modifications. *J. Physiol.*, **11**, 25–64.

Bradley, C., 1954. Organic factors in the psychopathology of childhood. In P. H. Hoch and J. Zubin (Eds.). *Psychopathology of childhood.* New York: Grune and Stratton, pp. 82–104.

Bradley, K., Easton, D. M., & Eccles, J. C., 1953. An investigation of primary inhibition. *J. Physiol.*, **122**, 474–488.

Bradley, P. B., 1957. Microelectrode approach to the neuropharmacology of the reticular formation. In Garattini and Ghetti, 1957. Pp. 207–216.

Bradley, P. B., 1958. The central action of certain drugs in relation to the reticular formation of the brain. In Jasper 1958b. Pp. 123–149.

Bradley, P. B., Deniker, P., & Radouco-Thomas, C., 1959 (Eds.). *Neuropsychopharmacology.* Amsterdam: Elsevier.

Brady, J. V., 1957. A comparative approach to the evaluation of drug effects upon behavior. In Fields, 1957. Pp. 111–141.

Brazier, Mary A. B., 1958. Studies of evoked responses by flash in man and cat. In Jasper, 1958b. Pp. 151–168.

Brazier, Mary A. B., 1959a. The historical development of neurophysiology. In Magoun, vol. I, 1959–1960. Pp. 1–58.

Brazier, Mary A. B., 1959b (Ed.). *The central nervous system and behavior.* Trans. First Conf. New York: Josiah Macy, Jr., Foundation.

Brazier, Mary A. B., 1960a. Long-persisting electrical traces in the brain of man and their possible relationship to higher nervous activity. In Jasper and Smirnov, 1960. Pp. 347–358.

Brazier, Mary A. B., 1960b (Ed.). *The central nervous system and behavior*. Trans. Third Conf. New York: Josiah Macy, Jr., Foundation.

Brazier, Mary A. B., 1961. Paired sensory modality stimulation studied by computer analysis. In Kline, 1961. Pp. 1054–1063.

Breese, B. B., 1899. On inhibition. *Psych. Rev. Monogr. Suppl.*, **3**, 1–65.

Bremer, F., 1925. Recherches sur le mécanisme de l'action de la strychnine sur le système nerveux: I. La strychnine et les phénomenes d'inhibition. *Arch. intern. physiol.*, **25**, 131–152.

Bremer, F., 1953. *Some problems of neurophysiology*. London: Athlone.

Bremer, F., 1954. The neurophysiological problem of sleep. In Delafresnaye, 1954. Pp. 137–158.

Bremer, F., & Stoupel, N., 1959. Facilitation et inhibition des potentiels évoqués corticaux dans l'éveil cérébral. *Arch. intern. Physiol.*, **67**, 240–275.

Brobeck, J. R., 1960. Regulation of feeding and drinking. In Magoun, vol. II, 1959–1960. Pp. 1197–1206.

Brodie, B. B., 1957. Serotonin and norepinephrine as antagonistic chemical mediators regulating the central autonomic nervous system. In Abramson, 1957. Pp. 323–341.

Brodie, B. B., & Shore, P. A., 1957. A concept for a role of serotonin and norepinephrine as chemical mediators in the brain. *Ann. N. Y. Acad. Med.*, **66**, 631–642.

Brookhart, J. M., 1960. The cerebellum. In Magoun, vol. II, 1959–1960. Pp. 1245–1280.

Brown, J. S., 1961. *The motivation of behavior*. New York: McGraw-Hill.

Brown, J. S., & Farber, I. E., 1951. Emotions conceptualized as intervening variables—with suggestions toward a theory of frustration. *Psychol. Bull.*, **48**, 465–495.

Brown-Séquard, C. E., 1853. Nouvel fait relatif à l'arrêt passif du coeur par la galvanisation du nerf vague. *CR Soc. Biol.*, **5**, 153–154.

Brown-Séquard, C. E., 1860. *Course of lectures on the physiology and pathology of the central nervous system*. Philadelphia: Collins.

Bruner, J. S., 1957. Neural mechanisms in perception. *Psychol. Rev.*, **64**, 340–358.

Bruner, J. S., & Postman, L., 1949. On the perception of incongruity: a paradigm. *J. Pers.*, **18**, 206–223.

Bruner, J. S., Goodnow, J. J., & Austin, G. A., 1956. *A study of thinking*. New York: Wiley.

Brunswik, E., 1939. Probability as a determiner of rat behavior. *J. exp. Psychol.,* **25,** 175–197.

Brunswik, E., 1943. Organismic achievement and environmental probability. *Psychol. Rev.,* **50,** 255–272.

Brunswik, E., 1944. Distal focussing of perception: size-constancy in a representative sample of situations. *Psychol. Monogr.* No. 254.

Brunswik, E., 1947. *Systematic and representative design of psychological research.* Berkeley, Calif.: Univer. California Press.

Brunswik, E., 1952. The conceptual framework of psychology. *Int. Encycl. unified Sci.,* **1** (10).

Brunton, T. L., 1874. Inhibition, peripheral and central. *West Riding Lunatic Asylum Med. Rep.,* **4,** 179–222.

Brunton, T. L., 1883. On the nature of inhibition, and the action of drugs upon it. *Nature,* **27,** 419–422, 436–439, 467–468, 485–487.

Bubnoff, N., & Heidenhain, R., 1881. Über Erregungs- und Hemmungsvorgänge innerhalb der motorischen Hirncentren. *Pflüg. Arch. ges. Physiol.,* **26,** 137–200. (Trans. in *Illinois Monogr. med. Sci.,* 1944, **4,** 173–210.)

Bureš, J., 1959. Reversible decortication and behavior. In Brazier, 1959b. Pp. 207–245.

Burks, H. F., 1958. Research on pseudo-mental retardation. In E. M. Bower and J. H. Rothstein (Eds.). Diagnostic problems in mental retardation. *Bull. Calif. State Dept. Educ.,* **27** (7), 40–43, 64.

Burns, B. D., 1951. Some properties of isolated cerebral cortex in the unanesthetized cat. *J. Physiol.,* **112,** 156–175.

Burns, B. D., 1958. *The mammalian cerebral cortex.* London: Arnold.

Butterfield, E. C., 1961. A provocative case of over-achievement by a mongoloid. *Amer. J. ment. Defic.,* **65,** 444–448.

Bykov, K. M. [1955]. Further development of the problem of the physiology and pathology of the corticovisceral system. In *Central nervous system and human behavior,* 1959. Pp. 147–166.

Bykov, K. M., 1957. *The cerebral cortex and the internal organs.* Trans. by W. H. Gantt. New York: Chemical Publ. Co.

Cabanis, G. [1802]. *Rapports du physique et du moral de l'homme* (4th ed.). Paris: Béchet, 1824, 2 vols.

Canali, G., & Grisoni, R., 1957. The action of serotonin, injected intravenously, on the epileptic patterns of the EEG in man. In Garattini & Ghetti, 1957. Pp. 289–291.

Cannon, W. B., 1927. *Bodily changes in hunger, pain, fear and rage.* New York: Appleton.

Cannon, W. B., & Rosenblueth, A., 1937. *Autonomic neuro-effector systems.* New York: Macmillan.

Caplan, G., 1961 (Ed.) *Prevention of mental disorders in children.* New York: Basic.

Carmichael, L., 1946a (Ed.) *Manual of child psychology.* New York: Wiley.

Carmichael, L., 1946b. The onset and early development of behavior. In Carmichael, 1946a. Pp. 43–166.

Carmichael, L., 1951. Ontogenetic development. In Stevens, 1951. Pp. 281–303.

Casselli, A., 1899. Untersuchungen über die reflexhemmende Function des oberen Schlundganglion der Languste. *Pfl. Arch. ges. Physiol.,* **74,** 158–163.

Central Nervous System and Human Behavior. Translations from the Russian medical literature. U.S. Dept. of Health, Educ. & Welfare, 1959, vol. I; 1960, vol. II.

Chernyshevsky, N. G., 1860. [The anthropological principle in philosophy.] *Sovremenik,* **80**(4); **81**(5). (Trans. in N. G. Chernyshevsky, *Selected philosophical essays.* Moscow: For. Lang. Pub. House, 1953.)

Chernyshevsky, N. G. [1863. *What is to be done?*] Trans. by B. R. Tucker, rev. and abridged by Ludmilla B. Turkevich. New York: Knopf (Vintage), 1961.

Chow, K. L., 1961. Brain functions. *Annu. Rev. Psychol.,* **12,** 281–310.

Chow, K. L., & John, E. R., 1958. Effects of intracerebral injection of anticholinesterase drugs on behavior in rats. *Science,* **128,** 781–782.

Clarke, Ann M., and Clarke, A. D. B. 1958 (Eds.) *Mental deficiency. The changing outlook.* Glencoe, Ill.: Free Press.

Clementi, A., 1929a. Stricnizzione della sfera corticale visiva ed epilessia da stimoli luminosi. *Arch. fisiol.,* **27,** 356–387.

Clementi, A., 1929b. Stricnizzione della sfera corticale uditiva ed epilessia sperimentale da stimoli acustici. *Arch. fisiol.,* **27,** 388–414.

Coghill, G. E., 1930. Individuation versus integration in the development of behavior. *J. gen. Psychol.,* **3,** 431–435.

Culler, E., & Mettler, F. A., 1934. Conditioned behavior in a decorticate dog. *J. comp. Psychol.,* **18,** 291–303.

Curtis, D. R., & Watkins, J. C., 1960. Investigations upon the possible synaptic transmitter function of gamma-aminobutyric acid and naturally occurring amino acids. In Roberts, 1960. Pp. 424–444.

Cyon, E., 1871. Hemmungen und Erregungen im Centralsystem der Gefässnerven. *Bull. Acad. Sci., St. Pétersb.* (*Akad. Nauk, Lening.*), **16,** 97–117.

Cyon, E., 1874. Zur Hemmungstheorie der reflectorischen Erregungen. In *Beiträge zur Anatomie und Physiologie als Festgabe Carl Ludwig.* Leipzig: Vogel. Pp. 166–172.

Dale, H. H., 1933. Nomenclature of fibres in the autonomic system and their effects. *J. Physiol.,* **80,** 10P–11P.

Darwin, E., 1794–1796. *Zoonomia, or the laws of organic life.* London: Johnson. 2 vols.

Delafresnaye, J. F., 1954 (Ed.) *Brain mechanisms and consciousness.* Springfield, Ill.: Thomas.

Delafresnaye, J. F., 1961 (Ed.) *Brain mechanisms and learning.* London: Blackwell.

Dennis, W., 1938. Infant development under conditions of restricted practice and of minimum social stimulation: a preliminary report. *J. genet. Psychol.,* **53,** 149–157.

Denny-Brown, D., 1960. Motor mechanisms–introduction: the general principles of motor integration. In Magoun, vol. II, 1959–1960. Pp. 781–796.

Descartes, R. [1650]. *The passions of the soul.* In *Essential works of Descartes,* trans. by L. Bair. New York: Bantam, 1961. Pp. 108–210.

Diamond, S., 1957. *Personality and temperament.* New York: Harper.

Diamond, S., 1960. Inhibition, disinhibition, and the percepts of psychologists. In J. G. Peatman and E. L. Hartley (Eds.), *Festschrift for Gardner Murphy,* New York: Harper, pp. 50–59.

Dilger, W. C., 1962. The behavior of lovebirds. *Scient. Am.,* **206**(1), 88–98.

Dodge, R., 1923. Habituation to rotation. *J. exp. Psychol.,* **6,** 1–35.

Dollard, J., & Miller, N. E., 1950. *Personality and psychotherapy.* New York: McGraw-Hill.

Domino, E. F., 1958. A pharmacologic analysis of some reticular and spinal cord systems. In Jasper 1958b. Pp. 285–312.

Down, J. L. H., 1866. Observations on an ethnic classification of idiots. *London Hosp., clin. Lectures & Reports,* **3,** 259–262.

duBois-Reymond, E., 1848–1849. *Untersuchungen über thierische Elektricität.* Berlin: Reimer. 2 vols.

Dumont, S., & Dell, P., 1960. Facilitation réticulaire des mécanismes visuels corticaux. *EEG & clin. Neurophysiol.*, **12**, 769–796.

Dunlap, K., 1928. A revision of the fundamental law of habit formation. *Science,* **67**, 360–362.

Durling, Dorothy, and Benda, C. E., 1952. Mental growth curves in untreated institutionalized mongoloid patients. *Amer. J. ment. Defic.*, **56**, 578–588.

Durop, G., & Fessard, A., 1935. L'electroencéphalogramme de l'homme; observations psycho-physiologiques relative à l'action des stimuli visuels et auditifs. *Année Psychol.*, **36**, 1.

Eccles, J. C., 1953. *The neurophysiological basis of mind.* Oxford: Clarendon.

Eccles, J. C., 1959. Neurophysiology–introduction. In Magoun, vol. I, 1959–1960. Pp. 59–74.

Eccles, J. C., 1961. The effects of use and disuse on synaptic function. In Delafresnaye, 1961. Pp. 335–348.

Eckhard, C., 1862. Über die Erection des Penis. *Sitzber. Akad. Wissenschaften, Vienna (math.-naturw. Kl.)*, **45** (Abt. 2): 542–543.

Economo, C. v., 1926. Die Pathologie des Schlafes. In A. Bethe *et al.* (Eds.), *Handbuch der normalen und pathologischen Physiologie,* Berlin: Springer, **17**, 591–610.

Egel, P. F., 1948. *Technique of treatment for the cerebral palsy child.* St. Louis: Mosby.

Egger, M. D., and Flynn, J. P., 1962. Amygdaloid suppression of hypothalamically elicited attack behavior. *Science,* **136**, 43–44.

English, H. B., & English, Ava C., 1958. *A comprehensive dictionary of psychological and psychoanalytical terms.* New York: Longmans, Green.

Escalona, Sibylle, 1953. Emotional development in the first year of life. In Senn, 1953. Pp. 11–92.

Estes, W. K., 1950. Toward a statistical theory of learning. *Psychol. Rev.*, **57**, 94–107.

Estes, W. K., 1954. Individual behavior in uncertain situations: an interpretation in terms of statistical association theory. In Thrall, Coombs, & Davis, 1954. Pp. 127–138.

Estes, W. K., MacCorquodale, K., Schoenfeld, W. N., & Verplank, W. S., 1954 (Eds.). *Modern learning theory: a critical analysis of five examples.* New York: Appleton-Century-Crofts.

Estes, W. K., & Straughan, J. H., 1954. Analysis of a verbal conditioning situation in terms of statistical learning theory. *J. exp. Psychol.*, **50,** 81–88.

Exner, S., 1882. Zur Kenntnis von der Wechselwirkung der Erregungen im Zentralnervensystem. *Pflüg. Arch. ges. Physiol.*, **28,** 487–506.

Exner, S., 1894. *Entwurf einer physiologischen Erklärung der psychischen Erscheinungen.* Leipzig: Deuticke.

Eysenck, H. J., 1955. Cortical inhibition, figural aftereffect, and theory of personality. *J. abnorm. soc. Psychol.*, **51,** 94–106.

Eysenck, H. J., 1957a. Drugs and personality. 1. Theory and methodology. *J. ment. Sci.*, **13,** 119–131.

Eysenck, H. J., 1957b. *The dynamics of anxiety and hysteria.* London: Routledge & Kegan Paul.

Eysenck, H. J., 1960. Drug postulates, theoretical deductions, and methodological considerations. In Uhr and Miller, 1960. Pp. 352–359.

Eysenck, H. J., 1961a. Classification and the problem of diagnosis. In Eysenck, 1961b. Pp. 634–696.

Eysenck, H. J., 1961b (Ed.). *Handbook of abnormal psychology.* New York: Basic.

Fano, G., 1895. Contribution à la localisation corticale des pouvoirs inhibiteurs. *Arch. ital. Biol.*, **24,** 438–446.

Feldberg, W., & Sherwood, S. L., 1953. A permanent cannula for intraventricular injections in cats. *J. Physiol.*, **120,** 3–4P.

Feldberg, W., & Vogt, Marthe, 1948. Acetylcholine synthesis in different regions of the central nervous system. *J. Physiol.*, **107,** 372–381.

Fenichel, O., 1945. *The psychoanalytic theory of neuroses.* New York: Norton.

Ferrier, D., 1876. *The functions of the brain.* London: Smith Elder.

Ferster, C. B., & Skinner, B. F., 1957. *Schedules of reinforcement.* New York: Appleton-Century-Crofts.

Fields, W. S., 1957 (Ed.) *Brain mechanisms and drug action.* Springfield, Ill.: Thomas.

Fisher, A. E., 1956. Maternal and sexual behavior induced by intracranial chemical stimulation. *Science,* **124,** 228–229.

Fisher, A. E., 1958. Discussant. In Jasper, 1958b. Pp. 252–258.

Florey, E., 1961a. Comparative physiology: transmitter substances. *Annu. Rev. Physiol.*, **23,** 501–528.

Florey, E., 1961b (Ed.) *Nervous inhibition.* New York: Pergamon.

Flugel, J. C., 1933. *A hundred years of psychology.* New York: Macmillan.

Flynn, J. P., MacLean, P. D., & Kim, C., 1961. Effects of hippocampal after-discharges on conditioned responses. In Sheer, 1961. Pp. 380–386.

Forbes, A., & Morison, B. R., 1939. Cortical response to sensory stimulation under deep barbiturate narcosis. *J. Neurophysiol.*, **2**, 112–128.

Fox, J., 1954. Freudian and Jungian approaches to development of ego and self. In Klopfer, Ainsworth, Klopfer, & Holt, vol. I, 1954. Pp. 701–715.

Frank, L. K., 1938. The fundamental needs of the child. *Ment. Hyg.*, **22**, 353–379.

French, G. M., 1959a. Locomotor effects of regional ablation of frontal cortex in rhesus monkeys. *J. comp. physiol. Psychol.*, **52**, 18–24.

French, G. M., 1959b. A deficit associated with hypermotility in monkeys with lesions of the dorsolateral frontal granular cortex. *J. comp. physiol. Psychol.*, **52**, 25–28.

French, J. D., 1958. Corticifugal connections with the reticular formation. In Jasper, 1958b. Pp. 491–505.

French, J. D., 1960. The reticular formation. In Magoun, vol. II, 1959–1960. Pp. 1281–1306.

French, J. D., Hernández-Peón, R., & Livingston, R. B., 1955. Projections from cortex to cephalic brain stem (reticular formation) in monkey. *J. Neurophysiol.*, **18**, 74–95.

Freud, S. [1900]. *The interpretation of dreams.* In Freud, 1938. Pp. 179–549.

Freud, S. [1905]. *Three contributions to the theory of sex.* In Freud, 1938. Pp. 551–629.

Freud, S. [1911]. Formulations regarding the two principles in mental functioning. In *Collected Papers,* vol. IV, London: Hogarth, 1925. Pp. 13–21.

Freud, S. [1920]. *Beyond the pleasure principle.* Trans. by J. Strachey. New York: Bantam, 1959.

Freud, S. [1925]. Negation. *Collected Papers,* vol. V, London: Hogarth, 1950. Pp. 181–185.

Freud, S., 1938. *Basic Writings,* trans. and edited by A. A. Brill. New York: Modern Library.

Freud, S., 1954. *The origins of psychoanalysis: letters to Wilhelm Fliess, drafts and notes, 1887–1902.* New York: Basic.

Freusberg, A., 1875. Über die Erregung und Hemmung der Thätigkeit der nervösen Centralorgane. *Pflüg. Arch. ges. Physiol.*, **10,** 174–208.

Frolov, Y. P., 1937. *Pavlov and his school.* New York: Oxford Univer. Press.

Frolov, Y. P. [1956]. Present-day cybernetics and the human brain. In *Central Nervous System and Human Behavior,* 1959. Pp. 685–695.

Galambos, R., 1954. Neural mechanisms of audition. *Psychol. Rev.,* **34,** 497–528.

Galambos, R., 1956. Suppression of auditory nerve activity by stimulation of efferent fibers to cochlea. *J. Neurophysiol.,* **19,** 424–431.

Galambos, R., 1961a. A glial-neural theory of brain function. *Proc. N.Y. Acad. Sci.,* **47,** 129–138.

Galambos, R., 1961b. Discussant. In Kline, 1961. Pp. 891–892.

Galambos, R., Meyers, R. E., & Sheatz, G. C., 1961. Extralemniscal activation of auditory cortex in cat. *Amer. J. Physiol.,* **200,** 23.

Gamper, E., 1926. Bau und Leistungen eines menschlichen Mittelhirnwesens (Arhinencephalie mit Encephalocele). Zugleich ein Beitrag zur Teratologie und Fasersystematik. *Ztschr. f. d. ges. Neurol. u. Psychiat.,* **102,** 154–235; **104,** 49–120.

Gantt, W. H., 1953. Principles of nervous breakdown: schizokinesis and autokinesis. *Ann. N.Y. Acad. Sci.,* **56,** 143–163.

Garattini, S., & Ghetti, V., 1957 (Eds.) *Psychotropic drugs.* Amsterdam: Elsevier.

Gardner, W. J., Licklider, J. C. R., & Weisz, A. Z., 1960. Suppression of pain by sound. *Science,* **132,** 32–33.

Gaskell, W. H., 1886. On the structure, distribution and function of the nerves which innervate the visceral and vascular systems. *J. Physiol.,* **7,** 1–80.

Gastaut, H., 1953. So-called "psychomotor" and "temporal" epilepsy—a critical study. *Epilepsia,* **2** (3 ser.), 59–76.

Gastaut, H., 1954. The brain stem and cerebral electrogenesis in relation to consciousness. In Delafresnaye, 1954. Pp. 249–279.

Gastaut, H., 1958. The role of the reticular formation in establishing conditioned reactions. In Jasper, 1958b. Pp. 561–588.

Gastaut, H., & Fischer-Williams, M., 1959. The physiopathology of epileptic seizures. In Magoun, vol. I, 1959–1960. Pp. 329–363.

Geleerd, Eliz., 1945. Some observations on temper tantrums in children. *Amer. J. Orthopsychiat.,* **15,** 238–246.

Gelhorn, E., 1957. *Autonomic imbalance and the hypothalamus.* Minneapolis: Univer. of Minnesota Press.

Gerard, R. W., 1961. The fixation of experience. In Delafresnaye, 1961. Pp. 21–32.

Gernandt, B. E., 1959. Vestibular mechanisms. In Magoun, vol. I, 1959–1960. Pp. 549–564.

Gesell, A., 1945 (In collaboration with C. S. Amatruda). *The embryology of behavior: the beginning of the human mind.* New York: Harper.

Gesell, A., & Ilg, Frances L., 1943. *Infant and child in the culture of today.* New York: Harper.

Gibbs, Erna L., & Gibbs, F. A., 1947. Diagnostic and localizing value of electroencephalographic studies in sleep. *Res. Publ. Ass. Res. nerv. ment. Dis.,* **26,** 366–376.

Gibbs, F. A., 1958. Abnormal electrical activity in the temporal regions and its relationship to abnormalities of behavior. *Res. Publ. Ass. nerv. ment. Dis.,* **36,** 278–294.

Gloor, P., 1960. Amygdala. In Magoun, vol. II, 1959–1960. Pp. 1395–1420.

Goldenberg, S., 1955. Testing the brain-injured child with normal IQ. In Strauss and Kephart, 1955. Pp. 144–164.

Goldstein, D. A., & Solomon, A. K., 1960. Determination of equivalent pore radius for human red cells by osmotic pressure measurement. *J. gen. Physiol.,* **44,** 1–17.

Goldstein, K., 1939. *The organism: a holistic approach to biology derived from pathological data in man.* New York: American Book.

Goldstein, K., 1942. *Aftereffects of brain injuries in war; their evaluation and treatment; the application of psychologic methods in the clinic.* New York: Grune and Stratton.

Goldstein, K., 1959. Abnormal mental conditions in infancy. *J. nerv. ment. Dis.,* **128,** 538–557.

Goltz, F., 1869. *Beiträge zur Lehre von den Functionen der Nervencentren des Frosches.* Berlin: Hirschwald.

Goltz, F., 1881. *Über die Verrichtungen des Grosshirns, gesammelte Abhandlungen.* Bonn: Strauss.

Gordon, H., 1923. *Mental and scholastic tests among retarded children.* London: Bd. of Educ. Pamphlet No. 44.

Granit, R., 1955. *Receptors and sensory perception.* New Haven: Yale Univer. Press.

Granit, R., 1959. Neural activity in the retina. In Magoun, vol. I, 1959–1960. Pp. 693–712.

Granit, R., & Kaada, B. R., 1952. Influence of stimulation of central nervous structures on muscle spindles in cat. *Acta physiol. Scandinav.*, **27**, 130–160.

Grant, D. A., Hake, H. W., & Hornseth, J. P., 1951. Acquisition and extinction of a verbal conditioned response with differing percentages of reinforcement. *J. exp. Psychol.*, **42**, 1–5.

Grastyán, E., 1959. The hippocampus and higher nervous activity. In Brazier, 1959b. Pp. 119–193.

Grastyán, E., 1961. The significance of the earliest manifestations of conditioning in the mechanism of learning; pp. 242–251. In Delafresnaye, 1961.

Grastyán, E., Lissák, K., & Kékesi, F., 1956. Facilitation and inhibition of conditioned alimentary and defensive reflexes by stimulation of the hypothalamus and reticular formation. *Acta Physiol. Acad. Scient. Hungar.*, **9**, 133–151.

Green, J. D., 1960. The hippocampus. In Magoun, vol. II, 1959–1960. Pp. 1373–1389.

Green, J. D., & Arduini, A., 1954. Hippocampal electrical activity in arousal. *J. Neurophysiol.*, **17**, 533–557.

Griffith, C. R., 1920. An experimental study of dizziness. *J. exp. Psychol.*, **3**, 89–125.

Grisoni, R., Canali, G., & Pacini, L., 1959. The action of iproniazid on the epileptic patterns of the EEG in man. In Bradley, Deniker, & Radouco-Thomas, 1959. Pp. 584–586.

Grossman, S. P., 1960. Eating or drinking eliminated by direct adrenergic or cholinergic stimulation of hypothalamus. *Science*, **132**, 301–302.

Grossman, S. P., 1961. Effects of adrenergic and cholinergic blocking agents on eating and drinking elicited normally or by chemostimulation of the brain. *Amer. Psychol.*, **16**, 448. (Abstract)

Grundfest, H., 1959a. Evolution of conduction in the nervous system. In Bass, 1959. Pp. 43–86.

Grundfest, H., 1959b. Synaptic and ephaptic transmission. In Magoun, vol. I, 1959–1960. Pp. 147–197.

Grundfest, H., 1960a. Central inhibition and its mechanism. In Roberts, 1960. Pp. 47–65.

Grundfest, H., 1960b. Comparative studies on electrogenic membrane. In Roberts, 1960. Pp. 118–126.

Grundfest, H., 1961. The interpretation of electrocortical potentials. In Kline, 1961. Pp. 877–889.

Guthrie, E. R., 1930. Conditioning as a principle of learning. *Psychol. Rev.*, **37**, 412–428.

Guthrie, E. R., 1934. Pavlov's theory of conditioning. *Psychol. Rev.*, **41**, 199–206.

Guthrie, E. R., 1935. *The Psychology of learning*. New York: Harper.

Guthrie, E. R., 1937. *Psychology of human conflict*. New York: Harper.

Guthrie, E. R., 1942. Conditioning: a theory of learning in terms of stimulus, response, and association. *41st Yearb. nat. Soc. Stud. Educ.*, 17–60, Part II.

Guthrie, E. R., 1959. Association by contiguity. In Koch, vol. II, 1959. Pp. 158–195.

Hadamard, J., 1945. *The psychology of invention in the mathematical field*. Princeton: Univer. Press.

Hagbarth, K.-E., & Kerr, D. I. B., 1954. Central influences on spinal afferent conduction. *J. Neurophysiol.*, **17**, 295–307.

Hake, H. W., & Hyman, R., 1953. Perception of the statistical structure of a random series of binary digits. *J. exp. Psychol.*, **45**, 64–74.

Hall, G. S., 1923. *Life and confessions of a psychologist*. New York: Appleton.

Haller, A. v. [1755]. *A dissertation on the sensible and irritable parts of animals*. London: Nourse. Reprinted 1936, Baltimore: The Johns Hopkins Press.

Harlow, H. F., 1949. The formation of learning sets. *Psychol. Rev.*, **56**, 51–65.

Harlow, H. F., 1958. The evolution of learning. In Roe and Simpson, 1958. Pp. 269–290.

Harlow, H. F., 1959a. The development of learning in the rhesus monkey. *Amer. Sci.*, **47**, 459–479.

Harlow, H. F., 1959b. Learning set and error factor theory. In Koch, vol. II, 1959. Pp. 492–537.

Harlow, H. F., 1962. The heterosexual affectional system in monkeys. *Amer. Psychologist*, **17**, 1–9.

Harlow, H. F., & Woolsey, C. N., 1958 (Eds.) *Biological and biochemical bases of behavior*. Madison: Univer. Wisconsin Press.

Head, H., 1921. Release of function in the nervous system. *Proc. Roy. Soc. London*, **92B**, 184–208.

Head, H., & Holmes, G., 1911. Sensory disturbances from cerebral lesions. *Brain,* **34,** 102–254.

Heath, R. G., 1961. Studies toward correlating behavior with brain activity. In Kline, 1961. Pp. 1106–1121.

Heath, R. G., & Mickle, W. A., 1960. Evaluation of seven years' experience with depth electrode studies in human patients. In Ramey & O'Doherty, 1960. Pp. 214–241.

Hebb, D. O., 1949. *The organization of behavior.* New York: Wiley.

Hebb, D. O., 1951. The role of neurological ideas in psychology. *J. Pers.,* **20,** 39–55.

Heck, L., 1920. Über die Bildung einer Assoziation beim Regenwurm auf Grund von Dressurversuchen. *Lotos Naturwiss. Z.,* **68,** 168–190.

Heidenhain, R., 1881. Über Erregung und Hemmung. *Pflüg. Archiv. ges. Physiol.,* **26,** 546–557.

Helmholtz, H. L. F. v. [1847]. *Über die Erhaltung der Kraft.* Reprinted in *Wissenschl. Abhandl.,* **1,** 12–75.

Herbart, J. F. [1816]. *Lehrbuch zur Psychologie.* In Herbart, vol. V, 1850.

Herbart, J. F. [1824–1825]. *Psychologie als Wissenschaft, neu gegrundet auf Erfahrung, Metaphysik und Mathematik.* In Herbart, vols. V–VI, 1850.

Herbart, J. F., 1850–1852. *Sämmtliche Werke.* Ed. by G. Hartenstein. Leipzig: Voss. 12 vols.

Hering, E. [1888]. *Zur Theorie der Vorgänge in der lebendigen Substanz.* In Hering, 1921. Pp. 53–103.

Hering, E. [1899]. *Zur Theorie der Nerventätigkeit.* In Hering, 1921. Pp. 105–131.

Hering, E., 1921. *Fünf Reden.* Leipzig: Engelmann.

Hering, H. E., 1902. Die intracentrallen Hemmungsvorgänge in ihrer Beziehung zur Skelettmuskulatur. *Erg. Physiol.,* **1** (Abt. 2), 503–533.

Hering, H. E., & Sherrington, C. S., 1897. Über Hemmung und Kontraktion willkürlicher Muskeln bei elektrischer Reizung der Grosshirnrinde. *Pfl. Arch. ges. Physiol.,* **68,** 222–228.

Hernández-Peón, R., 1960. Neurophysiological correlates of habituation and other manifestations of plastic inhibition (Internal inhibition). In Jasper and Smirnov, 1960. Pp. 101–114.

Hernández-Peón, R., & Brust-Carmona, H., 1961. Functional role of subcortical structures in habituation and conditioning. In Delafresnaye, 1961. Pp. 393–412.

Hernández-Peón, R., Scherrer, H., & Jouvet, M., 1956. Modification of electric activity in cochlear nucleus during attention in unanesthetized cat. *Science,* **123,** 331–332.

Herrick, C. J., 1956. *The evolution of human nature.* Austin: Univer. of Texas Press.

Hess, E. H., 1956. Space perception in the chick. *Scient. Amer.,* **195**(1), 71–80.

Hess, E. H., 1959. Two conditions limiting critical age for imprinting. *J. comp. physiol. Psychol.,* **52,** 515–518.

Hess, E. H., 1960. Effects of drugs on imprinting behavior. In Uhr and Miller, 1960. Pp. 268–271.

Hess, W. R., 1929a. Hirnreizversuche über den Mechanismus des Schlafes. *Arch. f. Psychiat.,* **86,** 287–292.

Hess, W. R., 1929b. Lokalisatorische Ergebnisse der Hirnreizversuche mit Schlafeffekt. *Arch. f. Psychiat.,* **88,** 813–816.

Hess, W. R., 1944. Das Schlafsyndrom als Folge dienzephaler Reizung. *Helvet. physiol. pharmacol. acta,* **2,** 305–344.

Hess, W. R., 1954. The diencephalic sleep center. In Delafresnaye, 1954. Pp. 117–125.

Hess, W. R., 1957. *The functional organization of the diencephalon.* New York: Grune & Stratton.

Hilgard, E. R., 1956. *Theories of learning* (2d ed.) New York: Appleton-Century-Crofts.

Himwich, H. E., 1957 (Ed.) *Tranquilizing drugs.* Washington, D.C.: A.A.A.S.

Hinde, R. A., & Tinbergen, N., 1958. The comparative study of species-specific behavior. In Roe and Simpson, 1958. Pp. 251–268.

Hippocrates. *The aphorisms of Hippocrates.* Trans. by Thomas Coar. London: Valpy, 1822.

Hobbes, T. [1651]. *Leviathan.*

Hobbes, T. [1655]. *De corpore.*

Hoch, P. H., 1958. Psychoses-producing and psychoses-relieving drugs. *Res. Publ. nerv. & ment. Dis.,* **36,** 335–346.

Hofstaetter, P. R., 1954. The changing composition of "intelligence": a study in *t*-technique. *J. genet. Psychol.,* **85,** 159–164.

Holmes, S. J., 1911. *The evolution of animal intelligence.* New York: Holt.

Holst, E. v., 1932. Untersuchungen über die Funktionen des Zentralnervensystems beim Regenwurm. *Zool. Jb.* (*Abt. Zool.*), **51**, 547–588.

Holst, E. v., 1933. Weitere Versuche zum nervösen Mechanismus der Bewegung beim Regenwurm. *Zool. Jb.* (*Abt. Zool.*), **53**, 67–100.

Hooker, D., 1943. Reflex activities in the human fetus. In Barker, Kounin, and Wright, 1943. Pp. 17–28.

Hovey, H. B., 1929. Associative hysteresis in flatworms. *Physiol. Zool.*, **2**, 322–333.

Howell, M. H., 1925. Inhibition. *Physiol. Rev.*, **5**, 161–181.

Hoyle, G., 1958. The leap of the grasshopper. *Scient. Amer.* **198**(1), 30–35.

Hull, C. L., 1929. A functional interpretation of the conditioned reflex. *Psychol. Rev.*, **36**, 498–511.

Hull, C. L., 1934. Learning, II: the factor of the conditioned reflex. In Murchison, 1934. Pp. 382–455.

Hull, C. L., 1943. *Principles of behavior*. New York: Appleton-Century-Crofts.

Hull, C. L., 1952. *A behavior system: an introduction to behavior theory concerning the individual organism*. New Haven: Yale Univ. Press.

Hume, D. [1739]. *A treatise of human nature*. Garden City, N.Y.: Doubleday. 1961.

Humphrey, G., 1933. *The nature of learning in its relation to the living system*. New York: Harcourt-Brace.

Humphreys, L. G., 1939. Acquisition and extinction of verbal expectations in a situation analogous to conditioning. *J. exp. Psychol.*, **25**, 294–301.

Hunt, J. McV., 1944 (Ed.) *Personality and the behavior disorders*. New York: Ronald. 2 vols.

Ingalls, T. H., 1952. Mongolism. *Scient. Amer.*, **186**(2), 60–66.

Ingram, W. R., 1960. Central autonomic mechanisms. In Magoun, vol. II, 1959–1960. Pp. 951–978.

Ittleson, W. H., & Cantril, H., 1954. *Perception: A transactional approach*. Garden City: Doubleday.

Ivanov-Smolensky, A. G., 1954. *Essays on the patho-physiology of the higher nervous activity*. Trans. from 2nd Russian ed., 1952. Moscow: Foreign Languages Publ. House.

Jackson, J. H., 1958. *Selected writings*. New York: Basic. 2 vols.

James, A., 1881. The reflex inhibitory center theory. *Brain*, **4**, 287–302.

James, W., 1890. *Principles of psychology*. New York: Holt. 2 vols.

Jarbur, S. J., & Towe, A. L., 1960. Effect of pyramidal tract activity on dorsal column nuclei. *Science*, **132**, 547–548.

Jarvik, M. E., 1951. Probability learning and a negative recency effect in the serial anticipation of alternative symbols. *J. exp. Psychol.*, **41**, 291–297.

Jasper, H. H., 1958a. Recent advances in our understanding of ascending activities of the reticular system. In Jasper, 1958b. Pp. 319–331.

Jasper, H. H., 1958b (Ed.) *Reticular formation of the brain*. Boston: Little, Brown.

Jasper, H. H., 1960. Unspecific thalamocortical relations. In Magoun, vol. II, 1959–1960. Pp. 1307–1322.

Jasper, H. H., 1961. Discussant. In Kline, 1961. Pp. 970–973.

Jasper, H., Ricci, G., & Doane, B., 1960. Microelectrode analysis of cortical cell discharge during avoidance conditioning in the monkey. In Jasper and Smirnov, 1960. Pp. 137–156.

Jasper, H. H., & Shagass, C., 1941. Conditioning the occipital alpha rhythm in man. *J. exp. Psychol.*, **228**, 373–388.

Jasper, H. H., & Smirnov, G. D., 1960 (Eds.) Moscow colloquium on electroencephalography of higher nervous activity. *EEG clin. Neurophysiol.*, Suppl. no. 13.

Jaynes, J., 1956. Imprinting: the interaction of learned and innate behavior: I. Development and generalization. *J. comp. physiol. Psychol.*, **49**, 201–206.

Jeffress, L. A., 1951 (Ed.) *Cerebral mechanisms in behavior*. New York: Wiley.

Jensen, A. R., 1961. On the reformulation of inhibition in Hull's system. *Psychol. Bull.*, **58**, 274–298.

John, E. R., 1961. Higher nervous function: brain functions and learning. *Ann. Rev. Physiol.*, **23**, 451–484.

John, E. R., Killam, K. F., Wenzel, B. M., & Tschirgi, R. D., 1959. Effects of intraventricular injections of gamma-aminobutyric acid on performance of conditioned responses in cats. In Roberts, 1959. Pp. 554–561.

Jones, E., 1953. *The life and work of Sigmund Freud. Volume I: The formative years and the great discoveries (1856–1900)*. New York: Basic.

Jones, H. G., 1958. The status of inhibition in Hull's system: a theoretical revision. *Psychol. Rev.*, **65**, 179–182.

Jones, M. R., 1953– (Ed.) *Nebraska symposia on motivation.* Lincoln: Univer. of Nebraska Press. (Has appeared annually since 1953.)

Jordan, H. J., 1901. Die Physiologie der Locomotion bei Aplysia limacina. *Z. Biol.*, **41**, 196–238.

Jordan, H. J., 1929. *Allgemeine vergleichende Physiologie der Tiere.* Berlin: de Gruyter.

Jouvet, M., 1961. Recherches sur les mécanismes neurophysiologiques du sommeil et de l'apprentissage négative. In Delafresnaye, 1961. Pp. 445–475.

Jung, R., 1954. Discussant. In Delafresnaye, 1954. P. 198.

Jung, R., & Hassler, R., 1960. The extrapyramidal motor system. In Magoun, vol. II, 1959–1960. Pp. 863–927.

Jung, R., & Tönnies, J. F., 1950. Hirnelektrische Untersuchungen über Entstehung und Erhaltung von Kramfentladungen: die Vorgänge am Reizort und die Bremsfähigkeit des Gehirns. *Arch. Psychiat.* **185**, 701–735.

Kaada, B. R., 1959. Discussant. In Bradley, Deniker & Radouco-Thomas, 1959. Pp. 38–45.

Kaada, B. R., 1960. Cingulate, posterior orbital, anterior insular and temporal pole cortex. In Magoun, vol. II, 1959–1960. Pp. 1345–1372.

Kanner, L., 1943. Autistic disturbances of affective contact. *Nerv. Child,* **2**, 217–250.

Kanner, L., 1957. *Child psychiatry* (3rd ed.) Springfield, Ill.: Thomas.

Kantor, J. R., 1947. *Problems of physiological psychology.* Bloomington: Principia Press.

Kawi, A., & Pasamanick, B., 1959. Prenatal and paranatal factors in the development of childhood reading disorders. *Monogr. Soc. Res. Child Develpm.*, **24** (4).

Kerr, D. I. B., & Hagbarth, K.-E., 1955. An investigation of olfactory centrifugal fiber system. *J. Neurophysiol.*, **18**, 362–374.

Killam, K. F., & Killam, E. K., 1958. Drug action on pathways involving the reticular formation. In Jasper, 1958b. Pp. 111–122.

Kirchner, F., & Michäelis, C., 1911. *Wörterbuch der philosophischen Grundbegriffe* (6th ed.) Leipzig: Meiner.

Kirk, S. A., 1958. *Early education of the mentally retarded.* Urbana: Univer. Illinois Press.

Kleitman, N., 1939. *Sleep and Wakefulness.* Chicago: Univer. Chicago Press.

Kline, N. F., 1961 (Ed.) Pavlovian conference on higher nervous activity. *Ann. N.Y. Acad. Sci.*, **92**, 813–1198.

Klopfer, B., 1924. Das Problem der seelischen Hemmungen. *Arch. f. d. ges. Psychol.*, **47**, 45–93.

Klopfer, B., Ainsworth, Mary D., Klopfer, W. G., & Holt, R. R., 1954 (Eds.). *Developments in the Rorschach technique*. Vol. 1. *Technique and theory*. Yonkers, N.Y.: World.

Klüver, H., 1933. *Behavior mechanisms in monkeys*. Chicago: Chicago Univ. Press.

Klüver, H., & Bucy, P. C., 1939. Preliminary analysis of functions of the temporal lobes in monkeys. *Arch. Neurol. Psychiat.*, **42**, 979–1000.

Knowlton, F. J., & Moore, A. R., 1917. Note on the reversal of reciprocal inhibition in the earthworm. *Amer. J. Physiol.*, **44**, 490–491.

Koch, S., 1954. Clark L. Hull. In Estes, MacCorquodale, Schoenfeld, & Verplanck, 1954. Pp. 1–178.

Koch, S., 1959 (Ed.) *Psychology: a study of a science*. New York: McGraw-Hill. (2 vols.)

Koelle, G. B., 1959. Neurohumoral agents as a mechanism of nervous integration. In Bass, 1959. Pp. 87–114.

Kogan, A. B., 1960. The manifestations of processes of higher nervous activity in the electrical potential of the cortex during free behavior of animals. In Jasper and Smirnov, 1960. Pp. 51–64.

Kohler, I., 1951. Über Aufbau und Wandlungen der Wahrnehmungswelt; insbesondere über "bedingte Empfindungen." *Sitzber. Österr. Akad. Wiss. (phil. hist. Kl.)*, **227**, Abh. 1, 118.

Köhler, W., 1920. *Die physischen Gestalten in Ruhe und im stationären Zustand*. Braunschweig: Vieweg.

Köhler, W., 1925. *The mentality of apes*. New York: Harcourt, Brace.

Köhler, W., 1929. *Gestalt Psychology*. New York: Liveright.

Köhler, W., 1940. *Dynamics in psychology*. New York: Liveright.

Köhler, W., & Wallach, H., 1944. Figural after-effects: an investigation of visual processes. *Proc. Amer. Phil. Soc.*, **88**, 269–357.

Konorski, J., 1948. *Conditioned reflexes and neuron organization*. Trans. by S. Garry. London: Cambridge Univer. Press.

Konorski, J., 1960. The cortical "representation" of unconditioned reflexes. In Jasper and Smirnov, 1960. Pp. 81–90.

Konorski, J., & Miller, S., 1937. On two types of conditioned reflex. *J. genet. Psychol.*, **16**, 264–272.

Koshtoyants, Kh. S., 1946. *Ocherki po istorii fiziologii v Rossii.* [Essays on the history of physiology in Russia]. Moscow: Akad. Nauk.

Koshtoyants, Kh. S., 1957. *Osnovy sravnitel'noi fiziologii, II. Sravnitel'noi fiziologii nervnoi sistemy.* [Foundations of comparative physiology, vol. II; Comparative physiology of the nervous system.] Moscow: Akad. Nauk.

Kounin, J. S., 1943. Intellectual development and rigidity. In Barker, Kounin, and Wright, 1943. Pp. 179–198.

Kudo, R. R., 1954. *Protozoology* (4th ed.) Springfield, Ill.: Thomas.

Kunstman, K. I., & Orbeli, L. A., 1921. [Demonstration of a dog with deafferented hind leg.] *Russk. fiziol. Zh.*, **4**, 253–255.

Ladd, G. T., & Woodworth, R. S., 1911. *Elements of physiological psychology* (2nd ed.) New York: Scribner.

Lange, F. A. [1873–1875]. *Geschichte des Materialismus.* Iserlohn: Baedeker, 1881. (Trans. by E. C. Thomas, reprinted 1950, New York: Humanities Press.)

Lange, L., 1888. Neue Experimente über den Vorgang der einfachen Reaction auf Sinneseindrucke. *Philos. Stud.*, **4**, 479–510.

Lansing, R. W., 1957. Relation of brain and tremor rhythms to visual reaction time. *EEG & clin. Neurophysiol.*, **9**, 497–504.

Lashley, K. S., 1950. In search of the engram. *Soc. exp. Biol., Symp. no. 4: Physiological mechanisms in animal behavior,* 454–482.

Lashley, K. S., 1951. The problem of serial order in behavior. In Jeffress, 1951. Pp. 112–136.

Lashley, K. S., 1958. Cerebral organizations and behavior. In Solomon, Cobb, & Penfield, 1958. Pp. 1–14.

Lashley, K. S., Chow, K. L., & Semmes, Josephine, 1951. An examination of the electrical field theory of cerebral integration. *Psychol. Rev.*, **58**, 123–136.

Law, T., & Meager, W., 1958. Hypothalamic lesions and sexual behavior in the female rat. *Science,* **128**, 1626–1627.

Leao, A. A. P., 1944. Spreading depression of activity in the cerebral cortex. *J. Neurophysiol.*, **7**, 359–390.

Leibnitz, G. W. [1714]. *Principes de la nature et de la grâce, fondés en raison.*

Lejeune, L., Gautier, Marthe, & Turpin, R., 1959. Les chromosomes humains en culture de tissus. *C.R. Acad. Sci., Paris,* **248**, 602–603.

Lennox, W. G., with collaboration of Margaret A. Lennox, 1960. *Epilepsy and related disorders.* Boston: Little, Brown. (2 vols.)

Leuba, C., 1955. Toward some integration of learning theories: the concept of optimal stimulation. *Psychol. Rep.*, **1**, 27–33.

Lewes, G. H., 1877. *The physical basis of mind.* London: Trübner.

Lewin, K., 1935. *A dynamic theory of personality.* New York: McGraw-Hill.

Liddell, E. G. T., & Sherrington, C. S., 1924. Reflexes in response to stretch (myotatic reflexes). *Proc. Roy. Soc., London,* **96B,** 212–242.

Liddell, H. S., 1959. Discussant; in Brazier, 1959a, pp. 188–194.

Limbaugh, C., 1961. Cleaning symbiosis, *Scient. Amer.*, **205**(2), 42–49.

Lindsley, D. B., 1951. Emotion. In Stevens, 1951. Pp. 473–516.

Lindsley, D. B., 1952. Psychological phenomena and the electroencephalogram. *EEG & clin. Neurophysiol.*, **4**, 443–456.

Lindsley, D. B., 1960. Attention, consciousness, sleep and wakefulness. In Magoun, vol. III, 1959–1960. Pp. 1553–1593.

Lindsley, D. B., 1961. Common factors in sensory deprivation, sensory distortion, and sensory overload. In Solomon, 1961. Pp. 174–194.

Lindsley, D. B., Bowden, J., & Magoun, H. W., 1949. Effect upon the EEG of acute injury to the brain stem activating system. *EEG & clin. Neurophysiol.*, **1**, 475–486.

Lindsley, D. B., & Cutts, Katherine K., 1940. Electroencephalograms of "constitutionally inferior" and behavior problem children: comparison with those of normal children and adults. *Arch. Neurol. Psychiat.*, **44**, 1199–1212.

Lindsley, D. B., and Henry, C. E., 1942. The effect of drugs on behavior and the electroencephalograms of children with behavior disorders. *Psychosom. Med.*, **4**, 140–149.

Lindsley, D. B., Schreiner, L. H., Knowles, W. B., & Magoun, H. W., 1950. Behavioral and EEG changes following chronic brain stem lesions in the cat. *EEG & clin. Neurophysiol.*, **2**, 483–498.

Lissák, K. [1955]. New experimental aspects in investigating diencephalic mechanisms and processes of higher nervous activity. In *Central Nervous System and Human Behavior,* vol. I, 1959. Pp. 277–286.

Lissák, K., & Grastyán, E., 1960. The changes of hippocampal electrical activity during conditioning. In Jasper and Smirnov, 1960. Pp. 271–280.

Livingston, R. B., 1957. Neurophysiology of the reticular formation. In Fields, 1957. Pp. 3–14.

Livingston, R. B., 1958. Central control of afferent activity. In Jasper, 1958b. Pp. 177–185.

Livingston, R. B., 1959. Central control of receptors and sensory transmission systems. In Magoun, vol. I, 1959–1960. Pp. 741–760.

Livingston, W. K., Haugen, R. P., & Brookhart, J. M., 1954. Functional organization of the nervous system. *Neurology*, **4**, 485–496.

Lloyd, D. P. C., 1941. A direct central inhibitory action of dromically conducted impulses. *J. Neurophysiol.*, **4**, 184–190.

Lloyd, D. P. C., 1960. Spinal mechanisms involved in somatic activities. In Magoun, vol. II, 1959–1960. Pp. 929–949.

Locke, J. [1690]. *An essay concerning human understanding*. Collated and annotated by A. C. Fraser, 2 vols. Oxford: Clarendon, 1894. Dover reprint, 1959.

Loeb, J., 1900. *Comparative physiology of the brain and comparative psychology*. New York: Putnam.

Loewi, O., 1921–1922. Über humorale Überträgbarkeit der Herznervenwirkung. *Pfl. Arch. ges. Physiol.*, **189**, 239–242; **193**, 201–213.

Lorenz, K., 1952. *King Solomon's ring*. New York: Crowell.

Lucas, K., 1911. On the transfer of the propagated disturbance from nerve to muscle with special reference to the apparent inhibition described by Wedensky. *J. Physiol.*, **43**, 46–99.

Lucas, K., 1917. *The conduction of the nerve impulse*. London: Longmans, Green.

Luria, A. R., 1960a. Experimental analysis of the development of voluntary action in children. Trans. in *Central Nervous System and Human Behavior*, II, 1960. Pp. 529–535.

Luria, A. R., 1960b. The role of speech in child development. Trans. in *Central Nervous System and Human Behavior*, vol. II, 1960. Pp. 556–574.

McConnell, J. V., Jacobson, A. L., & Kimble, D. P., 1959. The effects of regeneration upon retention of a conditioned response in the planarian. *J. comp. physiol. Psychol.*, **52**, 1–5.

McCulloch, W. S., 1944. Cortico-cortical connections. In Bucy, P. C. (Ed.) *The precentral motor cortex*. Urbana: Univer. Illinois Press. Pp. 211–243.

McDougall, W., 1903. The nature of the inhibitory process within the nervous system. *Brain*, **26**, 153–191.

McDougall, W., 1905. *Physiological psychology*. London: Dent.

McGinnies, E., 1949. Emotionality and perceptual defense, *Psychol. Rev.*, **56,** 244–251.

McGraw, Myrtle B., 1937. The Moro reflex. *Amer. J. Dis. Child.*, **54,** 240–251.

McGraw, Myrtle B., 1940. Suspension grasp behavior of the human infant. *Amer. J. Dis. Child.*, **60,** 799–811.

McGraw, Myrtle B., 1946. Maturation of behavior. In Carmichael, 1946a. Pp. 332–369.

McIlwain, H., 1959. *Biochemistry and the central nervous system* (2nd ed.) London: Churchill.

McKendrick, J. G., 1874. On the inhibitory or restraining action which the encephalon exerts on the reflex centres of the spinal cord. *Edin. med. J.*, **19,** 733–737.

MacLean, P. D., 1955. The limbic system "visceral brain" in relation to central gray and reticulum of the brain stem. *Psychosom. Med.*, **17,** 355–366.

MacLean, P. D., 1959. The limbic system with respect to two basic life principles. In Brazier 1959b. Pp. 31–111.

Magoun, H. W., 1958. *The Waking Brain,* Springfield, Ill.: Thomas.

Magoun, H. W., 1959–1960 (Ed.) *Handbook of Physiology, Section 1: Neurophysiology*. Washington, D.C.: Amer. Physiol. Society. 3 vols.

Magoun, H. W., 1961. Recent contributions to the electrophysiology of learning. In Kline, 1961. Pp. 818–829.

Magoun, H. W., & Rhines, Ruth, 1946. An inhibitory mechanism in the bulbar reticular formation. *J. Neurophysiol.*, **9,** 165–171.

Magoun, H. W., & Rhines, Ruth, 1947. *Spasticity: the stretch-reflex and extrapyramidal systems,* Springfield, Ill.: Thomas.

Mahler, Margaret S., 1952. On child psychosis and schizophrenia: autistic and symbiotic infantile psychoses. *Psychoanal. Study of Child,* **7,** 286–305.

Mahler, Margaret S., Furer, M., & Settlage, C. F., 1959. *Severe emotional disturbances in childhood: psychosis.* In Arieti, vol. I, 1959. Pp. 816–839.

Maier, N. R. F., 1949. *Frustration*. New York: McGraw-Hill.

Majkowski, J., 1961. Discussant. In Kline, 1961. Pp. 973–975.

Marrazzi, A. S., 1957a. The effects of certain drugs on cerebral synapses. *Ann. N.Y. Acad. Sci.,* **66,** 496–507.

Marrazzi, A. S., 1957b. The effect of drugs on neurons and synapses. In Fields, 1957. Pp. 45–70.

Marrazzi, A. S., & Hart, E. R., 1957. An electrophysiological analysis of drugs useful in psychotic states. In Himwich, 1957. Pp. 9–21.

Masland, R. L., 1958. The prevention of mental retardation: a survey of research. *Amer. J. ment. Defic.*, **62**, 991–1112.

Mathews, B., & Whiteside, T. C. D., 1960. Tendon reflexes in free fall. *Proc. Roy. Soc. London*, **153B**, 195–204.

Mauthner, L., 1890. Zur Pathologie und Physiologie des Schlafes nebst Bemerkungen über die "Nona." *Wien. med. Wochenschr.*, **40**, 961–964, 1001–1004, 1049–1052, 1092–1095, 1144–1146, 1185–1188.

Meltzer, S. J., 1899. Inhibition. *N.Y. Medical J.*, **69**, 661–666, 699–703, 739–743.

Mercier, C., 1888a. Inhibition. *Brain*, **11**, 361–405.

Mercier, C., 1888b. *The nervous system and the mind. A treatise on the dynamics of the human organism.* London.

Messick, S. J., & Solley, C. M., 1957. Probability learning in children: some exploratory studies. *J. genet. Psychol.*, **90**, 23–32.

Mettler, F. A., & Mettler, Cecelia C., 1942. The effects of striatal injury. *Brain*, **65**, 242–255.

Michaels, J. J., 1955. *Disorders of character. Persistent enuresis, juvenile delinquency and psychopathic personality.* Springfield, Ill.: Thomas.

Miller, N. E., 1944. Experimental studies of conflict. In Hunt, vol. I, 1944. Pp. 431–465.

Miller, N. E., 1948. Theory and experiment relating psychoanalytic displacement to stimulus response generalization. *J. abnorm. soc. Psychol.*, **43**, 155–178.

Milner, P. M., 1957. The cell assembly: Mark II. *Psychol. Rev.*, **64**, 242–252.

Minkowski, M., 1928. Neurobiologische Studien am menschlichen Foetus. In Abderhalden *Handb. biol. Arbeitsmeth.*, pt. V, **5B**, 511–618.

Minz, B., 1955. *The role of humoral agents in nervous activity.* Springfield, Ill.: Thomas.

Mittelmann, B., 1954. Motility in infants, children and adults: patterning and psychodynamics. *Psychoanal. Study of Child*, **9**, 142–177.

Moore, A. R., 1910. On the nervous mechanism of the righting movements of the starfish. *Amer. J. Physiol.*, **27**, 207–211.

Moore, A. R., 1918. Reversal of reaction by means of strychnine in planarians and starfish. *J. gen. Physiol.*, **1**, 97–100.

Morgan, C. L., 1891. *Animal life and intelligence.* Boston: Ginn.

Morgan, C. L., 1894. *Introduction to comparative psychology.* London: Scott.

Morgan, C. L., 1896. *Habit and instinct.* London: Arnold.

Morrell, F., 1960. Microelectrode and steady potential studies suggesting a dendritic locus of closure. In Jasper and Smirnov, 1960. Pp. 65–80.

Morrell, F., 1961. Lasting changes in synaptic organization produced by continuous neuronal bombardment. In Delafresnaye, 1961. Pp. 375–392.

Morrell, F., Roberts, L., & Jasper, H. H., 1956. Effect of focal epileptogenic lesions and their ablation upon conditioned electrical responses of the brain in the monkey. *EEG & clin. Neurophysiol.*, **8**, 217–236.

Moruzzi, G., 1950. *Problems in cerebellar physiology.* Springfield, Ill.: Thomas.

Moruzzi, G., & Magoun, H. W., 1949. Brain stem reticular formation and activation of the EEG. *EEG & clin. Neurophysiol.*, **1**, 455–473.

Munk, H., 1890. *Über die Functionen der Grosshirnrinde* (2nd ed.) Berlin: Hirschwald.

Münsterberg, H., 1900. *Grundzüge der Psychologie.* Leipzig: Barth.

Münsterberg, H., 1914. *Psychology, general and applied.* New York: Appleton.

Murchison, C., 1934 (Ed.) *A Handbook of general experimental psychology.* Worcester, Mass.: Clark Univer. Press.

Murphy, G., 1947. *Personality: a bio-social approach.* New York: Harper.

Murphy, G., 1958. *Human potentialities.* New York: Basic.

Murphy, Lois B., 1961. Preventive implications of development in the preschool years. In Caplan, 1961. Pp. 218–248.

Myklebust, H. R., 1957. Aphasia in children. In Travis, 1957. Pp. 503–530.

Nauta, W. J. H., 1946. Hypothalamic regulation of sleep in rats; an experimental study. *J. Neurophysiol.*, **9**, 285–316.

Nielsen, J. M., 1951. Discussant. In Jeffress, 1951. Pp. 183–191.

Norton, Stata, 1957. Behavioral patterns as a technique for studying psychotropic drugs. In Garattini and Ghetti, 1957. Pp. 73–82.

Oddi, R., 1895. Il cervello ed il midollo spinale come centri di inibizione. *Accad. Lincei* (*Cl. fis.-mat.*) (5 ser.), **4**(2), 118–125.

Ogden, T. E., 1960. On the function of corticothalamic neurons. *Science,* **131,** 40–41.

Olds, J., 1955. Physiological mechanisms of reward. In Jones, M. R., 1955. Pp. 73–139.

Olds, J., 1956. A preliminary mapping of electrical reinforcing effects in the rat brain. *J. comp. physiol. Psychol.,* **49,** 281–285.

Olds, J., 1958. Effects of hunger and male sex hormone on self-stimulation of the brain. *J. comp. physiol. Psychol.,* **51,** 320–324.

Olds, J., 1959. Self-injection in the rat brain. In Bradley, Deniker, & Radouco-Thomas, 1959. Pp. 386–387.

Olds, J., Killam, K. F., & Eiduson, S., 1957. Effects of tranquilizers on self-stimulation of the brain. In Garattini and Ghetti, 1957. Pp. 235–243.

Olds, J., & Olds, M. E., 1961. Interference and learning in paleocortical systems. In Delafresnaye, 1961. Pp. 153–188.

Olszewski, J., 1954. The cytoarchitecture of the human reticular formation. In Delafresnaye, 1954. Pp. 54–80.

Orbeli, L. A., 1945. *Lektsii po voprosam vyshei nervnoi deiatel'nostii.* [Lectures on the question of higher nervous activity.] Moscow: Akad. Nauk.

Osgood, C. E., 1962. Studies on the generality of affective meaning systems. *Amer. Psychologist,* **17,** 10–28.

Pampiglione, G., & Falconer, M. A., 1960. Electrical stimulation of the hippocampus in man. In Magoun, vol. II, 1959–1960. Pp. 1391–1394.

Papez, J. W., 1937. A proposed mechanism of emotion. *Arch. Neurol. & Psychiat.,* **38,** 725–743.

Pavlov, I. P., 1927. *Conditioned reflexes.* Trans. by G. V. Anrep. Oxford: Clarendon Press.

Pavlov, I. P., 1928. *Lectures on conditioned reflexes.* Trans. by H. Gantt. New York: Intern. Pubs.

Pavlov, I. P., 1932. The reply of a physiologist to psychologists. *Psychol. Rev.,* **39,** 91–127.

Pavlov, I. P., 1957. *Experimental psychology and other essays.* New York: Philosophical Library.

Peckham, G. W., and Peckham, E. G., 1887. Some observations on the mental powers of spiders. *J. Morphol.,* **1,** 383–419.

Penfield, W., 1930. Diencephalic autonomic epilepsy. *Res. Publ. Assoc. nerv. ment. Dis.,* **9,** 645–663.

Penfield, W., 1938. The cerebral cortex in man. I: The cerebral cortex and consciousness. *Arch. Neurol. & Psychiat.*, **40**, 417–442.

Penfield, W., 1954. Studies of the cerebral cortex of man—a review and an interpretation. In Delafresnaye, 1954. Pp. 284–309.

Penfield, W., 1958. Functional localization in temporal and deep sylvian areas. In Solomon, Cobb, & Penfield, 1958. Pp. 210–236.

Penfield, W., & Jasper, H., 1954. *Epilepsy and the functional anatomy of the human brain.* Boston: Little, Brown.

Penfield, W., & Milner, B., 1958. Memory deficit produced by bilateral lesions in the hippocampal zone. *Arch. Neurol. & Psychiat,* **79**, 475–497.

Penfield, W., & Rasmussen, T., 1950. *The cerebral cortex of man.* New York: Macmillian.

Penfield, W., & Roberts, L., 1959. *Speech and brain mechanisms,* Princeton: Univer. Press.

Penrose, L. S., Ellis, J. R., & Delhanty, Joy D. A., 1960. Chromosomal translocations in mongolism and in normal relatives. *Lancet,* 1960 (II), 409–410.

Peterson, G. M., 1949. Changes in handedness in the rat by local application of acetylcholine to the cerebral cortex. *J. comp. physiol. Psychol.,* **42**, 404–412.

Pevzner, M. S., 1961. *Oligophrenia: mental deficiency in children.* New York: Consultants Bureau.

Pfeiffer, C. C., & Smythies, J. R., 1959 (Eds.) *International Review of Neurobiology,* vol. I. New York: Academic Press.

Pflüger, E. F. W., 1853. *Die sensorischen Funktionen des Rückenmarks der Wirbelthiere nebst einer neuen Lehre über die Leitungsgesetze der Reflexionen.* Berlin: Hirschwald.

Pflüger, E. F. W., 1857. *Über das Hemmungs-Nervensystem für die peristaltischen Bewegungen der Gedärme.* Berlin: Hirschwald.

Pillsbury, W. B., 1908. *Attention.* New York: Macmillan.

Plato. *Works,* trans. by B. Jowett. New York: Dial.

Polimanti, O., 1906. *Contributi alla fisiologia ed all'anatomia dei lobi frontali.* Rome: Bertero.

Postman, L., Bruner, J. S., & McGinnies, E., 1948. Personal values as selective factors in perception. *J. abnorm. soc. Psychol.,* **43**, 142–154.

Pribham, K. H., 1960. Theory in physiological psychology. *Ann. Rev. Psychol.,* **11**, 1–40.

Pribham, K., 1961a. Discussant. In Kline, 1961. Pp. 890–891.

Pribham, K., 1961b. Limbic system. In Sheer, 1961. Pp. 311–320.

Purpura, D. P., 1957. Experimental analysis of the inhibitory action of Lysergic acid diethylamide on cortical dendritic activity. *Ann. N.Y. Acad. Sci.*, **66**, 515–536.

Purpura, D. P., 1959. Discussant. In Bradley, Deniker, & Radouco-Thomas, 1959. Pp. 46–50.

Purpura, D. P., 1960. Pharmacological actions of ω-amino acid drugs on different cortical synaptic organizations. In Roberts, 1960. Pp. 495–514.

Ramey, E. R., & O'Doherty, D. S., 1960 (Eds.) *Electrical studies on the unanesthetized brain.* New York: Hoeber.

Rapaport, D., 1951. *Organization and pathology of thought.* New York: Columbia Univer.

Rasmussen, G. L., 1953. Further observations of the efferent cochlear bundle. *J. comp. Neurol.*, **99**, 61–74.

Ray, O. S., & Marrazzi, A. S., 1961. A quantitative behavioral correlate of psychotogen and tranquilizer actions. *Science*, **133**, 1705–1706.

Razran, G., 1930. Theory of conditioning and related phenomena. *Psychol. Rev.*, **37**, 25–43.

Razran, G., 1950. A note on London's historical survey of psychology in the Soviet Union. *Psychol. Bull.*, **47**, 146–149.

Razran, G., 1957. The dominance-contiguity theory of the acquisition of classical conditioning. *Psychol. Bull.*, **54**, 1–46.

Razran, G., 1961. The observable unconscious and the inferable conscious in current Soviet psychophysiology: interoceptive conditioning, semantic conditioning, and the orienting reflex. *Psychol. Rev.*, **68**, 81–147.

Razyenkov, I. P., 1959. *Izbrannye trudy.* [*Selected works*]. Moscow: Medgiz.

Renshaw, B., 1941. Influence of discharge of motoneurons upon excitation of neighboring motoneurons. *J. Neurophysiol.*, **4**, 167–183.

Retzlaff, E., 1957. A mechanism for excitation and inhibition of the Mauthner's cells in teleost: a historical and neurophysiological study. *J. comp. Neurol.*, **107**, 209–225.

Retzlaff, E., & Fontaine, Joan, 1960. Reciprocal inhibition as indicated by a differential staining reaction. *Science*, **131**, 104–105.

Reymert, M. L., 1950 (Ed.) *Feelings and emotions; the Mooseheart symposium.* New York: McGraw-Hill.

Rheingold, Harriet L., 1960. The measurement of maternal care. *Child Develpm.*, **31**, 565–576.

Rhines, Ruth, & Magoun, H. W., 1946. Brain stem facilitation of cortical motor response, *J. Neurophysiol.*, **9**, 219–229.

Ribble, Margaret A., 1944. Infantile experience in relation to personality development. In Hunt, vol. II, 1944. Pp. 621–651.

Ribot, T., 1889. *Psychologie de l'attention.* Paris: Alcan.

Riesen, A. H., 1947. The development of visual perception in man and chimpanzee. *Science,* **106**, 107–108.

Riesen, A. H., 1958. Plasticity of behavior: psychological series. In Harlow and Woolsey, 1958.

Riesen, A. H., 1961. Excessive arousal effects of stimulation after early sensory deprivation. In Solomon et al., 1961. Pp. 34–40.

Roberts, E., 1960 (Ed.) *Inhibition in the nervous system and gamma-aminobutyric acid.* New York: Pergamon.

Roe, Anne, & Simpson, G. G., 1958 (Eds.) *Behavior and Evolution.* New Haven: Yale Univer. Press.

Roeder, K. D., 1935. An experimental analysis of the sexual behavior of the praying mantis. *Biol. Bull.,* **69**, 203–220.

Roeder, K. D., 1937. The control of tonus and locomotor activity in the praying mantis. *J. exp. Zool.*, **76**, 353–374.

Roitbak, A. I., 1955. [Bioelectrical phenomena in the cortex of the cerebral hemispheres.] Tiflis: Akad. Nauk, Georgia.

Roitbak, A. I., 1956. [Dendrites and the process of inhibition.] *Gagrskie Besedy, II.* Tiflis: Akad. Nauk, Georgia. Pp. 165–200.

Rosenthal, J., 1862. *Die Atembewegungen und ihre Beziehungen zum Nervus vagus.* Berlin: Hirschwald.

Rosenzweig, M. R., Krech, D., & Bennett, E. L., 1958. Brain chemistry and adaptive behavior. In Harlow and Woolsey, 1958. Pp. 367–400.

Rothballer, A. B., 1956. Studies on the adrenaline-sensitive component of the reticular activating system. *EEG & clin. Neurophysiol.*, **8**, 603–621.

Rowland, V., 1959. Conditioning and brain waves. *Scient. Amer.*, **201**(2), 89–96.

Rubin, E., 1911. *Visuell wahrgenommene Figuren.* Copenhagen: Gyldendalska.

Russell, G. W., 1961. Interrelationships within the limbic and centrencephalic systems. In Sheer, 1961. Pp. 167–181.

Russell, R. W., 1958. Effects of "biochemical lesions" on behavior. *Acta Psychol.*, **14**, 281–294.

Russell, W. R., 1959. *Brain-memory-learning: a neurologist's view.* Oxford: Clarendon Press.

Sager, O., 1960. *Diencefalul.* Bucharest: Acad. Rep. Pop. Rumine. (Includes English summary.)

Samoilov, A. F. [1924]. [On the passage of excitation from the motor nerve to the muscle.] In Sechenov, Pavlov, and Wedensky, vol. II, 1952. Pp. 619–624.

Sandiford, P., 1942. Connectionism: its origin and major features. *41st Yearb. Nat. Soc. Study Educ.*, part II, 97–140.

Santanelli, R., Municchi, L., & Serra, C., 1961. EEG changes in epileptic patients induced by iproniazid treatment. *EEG & clin. Neurophysiol.*, **13**, 136.

Sarason, S. B., 1949. *Psychological problems in mental deficiency.* New York: Harper.

Sarason, S. B., and Gladwin, T., 1958. Psychological and cultural factors in mental subnormality: a review of research. *Genet. psychol. Monogr.*, **57**, 3–289.

Schain, R. J., & Yannett, H. Y., 1960. Infantile autism: an analysis of 50 cases and a consideration of certain relevant neurophysiological concepts. *J. Pediatrics*, **57**, 560–567.

Scheer, B. T., 1948. *Comparative physiology.* New York: Wiley.

Schiff, M. [1849]. Experimentelle Untersuchungen üker die Nerven des Herzens [*Arch. physiol. Heilk.*, 8]. Reprinted in *Gesammelte Beiträge zur Physiologie,* vol. II. Lausanne: Benda, 1894. Pp. 125–236 (4 vols.).

Schiff, M. [1873]. Abschied von der Erschöpfungstheorie [*Moleschott's Beitrage,* 11]. Reprinted in *Gesammelte Beiträge zur Physiologie,* vol. II. Lausanne: Benda, 1894. Pp. 551–567 (4 vols.).

Schlösser, W., 1880. Untersuchungen über die Hemmungen von Reflexen. *Arch. Anat. u. Physiol.* (*Physiologische Abt.*), Jg. 1880, 303–322.

Schmid, W., Lee, C. H., & Smith, Priscilla M., 1961. At the borderline of mongolism: report of a case with chromosome analysis. *Amer. J. ment. Defic.*, **66**, 449–455.

Schneider, J. A., 1958. Discussant. In Jasper, 1958b. Pp. 173–176.

Schneirla, T. C., 1939. A theoretical consideration of the basis for approach-withdrawal adjustments in behavior. *Psychol. Bull.*, **37**, 501–502.

Schneirla, T. C., 1959. An evolutionary and developmental theory of biphasic processes underlying approach and withdrawal. In Jones, M. R., 1959. Pp. 1–41.

Schreiner, L., & Kling, A., 1953. Behavioral changes following rhinencephalic injury in cat. *J. Neurophysiol.* **16**, 643–659.

Scoville, W. B., & Milner, B., 1957. Loss of recent memory after bilateral hippocampal lesions. *J. Neurol., Neurosurg. & Psychiat.*, **20**, 11–21.

Scripture, E. W. 1895. *Thinking, feeling, doing; an introduction to mental science.* New York: Putnam.

Sechenov, I. M. [1863a]. *Physiologische Studien über die Hemmungsmechanismus fur die Reflexthätigkeit des Rückenmarks im Gehirne des Frosches.* Berlin: Hirschwald. (Reprinted in Sechenov, 1935.) Appeared also as J. Setschenow, Études physiologiques sur les centres modérateurs des mouvements réflexes dans le cerveau de la grénouille. *Annales des sciences naturelles,* 1863, **19** (4 ser.), 109–134.

Sechenov, I., 1863b. *Refleksii golovnogo mozga.* [Reflexes of the brain.] St. Petersburg. (Engl. trans. in Sechenov, 1935.)

Sechenov, I., 1907. *Avtobiograficheskie zapiski.* [Autobiographic notes.] Moscow: Nauchnoe Slovo.

Sechenov, I., 1935. *Selected works.* Moscow: State Publ. House for biol. med. Liter. (Contains Engl. trans. of principal Russian writings, original text of French and German articles.)

Sechenov, I. M., & Pashutin, V. V. [1865. *Neue Versuche am Hirn und Rückenmark des Frosches.* Berlin.] Reprint of Russian edition, same year, in Sechenov, Pavlov, & Wedensky, 1952. Pp. 73–116, vol. III.

Sechenov, I. M., Pavlov, I. P. & Wedensky, N. E., 1952. *Fiziologiya nervnoi sistemy; izbrannye trudy* [Physiology of the nervous system; selected works]. 4 vols. Moscow: Gos. Izd. Med. Lit. (K. M. Bykov, ed.)

Senden, M. v. 1932. *Raum- und Gestaltauffassung bei operierten Blindgeborenen vor und nach der Operation.* Leipzig: Barth.

Senn, M., 1953 (Ed.) *Problems of infancy and childhood.* Trans. Sixth Conf. New York: Josiah Macy, Jr. Foundation.

Seward, J. P., & Seward, G. H., 1934. The effect of repetition on reactions to electric shock; with special reference to the menstrual cycle. *Arch. Psychol.,* **25**(168).

Sharpless, S., & Jasper, H., 1956. Habituation of the arousal reaction. *Brain,* **79,** 655–680.

Sheer, D. E., 1961 (Ed.) *Electrical stimulation of the brain.* Austin: Univer. of Texas Press.

Sherman, M., & Key, Cora B., 1932. The intelligence of isolated mountain children. *Child Develpm.,* **3,** 279–290.

Sherrington, C. S., 1906. *The integrative action of the nervous system.* Cambridge, Mass.: Yale Univer. Press.

Sherrington, C. S., 1925. Remarks on some aspects of reflex inhibition. *Proc. Roy. Soc., London,* **87B,** 519–545.

Sherrington, C. S., 1951. *Man on his nature* (2nd ed.) Cambridge: Univer. Press.

Sherrington, C. S., & Hering, H. E., 1897. Antagonistic muscles and reciprocal innervation. *Proc. Roy. Soc., London,* **62B,** 183–187.

Sherwood, S. L., 1955. Effect of drugs on the behavior of animals and on psychoses of man. In Abramson, 1955. Pp. 85–182.

Shirley, Mary M., 1931. Is development saltatory as well as continuous? *Psychol. Bull.,* **28,** 664–665.

Sholl, D. A., 1956. *The organization of the cerebral cortex.* New York: Wiley.

Shore, P. A., & Brodie, B. B., 1957. LSD-like effects elicited by reserpine in rabbits pretreated with iproniazid. *Proc. Soc. exp. Biol. & Med.,* **94,** 433–435.

Simonoff, L. N., 1866. Die Hemmungsmechanismen der Säugethiere experimentell bewiesen. *Arch. Anat. Physiol. wissensch. Med.,* 1866. Pp. 545–564.

Skinner, B. F., 1938. *The behavior of organisms: an experimental analysis.* New York: Appleton-Century-Crofts.

Skinner, B. F., 1950. Are theories of learning necessary? *Psychol. Rev.,* **57,** 193–216.

Skinner, B. F., 1953. *Science and human behavior.* New York: Macmillan.

Snyder, F. W., & Pronko, N. H., 1952. *Vision with spatial inversion.* Wichita, Kan.: Univer. Wichita Press.

Sokolov, E. N., 1960. Neuronal models and the orienting reflex. In Brazier, 1960b. Pp. 187–270.

Solley, C. M., & Murphy, G., 1960. *Development of the perceptual world.* New York: Basic.

Solomon, H. C., Cobb, S., & Penfield, W., 1958 (Eds.) *The human brain and behavior*. Baltimore: Williams and Wilkins.

Solomon, P., Kubzansky, P. E., Leiderman, P. H., Mendelson, J. H., Trumbull, R., & Wexler, D., 1961 (Eds.) *Sensory deprivation*. Cambridge: Harvard Univer. Press.

Soury, J., 1899. *Système nerveux centrale*. Paris: Carré et Naud.

Spence, K. W., 1956. *Behavior theory and conditioning*. New Haven: Yale Univer. Press.

Spence, K. W., 1958. Behavior theory and selective learning. In Jones, M. R., 1958. Pp. 73–107.

Sperry, R. W., 1951. Mechanisms of neural maturation. In Stevens, 1951. Pp. 236–280.

Sperry, R. W., 1958. Physiological plasticity and brain circuit theory. In Harlow and Woolsey, 1958. Pp. 401–424.

Sperry, R. W., 1959. The growth of nerve circuits. *Scient. Amer.*, **201**(5), 68–75.

Sperry, R. W., & Miner, Nancy, 1955. Pattern perception following insertion of mica plates into visual cortex. *J. comp. physiol. Psychol.*, **48**, 463–469.

Sprague, J. M., 1958. The distribution of dorsal root fibres on motor cells in the lumbosacral spinal cord of the cat, and the site of excitatory and inhibitory terminals in monosynaptic pathways. *Proc. Roy. Soc. London*, **149B**, 534–556.

Stanley, W. C., & Jaynes, J., 1949. The function of the frontal cortex. *Psychol. Rev.*, **56**, 18–32.

Stearns, P., Droulard, K., & Sahhar, F. U., 1960. Studies bearing on fertility of male and female mongoloids. *Amer. J. ment. Defic.*, **65**, 37–42.

Stevens, S. S., 1951 (Ed.) *Handbook of experimental psychology*. New York: Wiley.

Stratton, G. M., 1897. Vision without inversion of the retinal image. *Psychol. Rev.*, **4**, 341–360.

Strauss, A. A., & Kephart, N. C., 1955. *Psychopathology and education of the brain injured child*. Vol. II. *Progress in theory and clinic*. New York: Grune and Stratton.

Strauss, A. A., & Lehtinen, Laura E., 1947. *Psychopathology and education of the brain injured child*. New York: Grune and Stratton.

Teuber, H.-L., 1960. Perception. In Magoun, vol. III, 1959–1960. Pp. 1595–1668.

Thom, D. A., 1942. Convulsions of early life and their relation to the chronic convulsive disorders and mental defect. *Amer. J. Psychiat.*, **98**, 574–580.

Thompson, Clare W., and Magaret, Ann, 1947. Differential test responses of normals and mental defectives. *J. abn. soc. Psychol.*, **42**, 285–293.

Thorndike, E. L., 1898. Animal intelligence: an experimental study of the associative processes in animals. *Psychol. Rev. Monogr. Suppl.*, **2**, no. 8.

Thorndike, E. L., 1949. *Selected writings from a connectionist's psychology.* New York: Appleton-Century-Crofts.

Thorpe, W. H., 1956. *Learning and instinct in animals.* London: Methuen.

Thorpe, W. H., 1961. Some characteristics of the early learning period in birds. In Delafresnaye, 1961. Pp. 75–94.

Thrall, R. M., Coombs, C. H., & Davis, R. L., 1954 (Eds.). *Decision processes.* New York: Wiley.

Thurstone, L. L., 1947. *Multiple-factor analysis; a development and expansion of the factors of mind.* Chicago: Univer. of Chicago Press.

Tinbergen, N., 1951. *The study of instinct,* Oxford: Clarendon.

Tinbergen, N., 1960. The evolution of behavior in gulls. *Scient. American,* **203**(6), 118–130.

Tolman, E. C., & Brunswik, E., 1935. The organism and the causal texture of the environment. *Psychol. Rev.*, **42**, 43–77.

*Tolochinov, I., 1902. Contribution à l'étude de la physiol. et de la psychol. des glandes salivaires. *Verh. Nordisch Kongr.*, Helsingfors.

Travis, L. E., 1957 (Ed.) *Handbook of speech pathology.* New York: Appleton-Century-Crofts.

Trouton, D., & Eysenck, H. J., 1961. The effects of drugs on behaviour. In Eysenck, 1961b. Pp. 634–696.

Tucker, A. [1765]. *The light of nature pursued* (2 vols.). London: Charles Daly, 1836.

Ueberweg, F., 1898. *A history of philosophy.* Trans. from 4th Germ. ed. New York: Scribner. 2 vols.

Uhr, L., & Miller, J. G. (Eds.) 1960. *Drugs and behavior.* New York: Wiley.

Ukhtomsky, A. A., 1925. [The principle of dominants.] In Sechenov, Pavlov, Wedensky, vol. II, 1952. Pp. 262–266.

Ukhtomsky, A. A. [1926a]. [On the state of excitation in the dominant.] In Sechenov, Pavlov, & Wedensky, vol. II, 1952. Pp. 267–279.

Ukhtomsky, A. A. [1926b]. [On the drainage of excitation.] In Sechenov, Pavlov, & Wedensky, vol. II, 1952. Pp. 280–299.

Ukhtomsky, A. A. [1934]. [On the indications of lability (functional mobility) of physiological mechanisms.] In Sechenov, Pavlov, & Wedensky, vol. II, 1952. Pp. 506–511.

Ukhtomsky, A. A. [1937]. [From the history of the doctrine of nervous inhibition.] In Sechenov, Pavlov & Wedensky, vol. II, 1952. Pp. 532–540.

Verworn, M., 1895. *Allgemeine Physiologie.* Jena: Fischer.

Verworn, M., 1910. *Die Mechanik des Geisteslebens.* Leipzig: Teubner. 2 vols.

Verworn, M., 1913. *Irritability.* New Haven: Yale Univer. Press.

Volkmann, A. W., 1838a. Über Reflexbewegungen. *Arch. Anat. Physiol. wissenschaftl. Medizin,* **15**, 15–43.

Volkmann, A. W., 1838b. Von dem Baue und den Verrichtungen der Kopfnerven des Frosches. *Arch. Anat. Physiol. u. wissensch. Med.,* **15,** 70–89.

Voronin, L. G., & Sokolov, E. N., 1960. Cortical mechanisms of the orienting reflex and its relation to the conditioned reflex. In Jasper and Smirnov, 1960. Pp. 335–346.

Wada, J. A., 1961. Epileptogenic cerebral electrical activity and serotonin levels. *Science,* **134,** 1688–1689.

Waldeyer, H. W. G., 1891. Über einige neuere Forschungen im Gebiete der Anatomie des Centralnervensystems. *Deutsche med. Wochenschr.,* **17**(2), 1213–1218; 1244–1246; 1267–1269; 1287–1289; 1331–1332; 1352–1356.

Walker, E. L., 1958. Action decrement and its relation to learning. *Psychol. Rev.,* **65,** 129–142.

Waller, A. D., 1892. On the "inhibition" of voluntary and electrically excited muscular contraction by peripheral excitation. *Brain,* **15,** 35–64.

Wallin, J. E. W., 1949. *Children with mental and physical handicaps.* New York: Prentice-Hall.

Walter, W. G., 1950. Normal rhythms and their development, distribution and significance. In D. Hill and G. Parr (Eds.). *Electroencephalography.* New York: Macmillan. Pp. 203–227.

Walter, W. G., 1953. *The living brain.* New York: Norton.

Warren, H. C., 1896. *Buddhism in translations.* Cambridge: Harvard Univer. Press.

Washburn, Margaret F., 1916. *Movement and mental imagery.* Boston: Houghton Mifflin.

Watson, J. B., 1914. *Behavior: an introduction to comparative psychology.* New York: Holt.

Watson, J. B., 1916. The place of the conditioned reflex in psychology. *Psychol. Rev.,* **23,** 89–117.

Watson, J. B., 1924. *Behaviorism.* New York: Norton.

Wayner, M. J., Jr., & Zellner, D. K., 1958. The role of the suprapharyngeal ganglion in spontaneous alternation and negative movements in *Lumbricus terrestris L. J. comp. physiol. Psychol.,* **51,** 282–287.

Weber, E. F. W., 1846. Muskelbewegung. In R. Wagner *Handwörterbuch der Physiologie,* vol. III, pt. 2. Braunschweig: Vieweg. Pp. 1–122.

Weber, E. F. W., & Weber, E. H. W., 1845. Experimenta, quibus probatur nervos vagos rotatione machinae galvano-magneticae irritatos, motum cordi retardare et adeo intercipare. *Ann. Univ. Med., Milano,* **116,** 227–228.

Wedensky, N. E. [1886]. [On the relationship between stimulation and excitation in tetanus.] In Sechenov, Pavlov, & Wedensky, vol. II, 1952. Pp. 141–233.

Wedensky, N. E. [1897]. [On the reciprocal relationships between psychomotor centers.] In Sechenov, Pavlov, & Wedensky, 1952, vol. III. Pp. 181–188.

Wedensky, N. E., 1903. Die Erregung, Hemmung und Narkose. *Pfl. Arch. ges. Physiol.,* **100,** 1–144.

Weiskrantz, L., Mihailovič, L., & Gross, C. G., 1960. Stimulation of frontal cortex and delayed alternation performance in the monkey. *Science,* **131,** 1443–1444.

Welsh, J. H., 1957. Serotonin as a possible neurohumoral agent: evidence obtained in lower animals. *Ann. N.Y. Acad. Sci.,* **66,** 618–630.

Wendt, G. R., 1951. Vestibular functions. In Stevens, 1951. Pp. 1191–1223.

Werner, H., 1944. Development of visuo-motor performance on the marble-board test in mentally retarded children. *J. genet. Psychol.,* **64,** 269–279.

Wertheimer, Max, 1912. Experimentelle Studien über das Sehen von Bewegungen. *Z. Psychol.,* **61,** 161–265.

Wertheimer, Max, 1945. *Productive thinking.* New York: Harper.

Wertheimer, Michael, 1961. Psychomotor coordination of auditory and visual space at birth. *Science,* **134,** 1692.

Wikler, A., 1957. *The relation of psychiatry to pharmacology.* Baltimore: Williams & Wilkins.

Witt, P., 1954. Spider webs and drugs. *Scient. Amer.*, **191**(6), 80–86.

Wolman, B. B., 1960. *Contemporary theories and systems in psychology.* New York: Harper.

Wolpe, J., 1949. An interpretation of the effects of combinations of stimuli (patterns) based on current neurophysiology. *Psychol. Rev.*, **56,** 277–283.

Wolpe, J., 1958. *Psychotherapy by reciprocal inhibition.* Palo Alto: Stanford Univer. Press.

Woolley, D. W., 1958. Serotonin in mental disorders. *Ass. Res. nerv. ment. Dis.*, **36,** 381–400.

Woolley, D. W., & Shaw, E., 1954. A biochemical and pharmacological suggestion about certain mental disorders. *Science,* **119,** 587–588.

Worden, R. G., & Livingston, R. B., 1961. Brain-stem reticular formation. In Sheer, 1961. Pp. 263–277.

*Wulfson, S. H., 1898. [The work of the salivary glands.] Inaug. Dissert., St. Petersburg.

Wundt, W., 1871. *Untersuchungen zur Mechanik der Nerven und Nervencentren.* (Erste abt.) Erlangen: Enke.

Wundt, W., 1874. *Grundzüge der physiologischen Psychologie,* Leipzig: Engelmann. (2nd ed., 1880; 3rd ed., 1887; 4th ed., 1893; 5th ed., 1902–1903; Engl. trans. of 5th ed. [incomplete], Macmillan, 1904.)

Wyrwicka, W., & Dobrzecka, C., 1960. Relationship between feeding and satiation centers of the hypothalamus. *Science,* **132,** 805–806.

Yakovlev, P. I., 1959. Discussant. In Brazier, 1959a. Pp. 402–409.

Yannet, H., 1945. Diagnostic classification of patients with mental deficiency: distribution of 1330 institutionalized patients with review of incidence of convulsive disorders and non-cerebral developmental anomalies. *Amer. J. Dis. Child.*, **70,** 83–88.

Yerkes, R. M., 1912. The intelligence of earthworms. *J. anim. Behav.*, **2,** 332–352.

Yerkes, R. M., & Morgulis, S., 1909. The method of Pavlov in animal psychology. *Psychol. Bull.*, **6,** 257–273.

Zangwill, O. L., 1960. Speech. In Magoun, 1959–1960, vol. III. Pp. 1709–1722.

Ziehen, T., 1898. *Leitfaden der physiologischen Psychologie* (4th ed.) Jena: Fischer.

Index of Names

Index of Subjects

18 17